The Structure of Lipids

THE STRUCTURE OF LIPIDS
by Spectroscopic and X-Ray Techniques

With a chapter on Separation Techniques including thin layer and gas liquid chromatography

D. CHAPMAN
University Chemical Laboratory, Cambridge

distributed in the United States
by BARNES & NOBLE, Inc. NC
NEW YORK

First published 1965

Printed in Great Britain

Preface

Interest in the study of lipids has intensified considerably in the last ten years. Much of this interest has arisen because of the increasing concern over the causes of atherosclerosis and other lipid diseases. At the same time general interest in the biochemical reactions of fat metabolism and in the association of lipids and proteins has also grown considerably. Interest in the lipoproteins springs from many directions. They are thought to occur in cell membranes, to be involved in lipid transport in blood and are considered to be important in such various areas as neurological, physiological, biochemical and agricultural research. Enzyme activity in mitochondria has also been associated with lipid–protein interactions.

The lipid molecules are interesting molecules in their own right and exhibit many unusual properties. Many of them have more than one melting point and some have as many as four or five. This is associated with polymorphism and is related to the variety of ways in which hydrocarbon chains can pack together. Some lipids form liquid crystals where part of the molecule is in a liquid condition one hundred degrees or more below the true melting point. In the presence of water, lipids with polar head groups aggregate to form micelles which can also be of considerable biological importance.

In this book I have set out to show the kind of information which the different modern spectroscopic and X-ray techniques can provide about lipid molecules. To do this I have discussed first the simple lipids such as the monocarboxylic acids, long chain esters and alcohols, then glycerides, phospholipids and, finally, the natural lipoproteins, such as those which occur in the myelin sheath of nerve fibres. The particular feature of the techniques discussed is in the main that they are non-destructive and, in many cases, enable the biological material itself to be studied. It is certain that a great deal of our future understanding of the role of lipid molecules in biological systems will spring from the use of these techniques.

I have included in the first chapter a brief account of modern separation methods as the combination of these with the spectroscopic techniques will be particularly powerful. In a final chapter techniques other than X-ray and spectroscopic ones are also briefly mentioned.

The book is intended as a practical book for those carrying out research on lipids, but particularly for those carrying out research on their biophysical, biochemical and medical aspects.

D. CHAPMAN

Cambridge, 1964

Acknowledgements

I wish to thank the Master and Fellows of Gonville and Caius College, Cambridge, for their award of the Comyns-Berkeley Bye-Fellowship which enabled me to work in the University Chemical Laboratory, Cambridge. This gave me the opportunity to work in what was for me a number of new scientific areas. At the same time I began to appreciate much more the growing need in biochemical and medical research for basic physical knowledge on the cumbersome awkward lipid molecules on which I had previously worked. I have always found them interesting and rather fascinating but had previously considered them to be mainly of technological importance.

I also wish to thank colleagues at the University Chemical Laboratory and also the various Unilever laboratories, in particular Professor V. M. Clark and Professor G. Dijkstra, for useful discussions, and the secretarial assistance of the staff of these laboratories.

Contents

1. Introduction

The field of lipids

The field of lipids (lipides) is usually poorly defined, sometimes being associated only with a common solubility property. Substances ranging from the simple fatty acids and esters to complex sphingolipids, and from sterols, steroids to vitamins and colouring matters and flavours are often classified in this field. The definition more frequently accepted is that the term 'lipid' covers the esters of long-chain fatty acids and alcohols and closely related derivatives. As even this definition is somewhat vague we shall now outline more precisely the area and different classes of substance which we intend to discuss before considering the use of spectroscopy and other techniques for their study.

There is at present no internationally accepted system for nomenclature of these compounds and hence only the commonly used terms or most reasonable terms are adopted in this book.

FATTY ACIDS

The fatty acids are a basic unit in many lipid molecules and markedly determine their properties. In nature they occur only in small quantities in a free form, e.g. the lower fatty acids such as acetic, butyric and caproic occur in free form in milk fats. Whilst it was at one time considered that free fatty acids present in tissue extract were due to degradative action undergone in isolation procedures, it has now been established that free fatty acids are normal constituents of the tissue lipid pool.

The fatty acids found in the majority of mammalian lipids are straight chain, even numbered monocarboxylic, and the most predominant of these are lauric, myristic, palmitic and stearic acids. Small amounts of branched and odd numbered acids do occur naturally but only in small percentages. Unsaturated acids are particularly important and monoenoic (oleic acid), dienoic (linoleic acid), trienoic (linolenic acid) and tetraenoic acid (arachidonic acid) are known. Linoleic acid (*cis-cis* linoleic acid) is regarded as being particularly important in biology, and it and arachidonic acid are termed 'essential fatty acids'. The latter is found in liver, brain and depot lipids. Some of the variations on the fatty acid structure are:

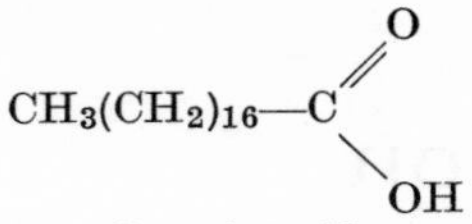

Stearic acid

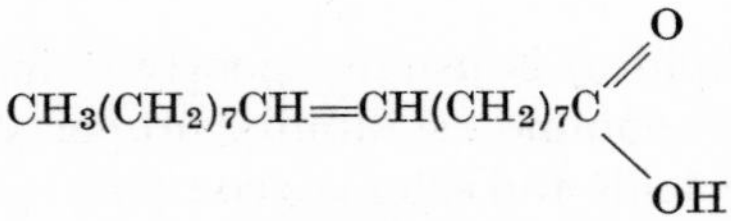

Oleic acid

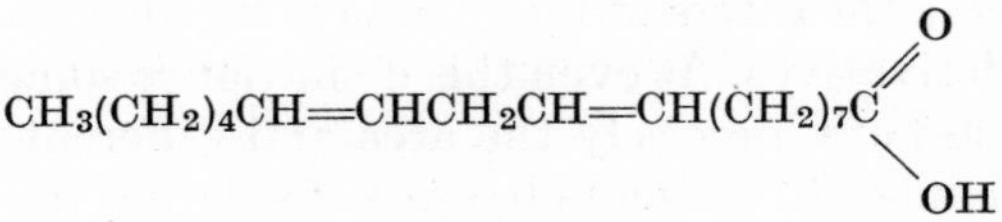

Linoleic acid

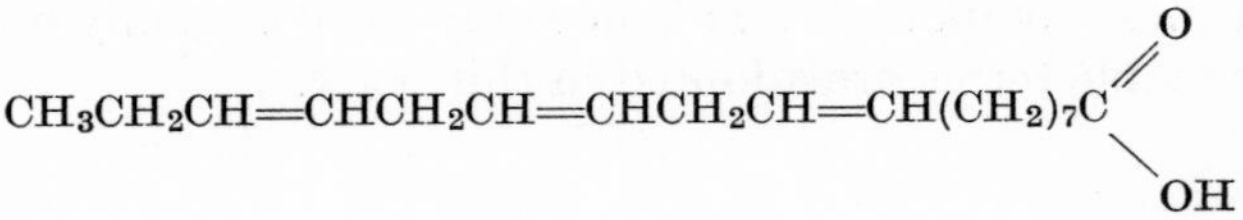

Linolenic acid

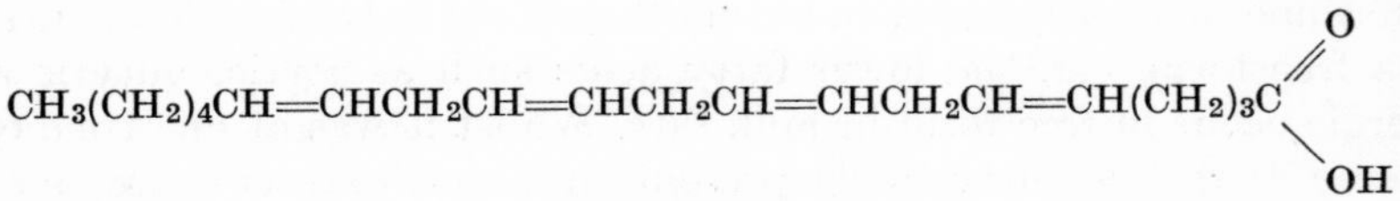

Arachidonic acid

SIMPLE LIPIDS

The simple lipids are amongst the most abundant fatty acid derivatives found in nature and exist in animal and plant tissue. The most predominant members of this class are the esters of the fatty acids with glycerol and also with cholesterol.

Glycerides

Five different derivatives are possible on esterification of glycerol with fatty acid and these are:

CH_2OCOR_1
|
$CHOCOR_2$
|
CH_2OCOR_3

Triglyceride

CH_2OCOR_1
|
$CHOCOR_2$
|
CH_2OH

1,2-Diglyceride

CH_2OCOR_1
|
CHO
|
CH_2OCOR_2

1,3-Diglyceride

CH_2OH
|
$CHOCOR_1$
|
CH_2OH

2-Monoglyceride

CH_2OCOR_1
|
$CHOH$
|
CH_2OH

1-Monoglyceride

where R_1, R_2 and R_3 are the long-chain hydrocarbon units of the fatty acids and may differ in length and in degree of unsaturation.

In mammalian tissues triglycerides are present to the largest extent, but diglycerides and monoglycerides are also present in certain tissues. The glycerides constitute well over 98% of the lipids of the adipose tissue of the mammal, 30% of the plasma and liver lipids, and less than 10% of the red blood cell lipid. There is the possibility of a number of permutations and combinations of fatty acids on the glycerol residue. Thus two different fatty acids, R_1 and R_2, can give rise to any one of six triglycerides, whilst three fatty acids, R_1, R_2 and R_3, can give eighteen triglycerides.

The mode of distribution of the fatty acids on the glycerol molecule in natural mixtures of glycerides is still not fully understood and many theories have been proposed and criticized relating to this. Thus there is a rule of even distribution, i.e. that each of the individual acids of a given glyceride tends to be distributed as evenly as possible amongst all the glyceride molecules. (An acid has to constitute greater than two-thirds of the total acid content before it can form any appreciable amounts of a monoacid-type triglyceride.) There is also a rule of random distribution, partial random distribution and a rule of restricted random distribution.

The diglycerides and monoglycerides can also undergo acyl migration or *trans* esterification. Thus the 2-monoglycerides can be converted predominantly to the 1-isomer whilst the 1,2-diglycerides can be converted to a predominance of the 1,3-isomer.

Cholesterol and cholesterol esters

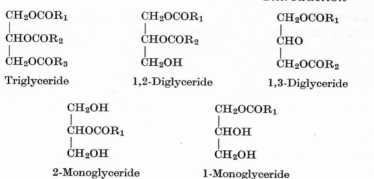

Whilst glycerol is by far the major polyhydroxy alcohol found esterified to long-chain fatty acids in mammals, another important alcohol is cholesterol. This is the only sterol found associated with long-chain fatty acids in mammals. There is particular interest in cholesterol esters at the present time because of their possible relation to atherosclerosis. There are three main sites of location of these esters, the adrenals, liver and plasma. Some uncertainty exists with regard to the fatty-acid composition of certain of these esters. Thus the lipid fractions present in the blood of rats were found not to contain oleic acid, although at least 50% of the esters of the human plasma are of the oleate type.

Glyceryl ethers

The glyceryl ethers can be represented by the formula

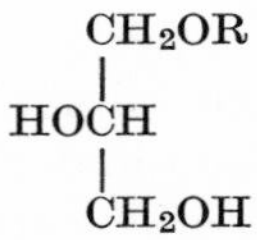

where R is usually palmityl, stearyl and oleyl. The R group is said to be found exclusively in the 1-position. They occur in marine animals, but only to a limited extent in land animals. Both D- and L-forms are possible but in nature the D-form is the predominant one.

Fatty alcohols and waxes

Although not found to any significant extent in land mammals the waxes do occur in aquatic animals and certain plants. The sperm whale contains considerable amounts of long-chain alcohols such as cetyl, stearyl and oleyl alcohols, esterified with long-chain acids. The waxes can be represented as carboxylic esters of the type:

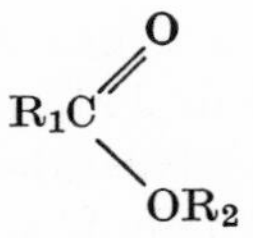

where R_1 is a long-chain fatty acid and R_2 is a long-chain alcohol. Natural leaf waxes contain alcohols such as myricyl alcohol $C_{30}H_{61}OH$ and myricyl palmitate occurs in high concentration in beeswax.

COMPLEX LIPIDS

The complex lipids consist of esters which may contain phosphorus, nitrogen bases, and sugars, in addition to long-chain fatty acids. First we may consider the phospholipids containing glycerol, i.e. the phosphoglycerides.

Phosphoglycerides

The phosphoglycerides, although apparently of little technological importance, are of widespread occurrence in nature and of great biochemical interest. These lipids have been associated with blood-clotting processes, as a source of choline in nervous tissue, as a matrix for the structure of the living cell, the transport of potassium and sodium ions and in many biological oxidations and as intermediates in the metabolism of fatty acids. Typical phosphoglycerides of importance are:

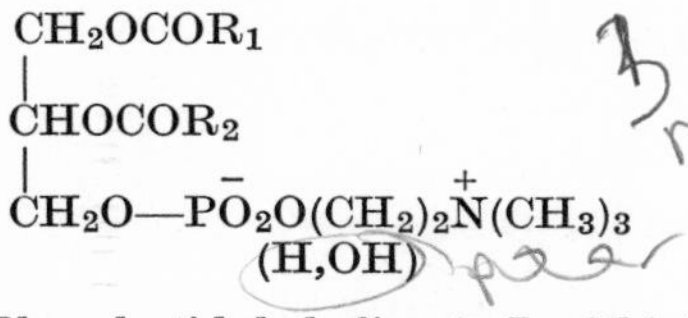

Phosphatidyl choline (α-Lecithin)

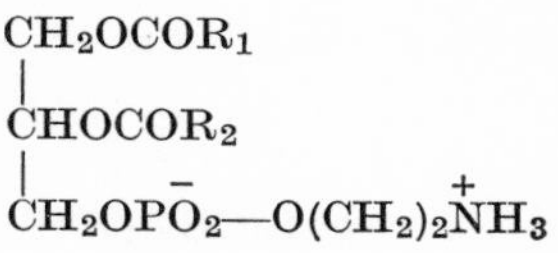

Phosphatidyl ethanolamine (α-Cephalin)

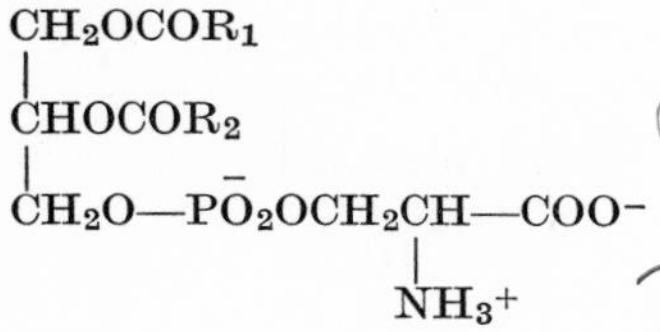

Phosphatidyl serine

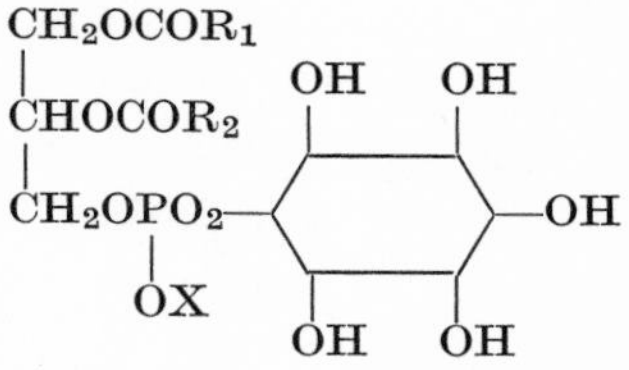

Phosphatidyl inositol (X is a cation)

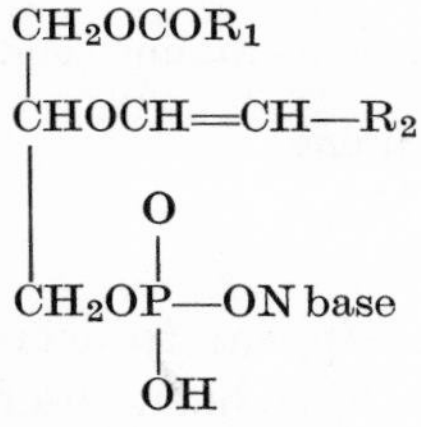

Plasmalogen (base, choline or ethanolamine)

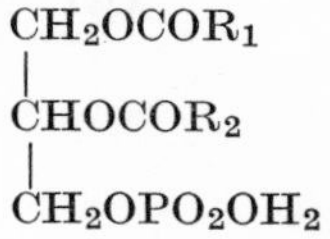

Phosphatidic acid

where R_1 and R_2 are the long-chain hydrocarbon units of the fatty acids. (With natural phosphoglycerides R_2 usually contains an unsaturated grouping.)

Sphingolipids

The sphingolipids are characterized by the derivation of its members from a number of long-chain hydroxylic bases; sphingosine, dihydrosphingosine, phytosphingosine and dehydrophytosphingosine. The first two occur in animal fats, particularly in pancreatic, brain and spinal lipids. The structure of some sphingosine-containing lipids are:

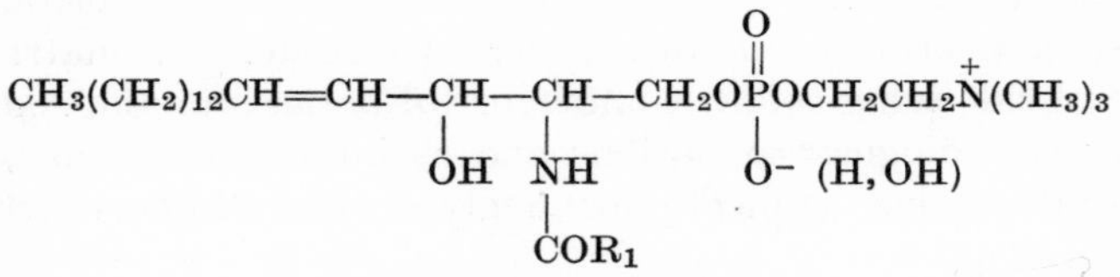

Sphingomyelin

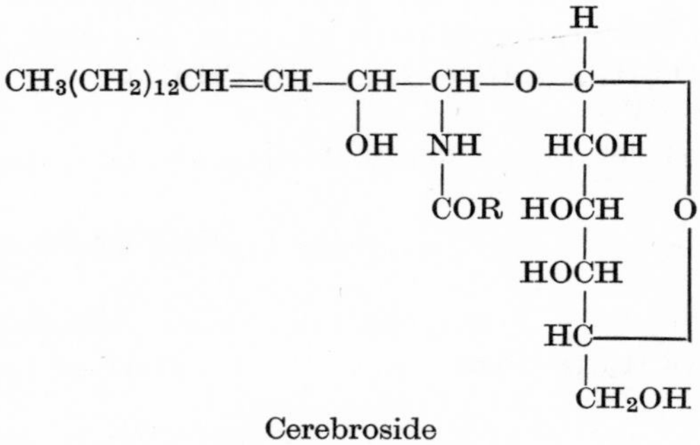

Cerebroside

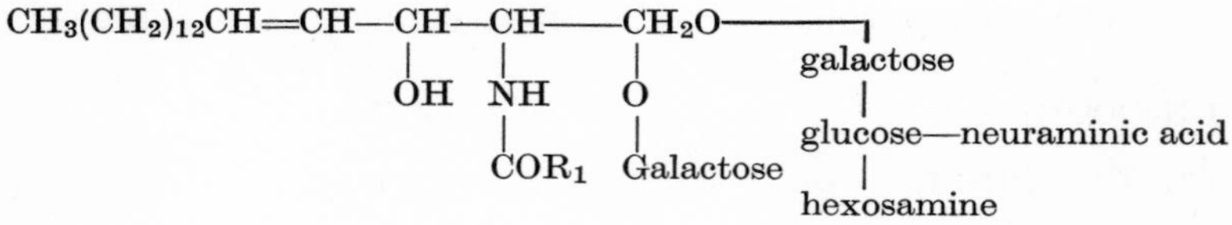

Ganglioside

Phytosphingosine and dehydrophytosphingosine appear to occur in plant sources only. Derivatives of phytosphingosine have been observed in soya-bean oil.

LIPOPROTEINS

In recent years it has become clear that lipids are also found to occur in an associated form along with proteins [1, 2, 3]. These lipoproteins occur in many systems and appear to be of considerable importance. Almost all biological membranes, cytoplasmic membranes, nuclear membranes, endoplasmic reticulum, cristae of mitochondria, lamellae of chloroplasts, myelin of nerve fibres, are composed of lipoproteins. They support the metabolic apparatus in mitochondria and the photosynthetic apparatus in chloroplasts, and are thought to be associated with enzymatic activity in mitochondrion [4]. The 'soluble' lipoproteins are considered to be responsible for the transport of lipids in blood. All or nearly all of the lipid components in blood plasma are combined with protein [5]. The nature of the bonding between lipid and protein is still unknown, although there have been speculations about this. As an individual lipoprotein particle may contain 1000 to 2000 lipid molecules, lipid–lipid interactions are important as well as lipid–protein interactions. In the nervous system a major part of lipids and proteins occur as lipoproteins. Some of these are similar to those found in plasma, i.e. soluble in water and insoluble in organic solvents, some occur which are insoluble in water and in organic solvents and a third group occurs which are insoluble in water and soluble in certain organic solvents. The latter group has been named the proteolipids [6].

REFERENCES

1. LOVERN, J. A. (1955) *The Chemistry of Lipids of Biochemical Significance.* Methuen.
2. MACHEBOEUF, M. A. (1937) 'Etat des Lipides dans la Matière Vivante Actualites', *Sci. et Ind.*, 448.
3. CHARGAFF, E. (1945) *Adv. Protein Chem.*, **1**, 1.
4. GREEN, D. E. and FLEISCHER, S. (1963) *Biochim. Biophys. Acta*, **70**, 544.
5. ONCLEY, J. L. (1955) *Harvey Lectures*, **50**, 71.
6. FOLCH, J. and LEES, M. (1951) *J. Biol. Chem.* **191**, 807.

2. Separation techniques

Many new techniques have become available in recent years for the separation of lipids from the complex mixtures in which they usually occur. Here we discuss them briefly, pointing to the particular features of the different methods.

We shall consider first the methods of separation available for the lipoproteins. As well as the general composition the fatty acid composition of the lipids in the lipoprotein complexes may significantly affect their behaviour and properties and can vary from particle to particle. This means that lipoprotein particles have first to be separated from each other and then the composition of the lipid mixtures determined according to the type of phospholipid, triglyceride and cholesterol esters present. Finally, in a complete analysis, the fatty-acid distribution is determined and the specific configuration of the fatty acid on the phospholipids or glycerol moiety deduced.

Separation of lipoproteins

One of the most characteristic properties of lipoproteins is their low density and hence the most widely used technique for separating them is by flotation using an ultracentrifuge. Determination of the sedimentation rate with varying density of the solvent can be used to differentiate the lipoproteins from other proteins of more normal density and to separate lipoproteins of differing density. The lipoproteins are themselves separated by means of their different densities; these differences reflect the densities of the individual components of the lipoproteins. There are two general procedures for separating different classes of plasma lipoproteins. In the first [1] the serum fraction is mixed with a quantity of salt solution (sometimes containing D_2O) providing a small molecule environment of a predetermined density. The lipoprotein molecules in the ultracentrifuge cell are subject to approximately the same buoyancy factor. The rate of flotation of the lipoprotein boundaries can be observed and the various components are characterized according to Svedberg's units of flotation. (The rate of flotation in a unit centrifugal field when the lipoprotein is suspended in an aqueous sodium chloride solution of density 1·063 at 26° is indicated by S_f notation.) Factors which affect the rate of flotation include the particle weight and size, as well as the difference in density between the medium and the lipoprotein complex.

Using this technique lipid-rich and lipid-poor proteins are easily separated. A diagram [1] illustrating the isolation of low-density lipoproteins is shown in Fig. 1, using a solvent density of 1·063 g/ml. The more dense α-lipoproteins are separated from the less dense β-lipoproteins at the density 1·063 g/ml. These lipoproteins correspond to those obtained by the fractionation by solubility of Cohn *et al.* [2].

A second method for separating lipoproteins is by creating a density gradient in the ultracentrifuge tube. This is done by varying the concentration of salt or solute. Density gradients can be created in this way so

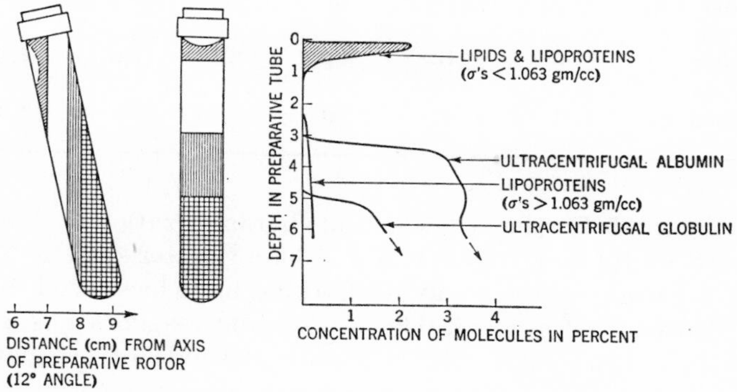

Fig. 1. Isolation of low-density lipoproteins in a solvent density of 1·063 g/ml. (Lindgren, F. T., Elliott, H. A., and Gofman, J. W., *J. Phys. Colloid Chem.*, **55**, 80 (1951).)

as to remain stable over a period of 18–24 h with density, say, between 1·06 at the bottom to 1·02 at the top, enabling clear separations of lipoproteins to be made. Each lipoprotein component with densities between these extremes concentrate in layers of solvent of equal density. The lighter lipoproteins concentrate at the top and heavier lipoproteins and other sedimentable material concentrate at the bottom of the tube. The distribution made on the basis of density need not correspond to a distribution dependent on S_f values. This is because with a particular density class there may be complexes of varying size, whilst for a given S_f class the complexes may vary with respect to both size and density. Sharp differentiation between the composition of each class can occur: thus the density class 0·98 contains considerable amounts of triglyceride and little cholesterol ester whilst the more dense lipoproteins contain more phospholipid than cholesterol. Table 1 shows the average composition of the major plasma lipoproteins determined by a number of different authors.

Table 1. *Composition of the major plasma lipoproteins* [3]

Type	Peptide	Phospholipid	Cholesterol Alcohol	Cholesterol Ester	Triglyceride	Non-esterified fatty acid
Chylomicrons	2·0	7·0	2·0	5·0	84·0	—
β-Lipoprotein (density 0·94–1·00)	8·0	18·0	7·0	12·0	50·0	2·0
β-Lipoprotein (density 1·03)	21·0	22·0	8·0	37·0	11·0	1·0
α-Lipoprotein (density 1·063–2·0)	50·0	22·0	3·0	14·0	8·0	3·0

Solubility methods for the isolation and characterization of lipoproteins have proved useful and, in particular, ethanol–water systems [3]. High polymers, especially anionic polysaccharides, have been used to precipitate low density lipoproteins. The use of zinc reagents has also been extensive [4]. Apparently, the different methods of estimating the quantities of the major lipoprotein classes give essentially the same results [5]. It has been suggested, however, that the use of high concentrations of salts, as is required for ultracentrifugal flotation of high-density lipoproteins, may be harmful [6]. Autoxidation has now been suggested to be associated [7, 8] with two types of alteration observed during the isolation and storage of lipoproteins of density class 1·035. This is discussed in the chapter on ultraviolet spectroscopy, page 49.

Electrophoretic methods have been extensively applied to lipoproteins. Whilst it has been difficult to use these methods satisfactorily for purification purposes, they are useful as analytical methods. Free electrophoresis and zonal electrophoresis, using paper, starch, agar and polyvinyl resin, have been used successfully. The method has been reviewed elsewhere [9].

Isolation and purification of lipids

The lipids themselves are usually extracted using a solvent system such as ethanol–ether or chloroform–methanol. This separates the lipids from the proteins and many other components. The solvent is removed by vacuum evaporation and the aqueous mixture is subjected to extraction with other solvents such as diethyl ether, petroleum ether or chloroform. After washing this solution the total lipid is obtained by removing the solvent. It may then contain phospholipids and simple lipids. Some contamination of the lipids can occur. The phospholipids in particular solubilize many non-lipid components such as sugars, free amino acids, sterols, urea and many inorganic substances. These may be removed by special washing techniques or by chromatographic techniques using column chromatography or paper chromatography.

In one special washing procedure, which is fairly commonly used, the chloroform–methanol extract from the tissue is mixed with 0·2 of its volume in water to which certain mineral salts are added (e.g. NaCl, KCl, $CaCl_2$ or $MgCl_2$). This results in a two-phase system. The upper phase contains predominantly non-lipid material and the lower phase contains essentially all of the lipid material. This procedure is simple and reduces the loss of lipids incidental to the washing process to a low level.

A number of techniques have been used for the detailed fractionation of the lipids. These include countercurrent distribution methods, paper chromatography methods and column chromatography. The method acquiring considerable importance at present is that of thin-layer chromatography. This is used to separate the lipids into their different classes and sometimes is preceded by column chromatography to obtain greater quantities of materials or followed by other thin-layer chromatographic techniques. Enzymatic hydrolysis and gas–liquid chromatographic techniques are also used to provide a detailed analysis of the lipids present.

COUNTER-CURRENT DISTRIBUTION

Counter-current distribution is a multiple-batch extraction technique [10] in which continuous portions of one solvent phase moving in one direction are equilibrated with a second solvent phase progressing in the opposite direction. The advantage of this technique is that large volumes of solvent can be easily handled so that large amounts of pure material can be obtained.

The efficiency of the technique is a direct function of the number of transfers employed. Counter-current methods have been used for the fractionation of phospholipids [10] and brain lipids [11]. Plant lipids [12] have also been separated. With plant lipids a 400-stage transfer with a solvent system of *n*-heptane–*n*-butanol–methanol–water was used. The phytosphingolipids were concentrated and showed a separation from phosphatidylinositol. Oleic, linoleic and linolenic acids have been separated using a solvent system of heptane–methanol–formamide and acetic acid [13]. With this system, however, oleic and palmitic acids and linoleic and myristic acids could not be separated. A solvent system using silver salts in the more aqueous phase has been introduced [14]. The reversible complexing between the double bonds of the unsaturated fatty acids and the silver ions produces a large change in the distribution coefficient of the unsaturated fatty acids. This enables the *cis*- and *trans*-isomers to be separated.

Chromatographic techniques

COLUMN CHROMATOGRAPHY

Column chromatography has been particularly useful in the isolation and purification of lipids. The materials used for the column include silicic

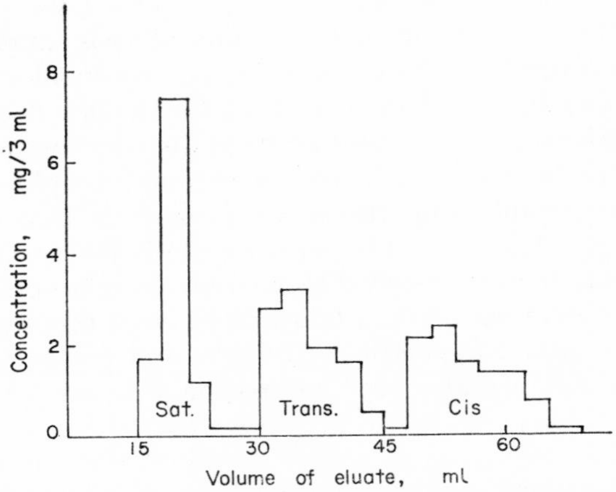

Fig. 2. Column chromatography of 10 mg each of a mixture of methyl stearate, elaidate and oleate. Adsorbent 2 g of silver nitrate on silica; column height 11 cm, column diameter 8 mm; eluent, benzene and light petroleum (10 + 90 to 30 + 70), rate 0·5 ml per minute (after de Vries[17]).

acid, aluminium oxide and magnesium oxide. Silicic acid has been used successfully for the fractionation of phospholipids and neutral lipids. Using this method the phospholipids of egg yolk have been separated and the two major components, phosphatidylethanolamine and phosphatidyl choline, separated [15]. The solvent used was 20% methyl alcohol in chloroform. The phospholipids from rat liver, beef liver and yeast have been separated using solvent mixtures of chloroform and methanol [16]. The more acidic type phospholipids are eluted first, next to the inositides and phosphatidyl choline types, and finally the sphingomyelins. The lysolecithin fraction tends to be found between lecithin and the sphingomyelin fraction. Adequate fractionation is usually obtained with 1 mg or less of phospholipid-phosphorus per gram of silicic acid. Overlapping and smearing fractions can occur if larger amounts are used. Fresh silicic acid dried overnight at 110° C is usually used but the activation of this material is not as important with the phospholipids as with the simple neutral lipids. (The silicic acid commercially available in England is quite different in adsorbtive properties from that in the United States. With the former only the triglycerides are adsorbed, whilst with the

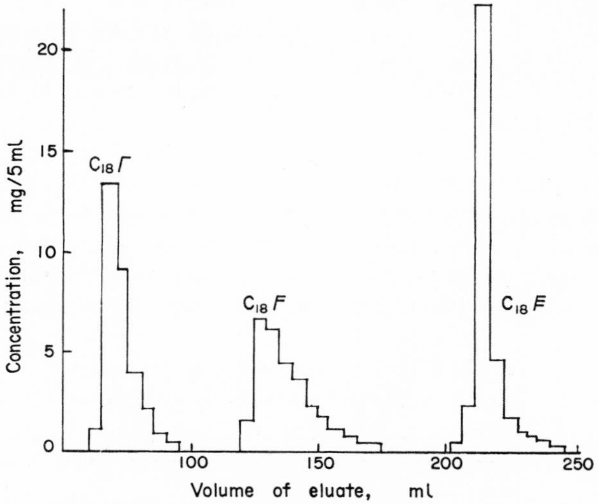

Fig. 3. Column chromatography of 30 mg each of a mixture of methyl oleate, linoleate and linolenate. Adsorbent 10 g of silver nitrate on silica; column height 23 cm, column diameter 14 mm; eluent, benzene and light petroleum (40 + 60 to 100 + 0), rate 0·5 ml per minute. (After de Vries[17]).

latter the phospholipids and neutral lipids can be adsorbed and eluted.) The use of silver ion complexes and saturated acids has considerably improved resolution [17]. Separations of methyl esters of saturated and unsaturated esters using silver nitrate impregnated silicic acid columns are illustrated in Figs. 2 and 3. Natural mixtures of cholesterol esters [18] and serum triglycerides [19] have also been fractionated using this technique. The triglycerides separate readily according to their degree of unsaturation.

Column partition chromatography and, in particular, reverse phase chromatography have been used to fractionate saturated acids [20]. In this way fractionation of acids from C_{12} to C_{24} has been possible. Paraffin oil is used as the stationary phase and acetone–water mixtures (containing paraffin oil) as the developing solvent. By hydrogenation and re-chromatography, saturated and unsaturated acids have also been separated [21]. Reversed phase chromatography has also been used to study [22] ingested ^{14}C-labelled stearic, palmitic, oleic and linoleic acids. Separation of stearic, palmitic and oleic acids is satisfactory, but the oleic acid appears with the palmitic acid.

Aluminium oxide has been shown to be particularly useful in the preparation of lecithin fractions. Using this material choline and non-choline containing phospholipids have been separated [23]. The loading is in the range from 1–2 mg phospholipid phosphorus per gram of aluminium oxide. The advantage of combining chromatography on aluminium oxide followed by chromatography on silicic acid has also been considered [24].

PAPER CHROMATOGRAPHY

Paper chromatography has been particularly useful with phospholipids and fatty acids. Using silicic acid impregnated paper [25] it has been possible to separate phosphatidyl ethanolamine, phosphatidyl choline and lysolecithin as shown in Table 2. The lysophosphatidylethanolamine

Table 2. *Chromatography of phospholipids on silicic acid impregnated filter paper*

Compounds	R_f
Lysolecithin	0·27
Lysophosphatidylethanolamine	0·44
Sphingomyelin	0·45
Plasmalogen	0·62
Lecithin	0·63
Phosphatidylethanolamine	0·80

and sphingomyelin tend to migrate together as do the plasmalogens and lecithins. Phospholipids have also been separated using glass-fibre filter paper impregnated with silicic acid and using methanol–ether solvents [26]. Two-dimensional chromatography on paper in phenol ammonia and in *t*-butanol trichloracetic acid has been shown to provide very good separation with compounds such as glycerylphosphorylcholine, glycerylphosphorylserine, glycerylphosphorylethanolamine, and an inositol phosphate derivative [27].

Fatty acids have been separated from C_2 to C_{24} using filter paper impregnated with high-boiling petroleum hydrocarbon as the stationary phase and using a mobile solvent such as aqueous acetic acid [28]. Using filter paper impregnated with silicone and a solvent system of 70% acetic acid it has been possible to separate unsaturated long-chain fatty acids [29].

The R_f values do not adequately identify or prove the structure of a compound but are useful in confirming or providing additional information.

THIN-LAYER CHROMATOGRAPHY

Although attempts have been made for a considerable number of years to obtain an open-column adsorption chromatography system for micro-analyses using a thin layer of powdered adsorbent on an inert support, only in recent years has any success been achieved in standardizing the method and applying it to a whole range of chemical compounds. Kirchner [30] used narrow glass strips to which the adsorbent was glued with starch adhesive and used silicic acid as the adsorbent layer. However, it was Stahl [31] who described the first practical equipment for the preparation and application of the required uniform layers.

The essentials of the method are as follows. A glass plate is covered with an aqueous slurry of an adsorbent powder containing a binder such as plaster of paris so that a uniform coherent film sticks to the glass. The plate is baked to remove water and to reactivate the adsorbent. The solution of the sample for analysis is spotted on to the film and the charged plate is placed in an enclosed tank containing a suitable solvent. The edge of the plate just dips into the solvent. The solvent is drawn upwards through the layer by capillary action and the components of the mixture are resolved. When the solvent has almost reached the top of the layer the plate is removed, dried and the positions of the components determined. This is done by spraying with a chromogenic reagent or with an indicator where substances are not self-coloured.

The technique is simple and rapid. Because the layers are made of fine grains almost all materials can be separated in 20–40 min and many simple mixtures in less than 10 min. The spots remain small and hence there is excellent separation even with closely related compounds. The sensitivity is often ten to one hundred times greater than paper methods. The technique can be used to fractionate large quantities of materials. Up to 50 mg of material has been separated and isolated on a single plate. The individual component is scraped from the plate and the compound extracted from the adsorbent. The layers may be acidic, neutral or alkaline and can be removed for documentation.

We shall now briefly described the experimental technique; additional details may be found elsewhere [32]. Commercial equipment is now available for thin-layer chromatography.

Production of thin layers

Glass plates, either square 20 × 20 cm or rectangular 5 × 20 cm or 10 × 20 cm of identical thickness (e.g. 6–8 mm) are arranged in a row on a template and coated with the slurry in one continuous operation. This is accomplished by means of a spreading device. (Several such devices can be obtained commercially.) This consists of a spreading trough of aluminium or stainless steel fixed to an aluminium bed on which the glass plates can be aligned. A variety of such devices can be used. The coated plates are stacked for drying in a drying rack and heated to 105–110° C for about 30 min. They are then available for use and can be stored over desiccant. An optimum thickness of 250 μ is used for many analytical problems but other layer thicknesses are also used.

Adsorbents

A variety of adsorbents can be used provided they have the correct particle size. Materials that have been used include silica gel, aluminium oxide, kieselguhr, cellulose powders and polyamide powders. Silica gel is the most generally useful. Whilst adsorbents prepared for column chromatography can be used for thin-film chromatography, the best results are obtained with particle size in the range 1–5 μ. Silica gel G, prepared for this work, can be obtained commercially. It is neutral and has a chromatographic activity near 11 on the Brockmann–Schodder scale. The silical gel also contains calcium sulphate for binding purposes.

The adsorbent is made into an aqueous slurry before it is spread on the plates and is thereby deactivated. It may then be dried in air at room temperature; this is sufficient to produce enough activity for many purposes. The activity depends upon the relative humidity of the atmosphere.

Spotting

The size of the spots have to be as small as possible. This is done by dropping a solution of the sample on to the film, using a micropipette or microsyringe, and placed about 15 mm from one edge of the film. For films of about 250 μ thick the ideal weight of sample is 5–15 μg per spot for linear development and 100–300 μg for semi-circular radial development.

Development

The plate is placed with the origin line at the bottom and parallel to the solvent surface in an enclosed tank containing a suitable solvent. The atmosphere of the tank is saturated with solvent vapour. The solvents must be dry and pure. A list of solvents, arranged in approximate order of eluting power, is shown in Table 3. Suitable solvents are found by trial and error.

Table 3. *Solvents in order of increasing eluting power*

Light petroleum
Cyclohexane
Carbon tetrachloride
Benzene
Chloroform
Ether
Ethyl acetate
1,2-Dichloroethane
Acetone
Ethanol
Methanol
Water
Pyridine
Acetic acid

Detection of components

After the plate is removed from the tank the solvent is allowed to evaporate at room temperature for about 3 min. When the compounds are colourless it is necessary to determine their positions by some suitable process. They can be detected (*a*) by examining films in filtered ultraviolet light. The fluorescent compounds are immediately observed, whilst inclusion of fluorescent agents enables those that absorb ultra-violet radiation to be detected. Zinc sulphide and zinc silicate in the adsorbent enables the position of compounds absorbing between 230 and 390 mμ to be revealed by quenching the fluorescence of the phosphors. (*b*) The film is sprayed with a reagent which forms coloured derivatives of the compounds present. Typical reagents include fluorescein–bromine, sulphuric acid, antimony trichloride, ferric chloride–sodium molybdate, iodine water, and others of a more special nature. When a layer is sprayed with concentrated sulphuric acid and heated to about 200° C for 10 min, most organic compounds, even long-chain saturated hydrocarbons, undergo carbonization and become visible as black or brown spots on a white background. Both saturated and unsaturated lipids may be detected by iodine as brown spots on a pale brown background. The iodine may be sprayed on in CCl_4 solution or the whole plate placed in iodine vapour. Saturated glycerides lose their brown colour more rapidly than unsaturated ones, but may be distinguished more positively by the use of a reagent such as potassium permanganate or osmium tetroxide. The relative volatility of some materials enables their location to be made. Sublimation from the heated layer to a nearby cooled plate is carried out. The sublimed spots are easily visible.

The sensitivity for detection depends upon the nature of the material and reagent but can be at least 1 μg and is often better.

There are a number of other methods of development that can also be used. These may be required where solvent systems produce only partial resolution of the components. One of these methods is multiple-stage development. After development, the solvent is allowed to evaporate completely and the chromatogram redeveloped either in the same or in a less polar solvent. This is useful for separating the less polar compounds, e.g. esters from the more polar compounds, such as free alcohols and acids. The saturated methyl esters of natural fatty acids have been separated from the unsaturated esters by converting the latter into mercuric acetate addition complexes and chromatographing the total mixture [33]. The first development was made with light petroleum and the saturated esters were carried to the front. The second development was made with *n*-propanol containing 1% acetic acid. This resolved the acetate complexes into four groups containing one, two, three and four or more double bonds per molecule. Other techniques include concentration gradient development, continuous development and two-dimensional development.

PARTITION CHROMATOGRAPHY

Thin-film chromatography is considered to be mainly an adsorptive process but it is possible to include a stationary phase and carry out partition chromatography. The aliphatic dicarboxylic acids from oxalic to sebacic acid have been separated from one another by partition chromatography [34] using kieselguhr G. Polyethylene glycol was used as the stationary phase and diisopropyl ether formic acid–water saturated with polyethylene glycol as the moving phase.

REVERSED PHASE PARTITION

By adapting the thin-layer technique for reversed phase partition chromatography, resolution can sometimes be obtained which is not otherwise possible.

This is illustrated by the separation of the methyl esters of the fatty acids containing 10 to 24 carbon atoms [35]. The layers of silica gel are impregnated with silicone oil using a silicone oil–ether solution. The developing solvent used is acetonitrile–acetic acid–water (70:10:25). The methyl esters of lauric, myristic, palmitic and stearic acids are easily separated, as also are oleic, linoleic and linolenic acids. The two series overlap each other, each double bond making the unsaturated ester behave like the saturated ester of two less methylene groups. The esters are detected by spraying with a solution of α-cyclodextrin then exposing to iodine vapour. The esters appear as white spots on a purple background.

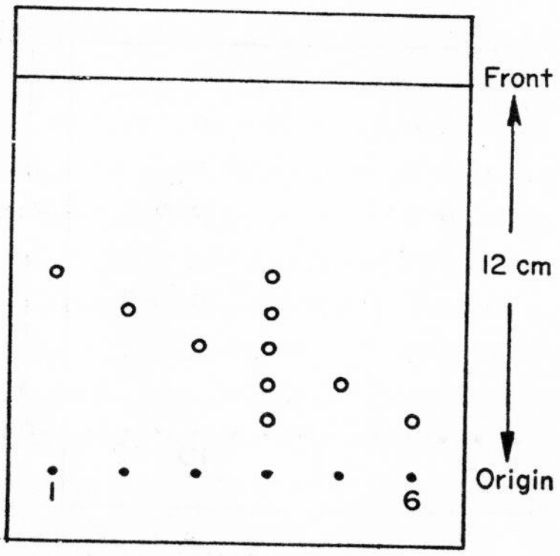

Fig. 4. Partition chromatography of aliphatic fatty alcohols using the thin film technique.

Stationary phase: *n*-undecane; *moving phase:* acetic acid/acetonitrile (1:3) 70% saturated with *n*-undecane. *Load:* 3 μg of each alcohol. *Time:* 80 min.

Key: **1**, lauryl; **2**, palmityl; **3**, stearyl; **4**, mixture of 1, 2, 3, 5 and 6; **5**, erucyl; **6**, behenyl.

Examples of the partition chromatographic technique are shown in Fig. 4 which shows the separation of aliphatic alcohols [36]. The stationary phase is *n*-undecane, the moving phase is acetic acid–acetonitrile (1:3) 70% saturated with *n*-undecane and a load of 3 μg. The separation of aliphatic monocarboxylic acids [36] is illustrated in Fig. 5. Here, the stationary phase was *n*-undecane and the moving phase acetic acid–acetonitrile (1:1) 70% saturated with *n*-undecane. A 10% solution of phosphomolybdic acid in ethanol is sprayed on to the film and the plate is heated to 120° C for suitable times, unsaturated acids about 10 min and saturated compounds longer. The minimum quantity of fatty acid that can be detected with this reagent is 1 μg for saturated acids and

0·5 μg for unsaturated acids. Critical pairs of acids, e.g. oleic and palmitic acids, are difficult to separate using the reversed-phase partition technique, but can be separated by thin-film adsorbtion chromatography. Glycerides can also be separated using this technique [37] and the separation of triglycerides is illustrated in Fig. 6. Here, the stationary phase is tetradecane standardized paraffin on kieselguhr, the moving phase is acetone–acetonitrile (4:1) 80% saturated with tetradecane standardized paraffin. The chromogenic reagent is 0·5% aqueous Rhodamine B (with examinations in u.v. light). The load of each triglyceride is 5 μg.

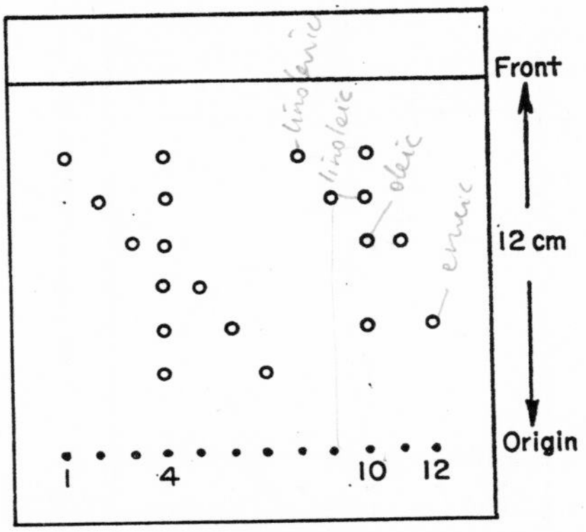

Fig. 5. Partition chromatography of aliphatic fatty acids using the thin film technique.

Stationary phase: n-undecane; *moving phase:* acetic acid/acetonitrile (1:1) 70% saturated with n-undecane. *Chromogenic reagent:* 10% phosphomolybdic acid in ethanol. *Load:* 6 μg of each acid. *Time:* 80 min.

Key: **1**, lauric; **2**, myristic; **3**, palmitic; **4**, mixture of 1–3 and 5–7; **5**, stearic; **6**, arachidic; **7**, behenic; **8**, linolenic; **9**, linoleic; **10**, mixture of 8, 9, 11 and 12; **11**, oleic; **12**, erucic.

In each case, using the same stationary phase, the moving phase is made more polar as the compounds become more polar. Acetone–acetonitrile mixtures are used for esters, a small amount of acetic acid in acetonitrile for alcohols and acetic acid in small amounts of acetonitrile for free monocarboxylic acids. If the same moving phase is used the R_f value of components decrease with increase of molecular weight and the molecular weight of the stationary phase.

Two-dimensional methods have also been used and this is illustrated in Fig. 7 where tri- and diglycerides are separated [36]. This is carried out by using dichloroethane for the first development and acetone–acetonitrile (7:3) and a stationary phase of n-undecane for the second development. The chromogenic reagent is 10% phosphomolybdic acid in ethanol.

Saturated and unsaturated cholesterol esters [38] have also been separated using this technique (Fig. 8). Here, tetralin–hexane (1:3) is used for the first development and methyl ethyl ketone–acetonitrile (7:3), with tetradecane standardized paraffin stationary phase, for the second development.

A variety of thin-layer techniques have been applied to the separation of the different glyceride types which may be present in neutral lipid

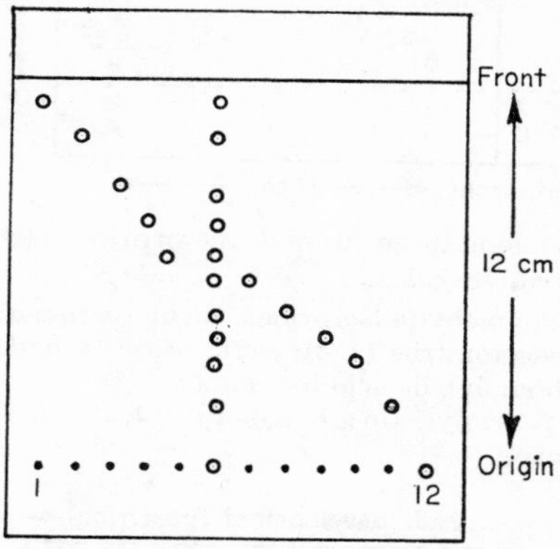

Fig. 6. Partition chromatography of triglycerides using the thin film technique.

Stationary phase: tetradecane standardized paraffin on kieselguhr. *Moving phase:* acetone/acetonitrile (4:1) 80% saturated with tetradecane standardized paraffin. *Chromogenic reagent*: 0·5% aqueous Rhodamine B (examined in ultraviolet light). *Load:* 5 μg of each triglyceride. *Time:* 40 min.

Key: Acids in the triglycerides:

1	Caprylic, caprylic, caprylic	**2**	Capric, capric, capric
3	Lauric, lauric, lauric	**4**	Capric, capric, stearic
5	Lauric, lauric, palmitic	**6**	Mixture of all samples
7	Myristic, myristic, myristic	**8**	Palmitic, palmitic, lauric
9	Capric, stearic, stearic	**10**	Palmitic, palmitic, palmitic
11	Stearic, stearic, palmitic	**12**	Stearic, stearic, stearic

material. Triglycerides, monoaceto-diglycerides and diaceto-monoglycerides have been easily separated by chromatography on silica gel G films [39, 40]. With diglycerides, resolution of 1,2- and 1,3-diglycerides has been achieved [41]. A method has been described for resolving saturated and unsaturated monoglycerides [41a]. This makes use of treatment with ozone at −60° C and reduction of the ozonide with hydrogen and Lindlar catalyst. This treatment causes the unsaturated compounds to rupture at the double bonds, leaving an omega aldehyde

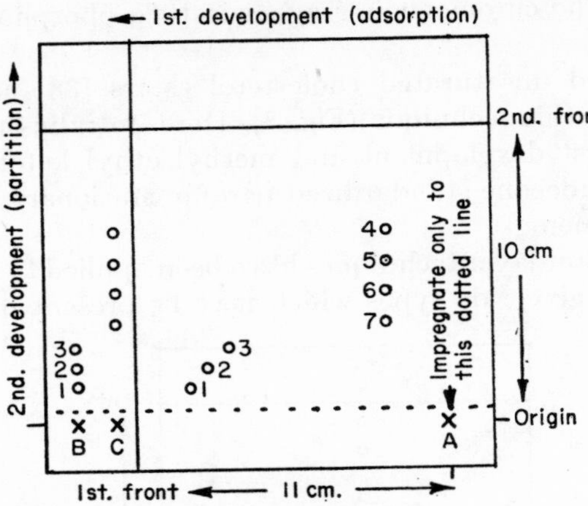

Fig. 7. Two-dimensional combined adsorption–partition chromatography of di- and triglycerides.

Solvents: 1st development (adsorption), dichloroethane; 2nd development (partition), acetone–acetonitrile (7:3); *static phase: n*-undecane. *Chromogenic reagent:* 10% phosphomolybdic acid in ethanol.

Key: **1**, triolein; **2**, trimyristin; **3**, trilaurin; **4**, dilaurin; **5**, dimyristin; **6**, dipalmitin; **7**, distearin.

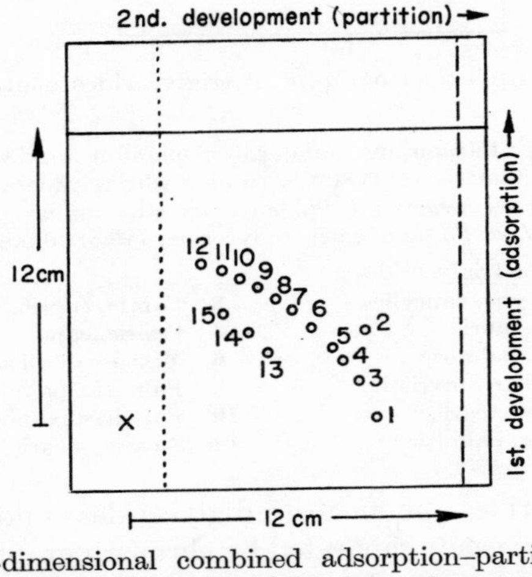

Fig. 8. Two-dimensional combined adsorption–partition chromatography of saturated and unsaturated cholesteryl esters.

Solvents: 1st development (adsorption), tetralin–hexane (1:3); 2nd development (partition), methyl ethyl ketone–acetonitrile (7:3); *static phase:* tetradecane standardized paraffin.

Key: **1**, cholesterol (all other samples are cholesteryl esters); **2**, formate; **3**, acetate; **4**, propionate; **5**, butyrate; **6**, caproate; **7**, caprylate; **8**, caprate; **9**, laurate; **10**, myristate; **11**, palmitate; **12**, stearate; **13**, oleate; **14**, linoleate; **15**, linolenate.

still attached to the glycerol; the saturated compounds are not affected. The aldehydic monoglyceride is easily separated from the saturated monoglyceride by thin-layer chromatography; however, the 1 and 2 isomers are not resolved. These can be distinguished by periodate oxidation of the 1:2 diol part of the 1-monoglyceride molecules. The 1:3 diols are unaffected. A similar treatment has been used for distinguishing saturated and unsaturated diglycerides. This method has also been extended to triglycerides and also to the positional arrangement of the fatty acids in lecithin [41b]. Only 5 mg of material is required. The two basic reactions of the method are demonstrated with glyceryl-1-linoleate-2,3-distearate as follows:

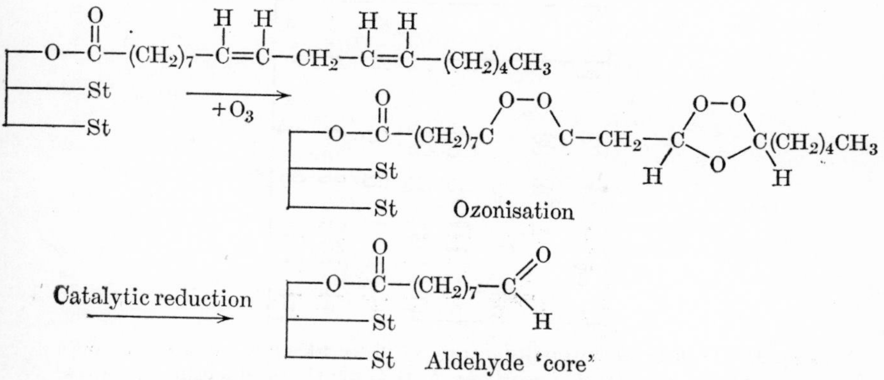

This triglyceride ozonide falls into the class having two ozonide groups; on reduction the ozonide gives an aldehyde core with one aldehyde group. Thin-layer chromatography is carried out on both the ozonides and the aldehyde 'cores'. The ozonides are separated on the basis of the number of ozonide groups–molecule, the aldehyde 'cores' are separated on the basis of the number of aldehyde groups–molecule. The fatty acids are methylated and analysed by gas–liquid chromatography. Application of the reversed-phase partition technique enables glycerides to be resolved into groups according to the total number of carbon atoms in the acid radicals. Tripalmitin is readily separated from trimyristin but not from palmitomyristo stearin, and the positional isomers are not resolved. However, PPP, PPO, POO and OOO (where P is palmitic and O is oleic acid) have been separated using three-fold elution in the reversed-phase process [42]. Triolein–tripalmitin and dioleopalmitin–dielaidopalmitin have also been resolved by three-stage development.

Thin-layer chromatography with the silica impregnated with silver nitrate has enabled the separation of glycerides to be made according to their degree of unsaturation [43, 44], and has also enabled resolution of certain isomeric unsaturated glycerides. These separations depend upon the ability of compounds possessing an olefinic double bond to form co-ordination complexes with silver ions (30 g of silica gel G and aqueous silver nitrate 60 ml, 12·5% solution, are mixed to form a slurry for layer preparation. Development is by the ascending method in a closed tank using a mixture of chloroform 99·5% and acetic acid 0·5% as the developing solvent. The plates are sprayed with an ethanolic solution (0·2%) of dibromo R-fluorescein). Resolution of some glycerides using this technique is shown in Fig. 9.

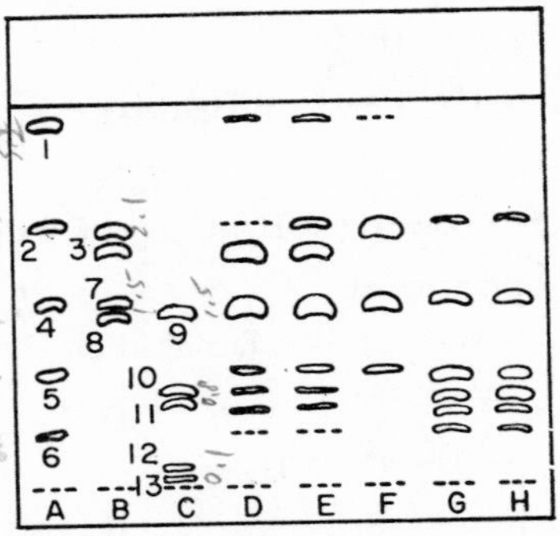

Fig. 9. Thin-layer chromatography of glycerides and natural fats on a silica gel G–silver nitrate adsorbent. A, B, C, synthetic glyceride mixtures; D, lard; E, interesterified lard; F, cocoa butter; G, cottonseed oil; H, groundnut oil.

Key: **1**, tristearin; **2**, 2-oleodistearin; **3**, 1-oleodistearin; **4**, 1-stearodiolein; **5**, triolein; **6**, trilinolein; **7**, 2-linoleodistearin; **8**, 1-linoleodistearin; **9**, 1,3-distearin; **10**, 1,2-diolein; **11**, 1,3-diolein; **12**, monostearin; **13**, monoolein. (Barrett, C. B., Dallas, M. S. J. and Padley, F. B. *Chem. and Ind.*, 1950, 1962.)

In the above manner a detailed picture of the positions of the fatty acids can be made. It enables glyceride composition to be determined directly and is therefore better than the method of using enzymatic hydrolysis, where the acids at the secondary glycerol hydroxyl group are determined and random distribution of the remaining acids is assumed.

Cis- and *trans*-isomers can also be separated using the impregnated silver nitrate technique [45] (see Figs. 10a and 10b). Cholesterol esters of unsaturated acids can also be readily separated [46].

Thin-layer chromatography is being increasingly applied to separations of the phospholipids [47, 48, 49, 50]. The solvents are usually the same as those used for resolving phospholipids by chromatography on silicic acid-impregnated paper and on silicic acid columns. A chromatogram of various phospholipids is shown in Fig. 11. The technique has also been applied to the structure of gangliosides [51].

The high resolving power of thin-layer chromatography makes it useful for providing information prior to column chromatography and it can be used to determine satisfactory solvents for such work. At times thin-layer chromatography can resolve mixtures which appear as a single fraction. The two techniques can be used in a complementary manner.

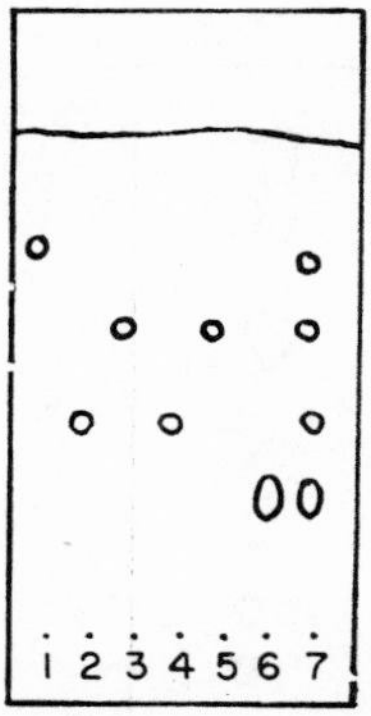

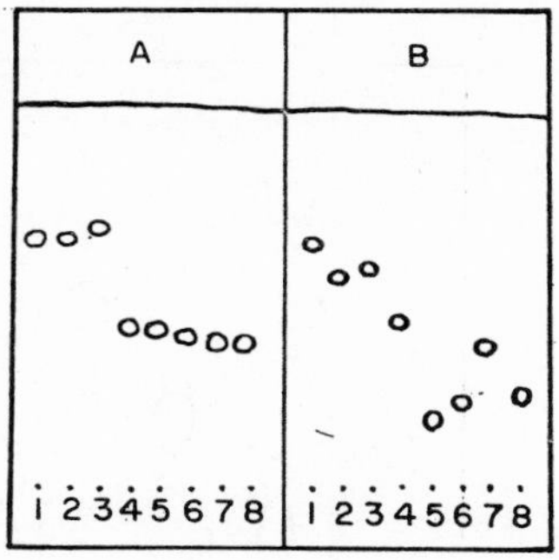

Fig. 10*a*. Thin-layer chromatogram of methyl esters on silver nitrate impregnated silica gel.

Key: **1**, stearate; **2**, oleate; **3**, elaidate; **4**, petroselinate; **5**, petroselaidate; **6**, linoleate; **7**, mixture of 1, 2, 3 and 6.

Developing solvent: diethyl ether–hexane (10+90). Spots were located in ultraviolet light after the plates had been sprayed with 2′,7′-dichlorofluorescein.

Fig. 10*b*. Thin-layer chromatogram of methyl esters on silica gel (A) and silver nitrate impregnated silica gel (B).

Key: **1**, *cis*-9,10-epoxyoctadecanoate; **2**, *cis*-9,10-epoxyoctadec-12-enoate; **3**, *cis*-12,13-epoxy-octadec-9-enoate; **4**, 12-hydroxyoctadecanoate; **5**, 12-hydroxyoctadec-9-enoate; **6**, 12-hydroxyoctadec-9-enoate; **7**, 9-hydroxyoctadecanoate; **8**, 9-hydroxy-octadec-12-enoate.

Developing solvent: diethyl ether–hexane (40+60). Spots were located in ultraviolet light after the plates had been sprayed with 2′,7′-dichlorofluorescein.

Separation of the major neutral lipids and phospholipids of pig sera was made by thin-layer chromatography [52] using chloroform–methanol–water (80:25:2 vol.) for the separation of the phospholipids and light petroleum–diethyl ether–acetic acid (90:10:1) for neutral lipids. The separated lipids are scraped from the plate and put directly into 5% (v/v) sulphuric acid in methanol and refluxed. After extraction the resultant methyl esters are analysed for fatty acid composition using gas–liquid chromatography. These results were compared with those obtained by column chromatography and showed that no loss of unsaturated fatty acids takes place. A comparison has been made of the determination of fatty-acid patterns of individual phospholipids (lecithin, lysolecithin and sphingomyelin) and neutral lipids of serum using gas–liquid chromatography after their separation by thin-layer chromatography [53]. Reproducible results were obtained. The results were compared with those obtained by column chromatography, and the fatty-acid composition of cholesterol esters, triglycerides and free fatty acids are in good

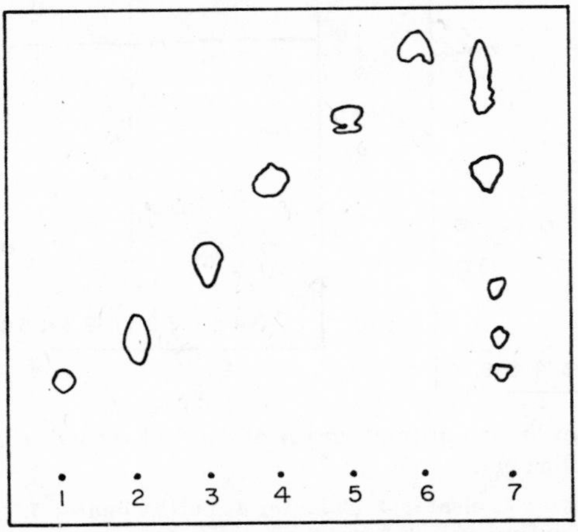

Fig. 11. Separation of phospholipids on silica gel.

Solvent: chloroform–methanol–water, 65/25/4, v/v/v. *Development time:* 2 hours. *Indicators:* Rhodamin B and Dragendorff reagent. *Amounts:* 50–100 γ, each.

Key: **1**, lysolecithin; **2**, sphingomyelin; **3**, lecithin; **4**, cephalin; **5**, cerebroside; **6**, cardiolipid; **7**, mixture.

agreement. With the phospholipids the agreement for values of lecithin and lysolecithin is moderately good, but with sphingomyelin agreement is poor. It is suggested that the speed of the thin-layer technique is useful, as the time for oxidation is thereby reduced.

Thin-layer chromatography has also been used with labelled lipids [54]. The lipid material is labelled by reacting their functional groups with ^{14}C-labelled diazomethane or with ^{14}C- or ^{3}H-labelled acetic anhydride. The ratios of the different lipid classes are determined by radiometry. Consecutively, each of the classes of labelled lipid derivatives is further resolved by reversed-phase paper partition chromatography. The ratios of the components of each class are then determined by scanning their respective activities with a radio chromatograph or by evaluating autoradiograms in a photodensitometer.

GAS–LIQUID CHROMATOGRAPHY

Gas–liquid chromatography has become quickly established as an indispensible tool for research with lipids since its development by Martin and James [55] in 1952. There are now numerous applications and the literature is extremely large. The general theory and practice of gas chromatographic methods are extensively treated in many review articles and books [56–60] and here we shall provide only a brief outline of the technique and its main application to the lipid field.

The basic equipment for the method consists of a column containing a stationary phase connected to a source of moving vapour phase and a detector capable of detecting the separated material. The substance for separation is placed on the column, driven through the column by a carrier gas and the materials are separated depending upon their differing interactions with the stationary phase. The separated materials are detected or characterized by measuring some chemical or physical property. A number of commercial instruments are now available for gas–liquid chromatography.

The size of samples required is small and usually varies from 0·5 to 30 μg. Solids are introduced either in solutions or in melts. Micrometer syringes are used to introduce the sample. The supporting materials for the columns are kieselguhr or ground firebrick, although other materials have been used. The stationary liquid phases are often non-polar materials, such as the paraffin greases and silicone products or of the polar type materials, polyesters. With non-polar phases, unsaturated and branched components emerge before the corresponding saturated ones, whereas with polar phases unsaturated acids emerge after the saturated ones. The efficiency of the separation column is the result of at least two factors, column efficiency and solvent efficiency. The column efficiency is often expressed as the height equivalent of a theoretical plate and is measured by the spread of a component when it passes through a column. The solvent efficiency depends on the distribution coefficients between the liquid and the gas phases and is expressed by the ratio of the retention volumes of two peaks. In each case the choice of stationary phase depends upon the particular separation required. Capillary columns have also been used [61]; these give better separation because of the extreme length of the column and the very small quantity of material required. Very sensitive detectors are, however, necessary. The carrier gases used in gas–liquid chromatography are commonly argon, helium, hydrogen and nitrogen. The detectors most frequently used are the gas density balance, the thermal conductivity cell and the β-ray argon ionization cell.[1] With the gas density balance the response depends only on the difference in concentration and molecular weight between the component and the carrier gas. Components are sometimes converted to CO_2 by combusting over cupric oxide before detection. Identification of the separated components is made by the comparison with standard materials. Within an homologous group the members can be identified by plotting the logarithm of retention times or retention volumes against the chain length or degree of unsaturation. A method has been described for determining the degree of unsaturation of straight-chain and branched-chain components. This is carried out by plotting the logarithm of the retention time measured on one stationary phase against similar values from a different stationary phase. The saturated components lie on one straight line and the unsaturated components lie on separate parallel lines [62]. Fractions may also be trapped and identified using the spectroscopic techniques, e.g. infra-red, ultraviolet, n.m.r. or mass spectroscopy [63], or chemical reaction techniques.

The concept of equivalent chain length (ECL) constants has been introduced [64]. These are for a specific column packing and a given carrier gas independent of experimental conditions, e.g. gas rate, temperature. ECL constants have the advantage over retention indices as being readily recognized as representing the number of carbon atoms or equivalent in a compound. The ECL of a saturated straight-chain acid having *n* carbon atoms is $n{\cdot}0$ in all liquid phases, e.g. stearic acid is 18·0.

For the gas–liquid chromatographic analysis of fatty acids [65] it is often necessary to prepare methyl esters on a micro-scale basis. A number of micro methods have been suggested for this purpose. Catalyzed transesterification in methanol followed by short-path distillation of the methyl esters is one method. Another method uses sodium and potassium methylate in excess methanol; it converts sterol esters, glycerides and phospholipids to methyl esters of their fatty acids. This is followed by separation of the esters from other materials by silicic acid chromatography. A third method uses 10% methanol in ether as solvent and diazo methane, care being taken to avoid an excess of the latter. This method is suitable for preparation of ^{14}C-methyl esters. A typical chromatogram [66] of the methyl esters of some serum fatty acids is shown in Fig. 12.

The method has been applied to the separation of *cis*, *trans* fatty acid isomers by a number of authors [67, 68, 69] as well as to the separation of the polyunsaturated epoxy acids and cyclic fatty acids. *Cis*- and *trans*-

[1] Flame ionization and electron capture detectors are also becoming widely used.

isomers of methyl palmitoleate, oleate and 4-octadecenoate have been separated on packed columns coated with Apiezon M and the *trans*-isomer shown to elute after the corresponding *cis*-isomer [67]. Methyl oleate and elaidate have been separated on a capillary column [70] coated with Apiezon L. Separation of the *cis-trans*-isomers of mono-unsaturated methyl esters has been accomplished using high-resolution capillary columns coated with diethylene glycol succinate polyester [69]. With a polyester liquid phase the *trans*-isomer elutes before the corresponding *cis*-isomer. An examination of the geometrical isomers of

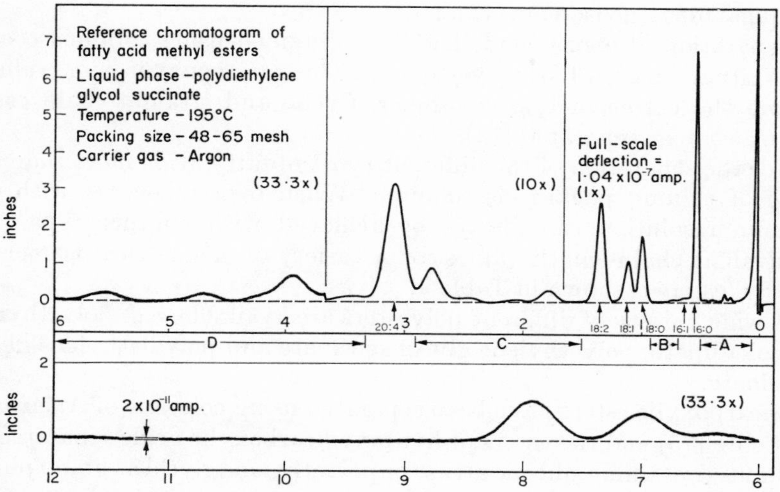

Fig. 12. Typical chromatogram of fatty acid methyl esters from a serum phospholipid fraction. Regions marked A, B, C, D correspond to prepalmitate, palmitoleate to stearate, linoleate to arachidonate and postarachidonate respectively. (After Nicholls [66].)

$\Delta^{9,12}$-octadecanoic acid shows a separation of the *cis-trans* from the *cis-cis* material but an overlap of the *trans-cis* and *trans-trans* compounds occurs with an Apiezon L capillary column. With the polyester column the *cis-cis* and *cis-trans* compounds overlap whilst the *trans-cis* and *trans-trans* acids are separated. Using both columns all the isomers can be resolved.

With Apiezon L columns no indication has been observed of any breakdown on the column of unsaturated fatty acids containing up to four double bonds. This is also the case with polyester stationary phases, but the temperature has to be as low as possible otherwise a loss of the slower-moving acids occurs when the column temperature exceeds 200° C.

Conjugated fatty acids have longer elution times on non-polar and polar liquid phases than their corresponding non-conjugated isomers and both types can be simultaneously analysed. With high-resolution columns the geometrical isomers can be separated [71]. The 9-*cis*, 11-*trans* and 10-*trans*, 12-*cis* octadecandienoates occur together but are separated from the 9-*trans*, 11-*trans* and 10-*trans*, 12-*trans* using an Apiezon L column isomer. There is no separation of *cis-trans* from *trans-cis* isomers. Trienoic acids are well separated from the corresponding dienoic acids in contrast to the unconjugated acids. Some isomerization has been observed of these acids which may limit analysis of the conjugated triene isomers [72].

Separation of epoxy acids has been obtained using columns coated with either Apiezon L or polyester [73]. The *trans*-epoxy isomer is eluted before the corresponding *cis*-isomer. Cyclic and straight-chain esters have also been separated [74].

For the separation of the different types of fatty acids more than one type of column packing is required. When overlap occurs with one column resolution can always be achieved with another type. The equivalent chain-length values for a variety of geometrical isomers of methyl esters is shown in Table 4.

A wide variety of different polyesters are available, e.g. polyethylene glycol adipate, polyethylene glycol succinate and polydiethylene glycol succinate.

Dicarboxylic esters have been separated using columns of Apiezon M on Celite [75] and the esters of hydroxydicarboxylic acids separated on columns containing silicone grease or polyethylene glycol as liquid phase.

The technique has also been extended to the analysis of glycerides despite their low volatility. Monoglycerides have been converted to the allyl esters of the corresponding fatty acids and separated using an Apiezon M column [76], and acetylated mono-, di- and triglyceride mixtures have been analysed on a silicone gum rubber column which was temperature programmed [77]. It was not possible to separate monoolein from monostearin. A number of triglycerides ranging from triacetin to tristearin in molecular weight have been separated using temperature-programmed columns from 250 to 400° C of silicone gum rubber and helium gas. Although the rate of programming was decreased as the temperature increased the glycerides are eluted at closer intervals [78, 79].

Further studies of this application are required to determine its limitations. One of the main problems is the necessity to obtain complete elution of all components before the column packing itself is eluted or the glycerides are decomposed.

Table 4. *Equivalent chain length (ECL) values for various geometric isomers of fatty-acid methyl esters* [69]

Compound	STATIONARY PHASE Apiezon	Polyester
Monoene acids		
Methyl palmitoleate	15·67	—
Methyl palmitelaidate	15·74	—
Methyl 4-*cis*-octadecenoate	17·72	—
Methyl 4-*trans*-octadecenoate	17·81	—
Methyl oleate	17·62	18.55
Methyl elaidate	17·72	18·50
Methyl ricinoleate	—	26·6
Methyl ricinelaidate	—	26·4
Diene acids		
Methyl 9-*cis*,12-*cis*-linoleate	17·48	19·36
Methyl 9-*cis*,12-*trans*-octadecadienoate	17·59	19·36
Methyl 9-*trans*,12-*cis*-octadecadienoate	17·64	19·44
Methyl 9-*trans*,12-*trans*-octadecadienoate	17·64	19·26
Methyl 9-*cis*,11-*trans*-octadecadienoate	18·20	—
Methyl 9-*trans*,11-*trans*-octadecadienoate	18·64	—
Methyl 10-*trans*,12-*cis*-octadecadienoate	18·20	—
Methyl 10-*trans*,12-*trans*-octadecadienoate	18·64	—
Methyl conjugated-*cis,cis*-octadecadienoate	18·4	20·4
Methyl conjugated-*cis,trans/trans,cis*-octadecadienoate	18·2	20·1
Methyl conjugated-*trans,trans*-octadecadienoate	18·6	20·7
Triene acids		
Methyl 9-*cis*,12-*cis*,15-*cis*-linolenate	17·48	20·44
Methyl 9-*trans*,12-*trans*,15-*trans*-octadecatrienoate	17·56	20·23
Methyl 9-*cis*,11-*trans*,13-*trans*-octadecatrienoate	19·1–19·4	22·1–22·5
Methyl 9-*trans*,11-*trans*,13-*trans*-octadecatrienoate	19·5–19·7	22·5–22·8
Epoxy acids		
Methyl 9,10-*cis*-epoxystearate	19·6	23·4
Methyl 9,10-*trans*-epoxystearate	19·5	22·6

In addition to the fatty acids and esters other lipid materials have been examined. Long-chain alcohols [80] and glyceride ethers in the form of their acetates have also been separated [81]. Radioactive fatty acids and esters have been collected [82] and columns have been directly connected to radio activity counters [83].

There have been many analyses of the fatty-acid composition of biologically interesting material using this technique, of which we include only a few here. Studies of the fatty acids from phosphatides and cerebrosides [84], human brain, hen brain [85] and rat brain [86], lecithin and cephalin fractions of mitochondria and microsomes from rat liver [87], the fat fractions from healthy and sick patients [88], human serum [89], and lipoprotein material [90] are among the many applications. A typical scheme due to Nelson and Freeman for the analysis of serum lipids and lipoproteins is shown in Fig. 13.

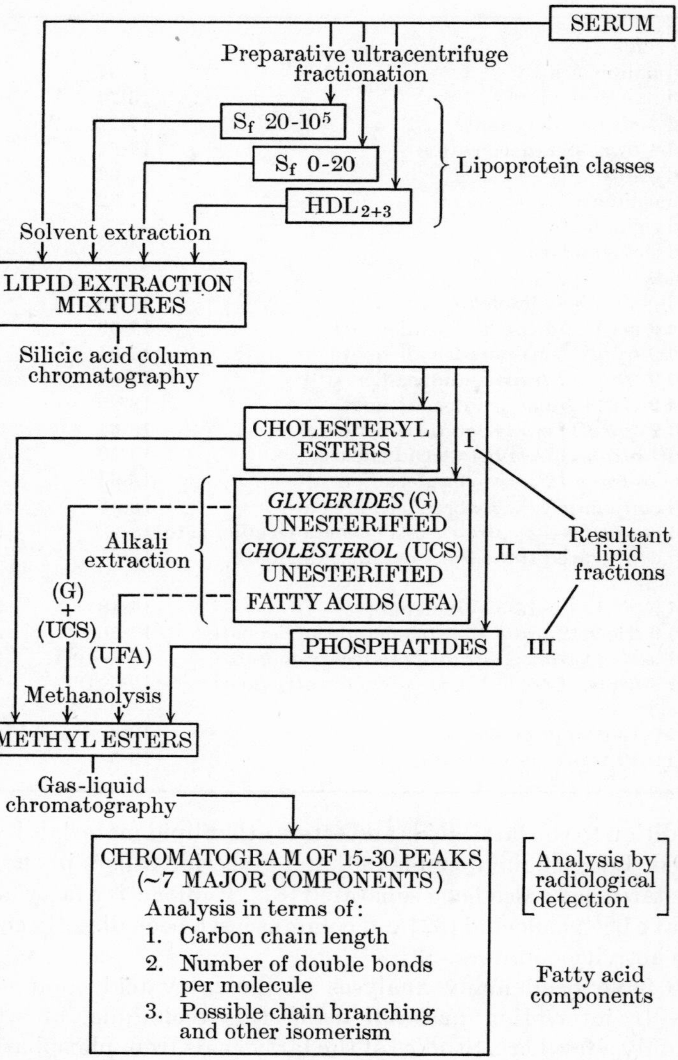

Fig. 13. Scheme for fatty acid analysis of the serum lipids and lipoproteins.

The combination of gas–liquid chromatography allied with enzymatic degradation is a particularly powerful technique for the study of the configuration of the fatty acids in glycerides. The pancreatic lipases specifically hydrolyse the fatty acids almost exclusively from the 1 and 3 positions of the glyceride [91]. The method has been applied to a variety of natural lipid material [92].

As the separation techniques are improved, combined with each other and linked with the spectroscopic techniques, which we will now discuss, the clearer will become our understanding of the detailed role which the lipids play in biological systems.

REFERENCES

1. LINDGREN, F. T., ELLIOT, H. A. and GOFMAN, J. W. (1951) *J. Phys. Colloid Chem.*, **55**, 80.
2. COHN, E. J., HUGHES, W. L. and WEARE, J. H. (1947) *J. Amer. Chem. Soc.*, **69**, 1753.
3. ONCLEY, J. L. (1960) in *Hormones in Human Plasma* (ed. H. N. Antoniades), p. 13. Little Brown & Co., Boston.
4. BERNFIELD, P. (1958) *The Lipoproteins, Methods and Clinical Significance*, p. 24. S. Karger, Basel.
5. ONCLEY, J. L. and GURD, F. R. N. (1953) *Blood Cells and Plasma Proteins*, p. 377. Academic Press.
6. KELTZ, A. and LOVELOCK, J. E. (1955) *Fed. Proc.*, **14**, 84.
7. GURD, F. R. N. (1948) *Studies on Human Serum β-Lipoprotein*, Ph.D. thesis, Harvard University.
8. RAY, B. R., DAVISSON, E. O. and CRESPI, H. L. (1954) *J. Phys. Chem.*, **58**, 841.
9. ONCLEY, J. L. (1958) *The Lipoproteins, Methods and Clinical Significance*, p. 14. S. Karger, Basel.
10. SCHOLFIELD, C. R., DUTTON, H. J., TANNER, F. W. and COWAN, J. C. (1948) *J. Amer. Oil Chemists' Soc.*, **25**, 368.
11. COLE, P. G., LATHE, G. H. and RUTHUEN, C. R. (1953) *Biochem. J.*, **55**, 17.
12. CARTER, H. E., CALANOS, D. E., GIGG, R. H., LAW, J. H., NAKAYAMA, T., SMITH, D. B. and WEBER, E. J. (1957) *Fed. Proc.*, **16**, 81.
13. AHRENS, E. H. and CRAIG, L. C. (1952) *J. Biol. Chem.*, **195**, 299.
14. DUTTON, H. J., SCHOLFIELD, C. R. and JONES, E. P. (1961) *Chem. & Ind.*, 1874.
15. LEA, C. H., RHODES, D. N. and STOLL, R. D. (1955) *Biochem. J.*, **60**, 353.
16. HANAHAN, D. J., DITTMER, J. C. and WARASHINA, E. (1957) *J. Biol. Chem.*, **228**, 685.

17. DE VRIES, B. (1962) Paper presented at the VIth Congress of the International Society for Fat Research, London.
18. HASHTI, E., NIKKARI, T. and JUVA, K. (1963) *Acta Chem. Scand.*, **17**, 538.
19. RENKONEN, O., RENKONEN, O. V. and HIRVISALO, E. L. (1963) *Acta Chem. Scand.*, **17**, 1465.
20. HOWARD, G. A. and MARTIN, A. J. P. (1950) *Biochem. J.*, **46**, 532.
21. POPJÁK, G. and TIETZ, A. (1954) *Biochem. J.*, **56**, 46.
22. DITTMER, J. C. (1958) Thesis, University of Washington.
23. RHODES, D. N. and LEA, C. H. (1957) *Biochem. J.*, **65**, 526.
24. HANAHAN, D. J. (1960) *Lipide Chemistry*, p 28. Wiley & Sons.
25. LEA, C. H., RHODES, D. N. and STOLL, R. D. (1955) *Biochem. J.*, **60**, 353.
26 DIECKERT, J. W. and REISER, R. (1956) *J. Amer. Oil Chemists' Soc.*, **33**, 123.
27a. DAWSON, R. M. C. (1954) *Biochim. Biophys. Acta*, **14**, 374.
27b. DAWSON, R. M. C. (1955) *Biochem. J.*, **59**, 5.
28. KAUFMAN, P. and NITSCH, W. H. (1955) *Fette u. Seifen*, **57**, 473.
29. MANGOLD, H. K., LAMP, B. J. and SHLENK, H. (1955) *J. Amer. Chem. Soc.*, **77**, 6070.
30. KIRCHNER, J. G. (1951) *Analyt. Chem.*, **23**, 420.
31. STAHL, E. (1956) *Pharmazie*,, **11**, 633.
32. TRUTER, E. V. (1963) *Thin-film Chromatography*. Cleaver-Hume Press.
33. MANGOLD, H. K. and KAMMERECK, R. (1961) *Chem. and Ind.*, 1032.
34. KNAPPE, E. and PETERI, D. (1962) *Z. analyt. Chem.*, **188**, 184.
35. MALINS, D. C. and MANGOLD, H. K. (1960) *J. Amer. Oil Chemists' Soc.*, **37**, 576.
36. KAUFMANN, H. P. and MAKUS, Z. (1960) *Fette u. Seifen*, **62**, 1014.
37. KAUFMANN, H. P. and KO, Y. S. (1961) *Fette u. Seifen*, **63**, 807.
38. KAUFMANN, H. P., MAKUS, Z. and DEICKE, F. (1961) *Fette u. Seifen*, **63**, 235.
39. GRUGER, E. H., MALINS, D. C. and GAUGLITZ, E. J. (1960) *J. Amer. Oil Chemists' Soc.*, **37**, 214.
40. MANGOLD, H. K. (1959) *Fette u. Seifen*, **61**, 877.
41a. PRIVETT, O. S. and BLANK, M. L. (1961) *J. Lipid Res.*, **2**, 37.
41b. PRIVETT, O. S. and BLANK, M. L. (1963) *J. Amer. Oil Chemists' Soc.*, **40**, 70.
42. KAUFMANN, H. P. and DAS, B. (1962) *Fette u. Seifen*, **64**, 214.
43. BARRETT, C. B., DALLAS, M. S. J. and PADLEY, F. B. (1962) *Chem. and Ind.*, 1950.
44. DE VRIES, B. (1962) *Chem. and Ind.*, 1049.
45. MORRIS, L. J. (1962) *Chem. and Ind.*, 1238.
46. MORRIS, L. J. (1963) *J. Lipid Res.*, **4**, 357.
47. HABERMANN, E., BANDFLOWER, G. and KRUSCHE, B. (1961) *Klin. Wochenschrift*, **39**, 816
48. WAGNER, H. (1960) *Fette u. Seifen*, **62**, 1115.

49. WAGNER, H., HÖRHAMMER, L. and WOLFF, P. (1961) *Biochem. Z.*, **334**, 175.
50. JATZKEWITZ, H. and MEHL, E. (1960) *Z. physiol. Chem.*, **320**, 251.
51. KUHN, R., WIEGANDT, H. and EGGE, H. (1961) *Angew. Chem.*, **73**, 580.
52. BOWYER, D. E., LEAT, W. M. F., HOWARD, A. N. and GRESHAM, G. A. (1963) *Biochem. J.*, **89**, 24P.
53. BOWYER, D. E., LEAT, W. M. F., HOWARD, A. N. and GRESHAM, G. A. (1963) *Biochim. Biophys. Acta*, **70**, 423.
54. MANGOLD, A. K. (1959) *Fette u. Seifen*, **61**, 877.
55. MARTIN, A. J. P. and JAMES, A. T. (1952) *Biochem. J.*, **50**, 679.
56. PHILIPS, C. (1956) *Gas Chromatography*. Butterworths, London.
57. KEULEMANNS, A. I. M. (1957) *Gas Chromatography*. Reinhold, New York.
58. DESTY, D. H. (1957) *Gas Chromatography*. Butterworths, London.
59. JAMES, A. T. (1960) *Methods of Biochemical Analysis* (ed. D. Glick), vol. 8. Interscience, New York.
60. KAUFMANN, H. P., MANKE, G. and LEHMANN, K. (1961) *Fette u. Seifen*, **63**, 1109.
61. BURCHFIELD, H. P. and STORRS, E. E. (1962) *Biochemical Applications of Gas Chromatography*. Academic Press, New York.
62. JAMES, A. T. (1959) *J. Chromatog.*, **2**, 552.
63. JANAK, J. (1960) *J. Chromatog.*, **185**, 684.
64. MIWA, T. K., MIKOLAJCZAK, K. L., EARLE, F. R. and WOLFF, I. A. (1960) *Analyt. Chem.*, **32**, 1739.
65. FONTELL, K., HOLMAN, R. T. and LAMBERTSEN, G. (1960) *J. Lipid Res.*, **1**, 391.
66. NICHOLS, A. V., REHNBORG, C. S. and LINDGREN, F. T. (1961) *J. Lipid Res.*, **2**, 203.
67. JAMES, A. T. and MARTIN, A. J. P. (1956) *Biochem. J.*, **63**, 144.
68. JAMES, A. T. (1959) *J. Chromatog.*, **2**, 552.
69. LITCHFIELD, C. C., REISER, R. and ISBELL, A. F. (1963) *J. Amer. Oil Chemists' Soc.*, **40**, 302.
70a. LIPSKY, S. R., LOVELOCK, J. E. and LANDOWNE, R. A. (1959) *J. Amer. Chem. Soc.*, **81**, 1010.
70b. LIPSKY, S. R., LANDOWNE, R. A. and LOVELOCK, J. E. (1959) *Analyt. Chem.*, **31**, 852.
71. BEERTHUIS, R. K., DIJKSTRA, G., KEPPLER, J. G. and RECOURT, J. H. (1959) *Ann. N.Y. Acad. Sci.*, **72**, 616.
72. MORRIS, L. J., HOLMAN, R. T. and FONTELL, K. (1960) *J. Lipid Res.*, **1**, 412.
73. MORRIS, L. J., HOLMAN, R. T. and FONTELL, K. (1961) *J. Lipid Res.*, **2**, 68.
74. BLACK, L. T. and EISENHAUER, R. A. (1963) *J. Amer. Oil Chemists' Soc.*, **40**, 272.
75. JAMES, A. T. (1957) *Gas Chromatography* (ed. D. H. Desty), p. 232. Butterworth, London.

76. MCINNES, A. G., HANSEN, R. P. and JESSOP, A. S. (1956) *Biochem. J.*, **63**, 702.

77. HUEBNER, V. R. (1959) *J. Amer. Oil Chemists' Soc.*, **36**, 262.

78. HUEBNER, V. R. (1961) *J. Amer. Oil Chemists' Soc.*, **38**, 628.

79. FRYER, F. H., ORMAND, W. L. and CRUMP, G. B. (1960) *J. Amer. Oil Chemists' Soc.*, **37**, 589.

80. CROPPER, F. R. and HEYWOOD, A. (1953) *Nature*, **172**, 1101.

81. BLOMSTRAND, R. and GÜRTLER, J. (1959) *Acta Chem. Scand.*, **13**, 1466.

82. JAMES, A. T., PEETERS, G. and LAURYSSENS, M. (1956) *Biochem. J.*, **64**, 726.

83. POPJÁK, G. J., LOWE, A. E., MOORE, D., BROWN, L. and SMITH, F. A. (1959) *J. Lipid Res.*, **1**, 29.

84. SWEELEY, C. C. (1959) *Biochim. Biophys. Acta*, **36**, 268.

85. JOHNSTON, P. V. and KOMMEROW, F. A. (1960) *Proc. Soc. Exp. Biol. Med.*, **104**, 201.

86. BEVAN, L. and BARTLEY, W. (1961) *Biochem. J.*, **79**, 159.

87. MACFARLANE, M. G., GRAY, G. M. and WHEELDON, L. W. (1961) *Biochem. J.*, **77**, 626.

88. JAMES, A. T., LOVELOCK, J. E., WEBB, J. and TROTTER, W. R. (1957) *Lancet*, **272**, 705.

89. NELSON, G. J. and FREEMAN, N. K. (1960) *J. Biol. Chem.*, **235**, 578.

90. REHNBORG, C. S., NICHOLS, A. V. and ASHIKAWA, J. K. (1961) *Proc. Soc. Exp. Biol. Med.*, **106**, 547.

91a. DESNUELLE, P., NAUDET, M. and CONSTANIN, M. J. (1954) *Biochim Biophys. Acta*, **13**, 491.

91b. MATTSON, F. H., and BECK, L. W. (1956) *J. Biol. Chem.*, **219**, 735.

92. COLEMAN, M. H. (1961) *J. Amer. Oil Chemists' Soc.*, **38**, 685.

3. Ultraviolet spectroscopy

Ultraviolet absorption spectroscopy was the earliest spectroscopic technique to be applied in chemistry and, to the field of lipids in particular, it has been of considerable value in many such studies. Whilst the use of other spectroscopic techniques has increased in recent years this branch of spectroscopy has continued to be valuable for studying unsaturation and changes in unsaturation of lipid molecules [1].

We shall first consider the basic theoretical background to ultraviolet absorption spectroscopy before going on to consider its applications to lipids.

Theoretical considerations

Ultraviolet absorption spectra arise from electronic transitions between energy levels in a molecule. The order of magnitude of the difference between electronic energy levels is ~ 100 kcal/mole whereas that between vibrational levels is ~ 5 kcal/mole and between rotational levels is $\sim 0{\cdot}01$ kcal/mole. Now the average thermal kinetic energy of a molecule at room temperature is ~ 1 kcal/mole and thus molecules will normally be in the lowest vibrational level of the ground electronic state but will possess several quanta of rotational energy. Thus when an electronic transition occurs the molecule may also undergo changes in vibrational and rotational energy. The consequence of this is that instead of obtaining a single line, a series of several lines are obtained which in the liquid or solvent are not usually resolved due to instrument resolution or to intermolecular effects, and an absorption band is observed.

The frequency or wavelength position of the ultraviolet absorption bands depend upon ΔE, the difference in the energy levels by the Bohr relationship, and these energy levels in turn depend upon the electrons concerned. Non-bonding lone-pair electrons are the least strongly bound in a molecule whilst within the bonding levels π-electrons have higher energies than corresponding σ-electrons. Within the antibonding levels this order is reversed. The order of energy levels is shown in Fig. 14. The $\sigma \rightarrow \sigma^*$ absorptions which occur with saturated compounds, e.g. the paraffins, occur in the far ultraviolet. The $n \rightarrow \pi^*$ transitions such as occur with carbonyl compounds generally lie to longer wavelengths than those arising from $\pi \rightarrow \pi^*$ transitions which occur with triple-bond and cumulative systems of double or triple bonds.

Olefins possess strong absorption bands in the 160 to 200 mμ region, due to an electron transition from a bonding to an anti-bonding π-orbital without a change of spin. When conjugated systems are examined it is found that the longer the conjugated unsaturated system the deeper the colour. Thus as the number of conjugated groups increase the maximum of the absorption band shifts from 200 to 400 mμ. Thus two ethylenic linkages on conjugation to C=C—C=C give rise to an absorption band of considerable intensity, about 230 mμ trienoic conjugation shifts the absorption to about 268 mμ, a tetraenoic system to 315 mμ, a pentaenoic system to 346 mμ and so on.

	Level	*Symbol*
↑	*Antibonding σ*	(σ^*)
	Antibonding π	(π^*)
E	*Non-bonding*	(n)
	Bonding π	(π)
	Bonding σ	(σ)

Fig. 14. Order of the electronic energy levels.

This empirical observation is nicely explained using the free-electron model [2], in which it is assumed that the π-electrons of a conjugated system move in a container of uniform potential with dimensions determined by the size of the molecule bounded by infinitely high potential walls. The quantization of the lower electronic energy levels is determined by the length of the conjugated system L and they have energies

$$E = h^2 j^2/8mL^2 \tag{3.1}$$

An electronic transition between levels of quantum numbers j and $j+1$ requires the absorption of light of frequency

$$\nu = h(2j+1)/8mL^2 \tag{3.2}$$

If account is taken of the potential variation, due to the alternation of double and single bonds, and the effective length of the polyene chain is taken to be one or two bond distances beyond the terminal conjugated atom, a relationship is obtained

$$\nu(\text{cm}^{-1}) = \nu_L + 3 \times 10^5/x^2 - \nu_l)/N \tag{3.3}$$

where x is the average bond distance in Å and N is the effective number of π-electrons, or number of bonds increasing by two for the addition of each ethylene or each acetylene group, and ν_l is the frequency of the convergence limit of the series [3].

INTENSITY

To describe the intensity of a band the Beer–Lambert relationship is used.

$$\log_{10}\frac{I_0}{I} = E = Kcl, \tag{3.4}$$

where I_0 is the intensity of the incident radiation,
I is the intensity of the transmitted radiation,
c is the concentration in gram/litre,
K is the specific extinction coefficient,
l is the path length in centimetres,

$$\log_{10}\frac{I_0}{I} = E \text{ is commonly termed the optical density.} \tag{3.5}$$

The numerical value of K depends upon the units in which c and l are expressed. The molecular extinction coefficient ϵ is defined by $\epsilon = E/cl$, where c is in g.-moles/l and l in centimetres.

The extinction 1 per cent 1 cm is given by

$$E^{1\%}_{1\,\text{cm}} = E/cl, \tag{3.6}$$

where c is in g/100 ml and l in cm.

$E^{1\%}_{1\,\text{cm}}$ does not involve the molecular weight and is used in ultraviolet spectrophotometric work for compounds of unknown or uncertain constitution.

The maximum extinction coefficient of an absorption band may be markedly affected by a change of phase or of solvent but the band area $A = \int K d\nu$ often remains constant, giving a better measure of absorption intensity. The band area is related to the oscillator strength.

In quantum theory the oscillator strength depends upon the absorption frequency ν and the electric transition moment length Q

$$f = 1{\cdot}085 \times 10^{-5}\,\nu Q^2 \tag{3.7}$$

where ν is in cm^{-1} and Q is in Å.

The transition moment length is a measure of the mean displacement of the electron during the transition and is given by

$$Q = \int \phi_n(\Sigma_i r_i)\,\phi_m\,dr \tag{3.8}$$

where ϕ_n and ϕ_m are the respective wave functions of the ground and excited state whilst r_i is a vector defining the position of the ith electron.

Electronic displacements of 1–3 Å give oscillator strengths of the order of unity. This corresponds to a maximum extinction coefficient in solution of about 10^5.

TERMINOLOGY

Some confusion exists over terminology and various alternative terms and symbols have been used. Some of the most common are shown in Table 5.

Table 5. *Alternative terms and symbols used in spectroscopy*

I_0	– the intensity of incident radiant energy
I	– the intensity of transmitted radiant energy
T	– transmittance $= \frac{I}{I_0}$ (also transmittancy and transmission)
$\%T$	– per cent transmittance $= T \times 100$ (also per cent transmittancy and per cent transmission)
E (or D)	– the optical density $= \log_{10} \frac{I_0}{I}$ (also absorbance A and absorbancy A_s)
K	– the specific extinction coefficient $= E/cl$ (also absorptivity K and absorbancy index a_s)
ϵ or E (or K)	– the molecular extinction coefficient $= KM$ (also molar absorptivity and molar absorbance index)
M	– molecular weight
c	– concentration
l (or b, d, x)	– the path length in centimetres

QUANTITATIVE ANALYSIS

A fairly frequent analytical problem is the determination of a single constituent after undergoing physical or chemical treatments to remove interfering materials having absorption. In this case it is first necessary to pick the best wavelength for measurement to be made. This is usually the absorption maximum since a small wavelength error makes only a very small error in the intensity determination. It is next necessary to test for adherence to the Beer–Lambert relationship by plotting optical density against concentration. If a linear relationship is obtained, comparison of the specific extinction coefficient with that given by a standard pure material enables the concentration of material present to be determined.

Occasionally, due to association or other effects, the solutions do not adhere to the Beer–Lambert relationship, i.e. the optical density–concentration curve shows marked curvature. In this case the specific extinction coefficient is not independent of concentration and measurements must be referred to the prepared curve.

Determination of two or more components

When two substances are present in a sample it is usually necessary to measure absorption at two wavelengths in order to determine both materials. The curves of the individual pure substances must also be known. From the curves one wavelength is chosen at which a single component is the sole or major absorber. Knowing the optical densities at the two wavelengths and the extinction coefficients of the pure substances at the two wavelengths the concentrations of the two substances can be determined.

This may be extended to more than two components by the same principle; a separate wavelength is chosen for each component. In the infra-red region, because of various complications, a simplified method of calculating concentrations of single components in a multicomponent system by using the baseline technique has become popular.

The most accurate optical density range for quantitative determinations is from 0·2 to 0·8 and cell lengths must be chosen to give suitable densities. The theoretical optimum value is 0·4343, which corresponds to 37% transmittance.

Experimental techniques

There are now several commercial instruments available for obtaining ultraviolet spectra. Until recently most instruments were of the manual or non-recording type, but at present many automatic recording instruments are available.

A typical recording instrument is the Unicam SP.700. This is a double-beam instrument made to record automatically the transmission of a sample relative to a reference in the ultraviolet, visible and near infra-red regions. For the ultraviolet region the source is a hydrogen arc-lamp and the dispersion unit a fused silica prism. The light, after emerging from the exit slit, is split into two parts and passed alternatively through the two cell compartments by a synchronous chopper unit. The beams are recombined on to a single photomultiplier detector. The resultant signal is amplified and distributed into separate channels corresponding to the reference and sample beam respectively. The transmittance of the sample cell with respect to the reference cell is indicated by the position of the pen on to a continuous chart recorder. Spectra are obtained with a linear wave number presentation and transmission 100% or 10% full scale, or optical density range 0–2 full scale.

Non-recording instruments include the Beckman D.U., Coleman 14 and Hilger Uvispek, whilst amongst the recording instruments are the Cary, General Electric, Beckman, Perkin Elmer and Optika spectrophotometers.

Cells used in the spectrophotometers for the ultraviolet region are of silica with path lengths ranging from 1 mm to 40 mm.

TECHNIQUE

Wavelength calibration is carried out by using suitable standards such as the emission lines from a mercury vapour lamp, by using suitable solutions, e.g. potassium chromate, or by an interference technique using closely spaced partially reflecting surfaces held parallel to one another and separated by a known small distance.

Calibration of the intensity scale is usually pre-set by the instrument manufacturer. Occasional checks can be made by the measurement of carefully prepared solutions.

Slit width can affect accurate quantitative determination. Since absorption bands have a finite width, the true intensity varies with the slit width. In some cases it is necessary to plot an optical density–slit width relationship for standard conditions and from which the optical density at zero slit width can be obtained by extrapolation. Usually a constant slit width is satisfactory.

The most common method for obtaining the ultraviolet spectrum is by dissolving the material in a suitable solvent. The solvent should be transparent over the wavelength region studied. Some of the commonly used solvents are: distilled water, ethyl alcohol, cyclohexane, heptane, octane and iso-octane. Distilled water is transparent between 200 and 700 mμ whilst ethyl alcohol is satisfactory down to 210 mμ. It is important that the ethyl alcohol does not contain traces of benzene or aromatic material. Solvents are now available on the market suitable for absorption spectroscopy, e.g. the Spectrosol solvents. It is quite usual to purify the crude solvents by some chromatographic treatment.

With the usual 1 cm cell a concentration of 10 to 40 mg/litre is usually adequate. The optimum optical density can be obtained by further dilution. It is important to appreciate that interaction may sometimes occur between the solvent and solute, giving rise to a different spectrum from that obtained in other solvents.

Applications to lipids

ABSORPTION SPECTRA OF FATTY ACIDS

The absorption spectra of the saturated and non-conjugated unsaturated fatty acids lie mainly in the vacuum ultraviolet region. Some investigations of the fatty acids have been made in this region [4]. The saturated acids such as acetic, caprylic and myristic have a broad but weak absorption band ($\epsilon \sim 50$) with a maximum near 205 mμ and a region of strong absorption beginning at 185 mμ and still increasing in intensity at 173 mμ. The measurements did not extend below this wavelength. The weak band at 205 mμ is found to be intensified in some branched-chain acids [5].

The acids containing one double bond, e.g. oleic acid, have the main wavelength absorption at 183 mμ and the absorption is more intense. A comparison of oleic and elaidic acid shows that the spectrum of the latter is shifted some 4 mμ towards the visible part of the spectrum and the maximum absorption increased by about 15%. The polyunsaturated acids with isolated double bonds such as linoleic and linolenic acids have similar absorption but of greater intensity, and this is usually additive in character. With the saturated acids the region above 220 mμ is almost transparent whilst the non-conjugated unsaturated acids show only unselective end absorption.

The acids containing one double bond which is conjugated with the carboxyl group show absorption λ_{max} near 208 to 210 mμ and a lower ϵ_{max} than do the conjugated dienes. Such α-ethylenic acids have been observed in the tubercle bacillus and the acid mycolipenic has been synthesized and studied [6]. The λ_{max} is found to be shifted to a longer wavelength by the introduction of a methyl group on one side of the ethylenic linkage [7, 8]. The nature of the branching appears to affect both the position λ_{max} and also ϵ_{max} with these acids [9].

Only one natural conjugated dienoic acid has been observed. This is 9,14-dihydroxyoctadec-10,12-dienoic acid, present in tung oil [10]. It has been suggested that this arises as a consequence of oxidation. (Many fats give rise to a peak at 230 mμ but this is considered to be the result of processing.) Stillingic acid (deca-2,4-dienoic acid) has the two double bonds conjugated to the carboxyl group. This was observed in stillingic oil and shows λ_{max} near 260 mμ and an extinction coefficient lower than that of the conjugated trienoic acids [11]. The higher homologue, dodeca-2,4-dienoic acid, has also been observed in the seed oil of *Sebastiana lingustrina* [12] and has a similar λ_{max}. The molecular extinction coefficient, however, appears to be higher than that for stillingic acid.

Conjugation of the unsaturated linkages brings the absorption bands into the easily accessible region. The data for the acids are given in Table 6. As the conjugation increases the extinction rises. With conjugation of three or more double bonds the absorption shows three peaks, a main one and subsidiary maxima on each side (Fig. 15). There is some doubt concerning the conjugated dienes about the presence of this

Table 6. λ_{max} *for various chromophores*

Chromophore	Type	Compound	λ_{max}
—C=C—	Ethylenic	Octene-3	185 mμ
—C=C—C=O	Conjugated ene-al	Croton aldehyde	217 mμ
$(—C=C—)_2$	Conjugated diene	9,11-Linoleic acid	232 mμ
—C=C—C=C—C=O	Conjugated diene-al	Sorbaldehyde	263 mμ
$(—C=C—)_3$	Conjugated triene	α-Elaeostearic acid	270 mμ
$(—C=C—)_4$	Conjugated tetraene	Parinaric acid	302 mμ

structure. It may occur with the *trans-trans*-isomer [13] but not the *cis*-isomers, although instrumental factors may be important in affecting resolution. As the number of double bonds increase the peaks spread further apart [14]. A relationship for the maximum of each peak has been

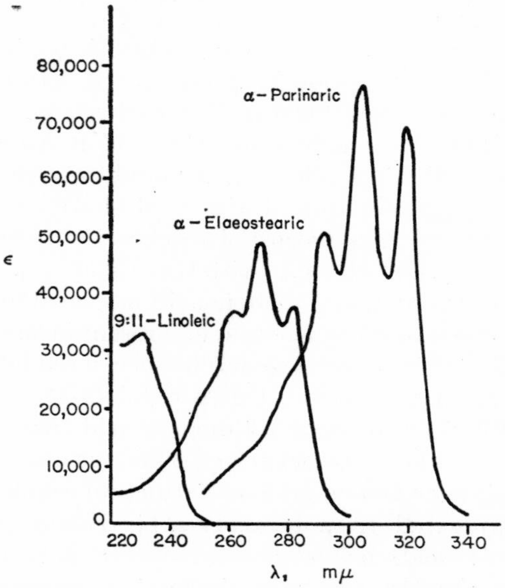

Fig. 15. Absorption spectra [1] of trans-trans 9:11 linoleic, α-elaeostearic and α-parinaric acids.
Solvent: ethanol.

put forward, i.e. $\lambda^2 = A + B_n$. Here, n is the number of conjugated double bonds and A and B are constants. A is the same for any acid and all the bands whilst B may be one of three constants, B_1, B_2 or B_3, each applicable to one band. These three constants differ in such a way that higher values of n cause the three bands to spread out.

Differences in absorption spectra also occur with the different geometrical isomers of the same acid. The all-*trans* form has the highest extinction coefficient and the *cis*-isomers usually have their maxima displaced to longer wavelengths. Such differences in spectra are observed in Fig. 16.

With acetylenic acids selective absorption in the accessible ultraviolet region only occurs when this group is conjugated with a double or another triple bond. A number of these acids have been observed in

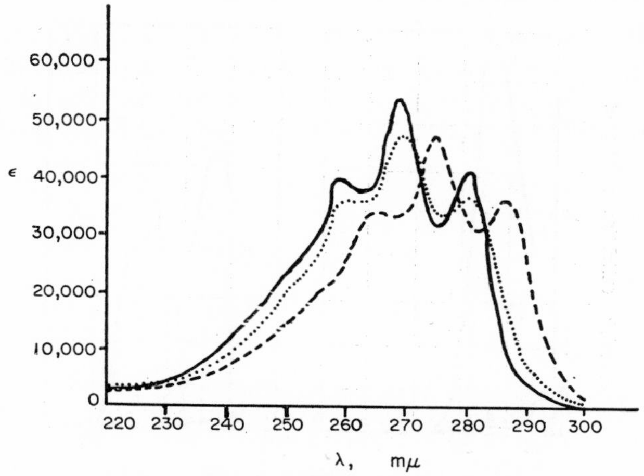

Fig. 16. Absorption spectra [1] of geometrical isomers of octadeca-9:11:13-trienoic acid. α-Elaeostearic (*cis-trans-trans*) .....; β-elaeostearic (*trans-trans-trans*) ——; and punicic acid (*cis-cis-trans*) ----.
Solvent: cyclohexane.

nature. Erythrogenic (isanic) acid or octadec-17-ene-9,11-diynoic acid has been observed in boleko nuts and the acid has been synthesized. The spectrum of the synthetic acid shows three sharp absorption bands [15] of low intensity between 227 and 254 mμ. Another acetylenic acid, octadec-11-en-9-ynoic acid, has also been studied [16]. It has λ_{max} at 229 mμ and ϵ_{max} 16,200 and an inflexion near 240 mμ.

ALKALI-ISOMERIZATION METHODS

Because most of the naturally occurring polyunsaturated fatty acids have their double bonds non-conjugated they do not show selective absorption in the accessible ultraviolet region. This has led to a tremendous interest in methods in which the double bonds in these acids are rearranged so as to form a conjugated system. The technique commonly used is that of alkali isomerization. The conjugation is induced in a non-conjugated polyene by treatment with alkali at an elevated temperature and the intensity of the resulting absorption is used as a measure of concentration.

The technique has its origin in the discovery that mixed fatty acids show stronger ultraviolet absorption after saponification [17, 18]. The intensity of the absorption is observed to increase with the time of the saponification and be particularly marked with the more unsaturated

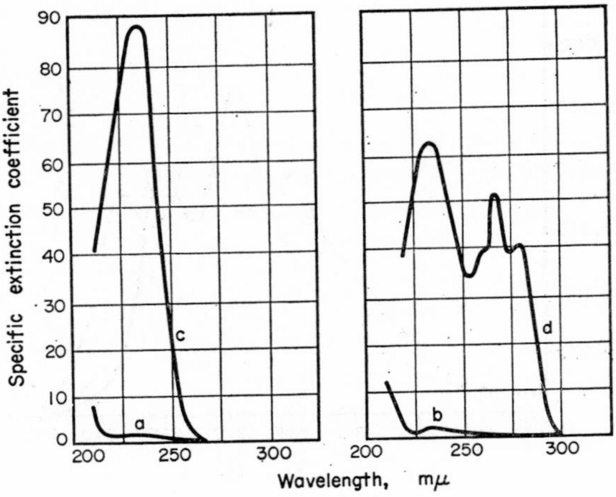

Fig. 17. Ultra-violet absorption spectra of normal linoleic (*a*) and linolenic (*b*) acids, and alkali-isomerized linoleic (*c*) and linolenic (*d*) acids.

acids. This was followed up by the discovery [19] that linolenic acid is convertible into an isomeric form giving an absorption spectrum similar to that of elaeostearic acid with λ_{max} at 270 mμ, and clearly migration of the double bond had occurred. Partial isomerization also takes place giving rise to a peak at 230 mμ, suggesting that migration of one of the two double bonds has occurred.

The first attempt to develop a spectrophotometric method for the direct determination of linoleic and linolenic acid was by Mitchell, Kraybell and Zscheile [20]. They used alkaline ethylene glycol and heated the material to 180° C. After cooling and diluting in ethanol the extinctions at 234 mμ and 268 mμ were determined and compared with a blank solution. The spectra of 9,12-linoleic acid before and after alkali isomerization are shown in Fig. 17. The absorption of the original is low.

Following this work many modifications of the method were published and it was extended to include arachidonic acid [21], pentanoic acids [22] and hexaenoic acids [23]. A complete method is issued by the American Oil Chemist's Society. A great deal of discussion and many reviews [1, 24, 25] of the method have been given, and here we merely make one or two brief comments about the method.

(*a*) *Time of heating*

The time of heating the unsaturated acids in alkali can be important since the newly formed conjugated system is susceptible to destructive processes, e.g. polymerization and cyclization can occur. With a mixture of acids isomerization occurs at different rates and picking the optimum time can be difficult.

(*b*) *Temperature*

A similar problem arises with the choice of an optimum temperature since the development of conjugation varies from acid to acid. Usually one selected temperature is used and reasonable reproducible results are obtained.

(*c*) *Solvent for isomerization*

The commonly used solvent is glycol but glycerol has also been used and both are accepted in standard procedures.

(*d*) *Concentration of alkali*

Potassium hydroxide is commonly used at a concentration of between 6 and 11%, although other materials may be used, e.g. sodium or lithium hydroxide. The formation of conjugated from unconjugated isomers is not complete under these conditions. This is particularly so with tetra- and penta-conjugated systems. The best concentration of alkali for these systems is just over 20% but there are nevertheless remaining difficulties.

(*e*) *Correction procedures*

Correction procedures are necessary to allow for the presence of conjugated diene material present before isomerization. This is done by examining the fat spectroscopically for conjugated di-, tri- and tetraenoic acids previous to isomerization. The extinction at 232 mμ is considered to arise from conjugated diene acids and absorption from the carboxyl groups. The latter absorption is found using pure stearic acid or methyl stearate. After subtraction the amount of diene acid is determined from extinction coefficients of the pure conjugated dienoic acids. The conjugated trienoic acids are determined from the extinction at 268 mμ.

It is important to note that, whilst correction procedures have been of value in increasing the scope and accuracy of the method, at times application of full correction procedures sometimes decreases the final accuracy of the determination!

(f) Possible exceptions

It is commonly accepted that for two double bonds to become conjugated they must be in a 1,4-diene system and similarly for three or more bonds. This may not be the case. Acids with 1,5 unsaturated systems are said by Japanese workers [26] to undergo conjugation.

(g) Accuracy

Despite enormous effort to improve the procedure, at present it is precise but of unknown accuracy. With tetra-enoic and higher unsaturated acids the method is least satisfactory. The general methods put forward are not capable of unlimited application. The method has been described as 'a long complicated exacting series of manipulations requiring above average skill and experience'.

The method has to be applied with caution. It is said to be readily applicable to those systems containing only *cis* acids but not those containing *cis-cis*, *cis-trans*, and *trans-trans* acids.

OXIDATION

A rather comprehensive study of oxidation of fatty acids, esters and fats has been made [27].

Oleic acid and elaidic acid were oxidized by exposing them in air in an oven at 68° and 63° C respectively, the acids being in alcoholic solutions. Alkaline solutions were also studied and equal volumes of 20% aqueous KOH added. The oxidation of oleic acid in alcohol did not produce appreciable changes in the absorption spectra, whereas the absorption in alkali increases progressively from the beginning of oxidation. It was concluded that if the increased absorption after 40 days is due to formation of conjugated trienes, then this amounted to about 0·1 and 0·26% triene content respectively. Oxidation of elaidic acid is similar to that of oleic acid but the absorption rises more rapidly during the early stages of oxidation. In both cases the greatest increases in absorption takes place in the later stage of the oxidation accompanied by the decomposition of peroxides, indicating that the compounds responsible for the increased absorption are secondary products produced by decomposition of the primary products.

Oxidation of dihydroxystearic acid shows an inflection at 2750 Å but the general absorption is greater than that of the oleates and elaidic acid.

The keto acids give very similar spectra. Linoleic acid shows almost identical spectra in alcohol and in alkali. Upon oxidation a marked increase in absorption occurs and is much greater with the alkali solution. Conjugated linoleic acid whose spectrum is unchanged by alkali becomes sensitive to alkali after oxidation. The absorption at 2350 Å decreases markedly whilst absorption above 2500 Å increases, bands appear at 2750 and 3800 Å. The increase in the absorption at 2750 Å is not directly related to peroxide value. Linolenic acid, ethyl linolenate, β-licanic acid, pseudo-eleostearic acid and α-eleostearic acid have also been studied. Oxidation of the non-conjugated trienes is accompanied by an increased absorption with the production of maxima at 2350 and 2750 Å. Oxidation of the conjugated trienes is accompanied by decreased absorption in the region 2600–2800 Å. It is concluded that since the absorption spectra of the pure acids are not affected by cold alkali the absorption bands which appear with autoxidation are due to oxygen-containing chromophores.

The unsaturated esters were examined at 37° C to be comparable with other enzymatic studies and the oxygen absorption was related to the spectroscopic absorption. With ethyl oleate oxidation is so slow that no appreciable change in spectrum is observed during the experiment. The rate of oxygen uptake is found to increase with the number of bonds present in the ester. The oxidation of ethyl, and possibly methyl, linolenate causes the formation of chromophores which exhibit fine structure in the spectra of their alcoholic and alkaline solutions. This is not observed with ethyl linoleate. The rate of formation of the chromophores absorbing at 2325 Å in oxidizing linolenate and the rate of oxygen uptake is found to be consistent with the postulated formation of a conjugated monohydroperoxide.

LIPOPROTEINS

Ultraviolet absorption studies [28] have been made with lipoproteins of the density class 1·035 in a study of alterations occurring during their isolation and storage which are attributed to autoxidation. The effect of age on the absorption spectrum is shown in Fig. 18. Above 410 mμ the change corresponds to the loss of the spectrum of carotenoid pigments. Below this wavelength there is a general rise in the absorption spectrum with a band near 274 mμ and another near 230–235 mμ. The latter is particularly apparent in fresh alcohol–ether extracts. These changes are associated with changes in fat autoxidation and compared to changes of absorption spectrum observed with the autoxidation of ethyl linoleate The latter changes have been associated with autoxidation steps, such as the formation of a hydroperoxide, rearrangement, splitting off water and formation of a conjugated diene ketone [29].

The ultraviolet absorption is markedly increased when strong alkali is added to an aged lipoprotein preparation or to an alcohol–ether extract, consistent with autoxidation steps occurring [28]. It is concluded that the spectral changes observed during storage in solution for 1 or 2 months represents alteration of a considerable proportion of the unsaturated fatty acids present.

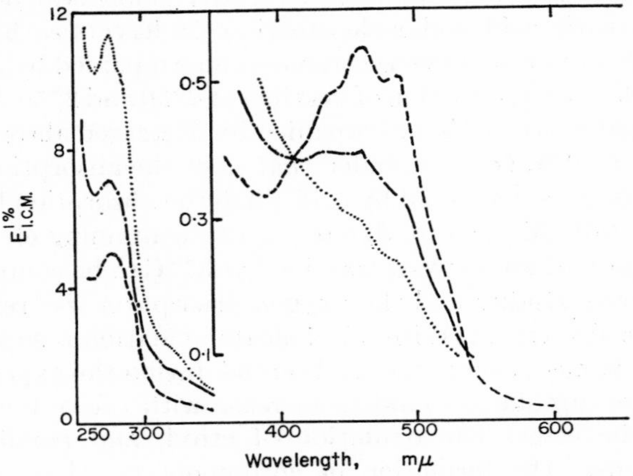

Fig. 18. Effect of age on absorption spectrum of β-lipoprotein. (Density class 1·035). ----- aged 3 days in solution; ..... aged 39 days in solution; —·—· aged 67 days as euglobulin precipitate, plus three days in solution. (Gurd, F. R. N., Ph.D. thesis, Harvard University.)

REFERENCES

1. PITT, G. A. J. and MORTON, R. A. (1957) *Progress in the Chemistry of Fats and Other Lipids*. Pergamon Press, London.
2. KUHN, H. (1948) *J. Chem. Phys.*, **16**, 840.
3. JAFFE, H. H. and ORCHIN, M. (1962) *Theory and Application of Ultra Violet Spectroscopy*. Wiley.
4. RUSOFF, I. I., PLATT, J. R., KLEVENS, H. B. and BURR, G. O. (1945) *J. Amer. Chem. Soc.*, **67**, 673.
5. CASON, J. and SUMRELL, G. (1951) *J. Org. Chem.*, **16**, 1177.
6. BAILEY, A. S., POLGAR, N. and ROBINSON, R. (1953) *J. Chem. Soc.*, 3031.
7. CASON, J. and SUMRELL, G. (1951) *J. Org. Chem.*, **16**, 1181.
8. CASON, J., ALLINGER, N. L. and WILLIAMS, D. E. (1953) *J. Org. Chem.*, **18**, 842.
9. BRANDE, E. A. and EVANS, E. A. (1955) *J. Chem. Soc.*, 3331.

10. DAVIS, S. B., CONROY, E. A. and SHAKESPEARE, N. E. (1950) *J. Amer. Chem. Soc.*, **72**, 124.
11. CROSSLEY, A. and HILDITCH, T. P. (1949) *J. Chem. Soc.*, 3353.
12. HOLMAN, R. T. and HANKS, D. P. (1955) *J. Amer. Oil Chemists' Soc.*, **32**, 356.
13. KASS, J. P. (1944) *Protective and Decorative Coatings* (ed. J. P. Matiello), vol. 4, p. 362.
14. HAMMOND, E. G. and LUNDBERG, W. O. (1953) *J. Amer. Oil Chemists' Soc.*, **30**, 438.
15. BLACK, H. K. and WEEDON, B. C. L. (1953) *J. Chem. Soc.*, 1785.
16. LIGTHELM, S. P., SCHWARTZ, H. M. and VON HOLDT, M. M. (1952) *J. Chem. Soc.*, 1088.
17. MORTON, R. A., HEILBRON, I. M. and THOMPSON, A. (1931) *Biochem. J.*, **25**, 20.
18. GILLAM, A. E., HEILBRON, I. M., HILDITCH, T. P. and MORTON, R. A. (1931) *Biochem. J.*, **25**, 30.
19. MOORE, T. (1937) *Biochem. J.*, **31**, 138.
20. MITCHELL, J. H., KRAYBELL, H. R. and ZSCHEILE, F. P. (1943) *Ind. Eng. Chem.*, **15**, 1.
21. BRUCE, B. A. and SWAIN, M. L. (1945) *J. Opt. Soc. Amer.*, **35**, 532.
BRUCE, B. A. and SWAIN, M. L., SCHAEFFER, B. B. and AULT, W. C. (1945) *Oil and Soap*, **22**, 219.
22. HERB, S. F. and RIEMENSCHNEIDER, R. W. (1952) *J. Amer. Oil Chemists' Soc.*, **29**, 456.
23. HAMMOND, E. G., and LUNDBERG, W. O. (1953) *J. Amer. Oil Chemists' Soc.*, **30**, 433.
24. O'CONNOR, R. T. (1955) *J. Amer. Oil Chemists' Soc.*, **32**, 616.
25. HERB, S. F. (1955) *J. Amer. Oil Chemists' Soc.*, **32**, 153.
26. TOYAMA, Y. and SHIMO-OKA, T. (1954) *Mem. Fac. Eng. Nagoya Univ.*, **5**, 323.
27. HOLMAN, R. T., LUNDBERG, W. O., LAUER, W. M. and BURR, G. O. (1945) *J. Amer. Chem. Soc.*, **67**, 1285, 1386, 1390; (1946) *Oil and Soap*, **23**, 10.
28. GURD, F. R. N. (1948) Thesis Ph.D., Harvard University.
29. HOLMAN, R. T. (1946) *Trans. 1st Conf. Biol. Antioxidants*, 37.

4. Infra-red and Raman spectroscopy

Considerable use has been made of infra-red spectroscopy in the field of lipids [1–3]. Lipids have been examined in the vapour, liquid and solid state and in solution. Because of the long hydrocarbon chains present in most lipid material polymorphism can occur and this brings complications to the infra-red spectra of the material in the solid state. At the same time these spectra can provide a considerable amount of additional information. Increasing use is being made of the technique for qualitative and quantitative estimations on lipid material and studies of solid state behaviour combined with X-ray methods are also increasing.

The use of Raman spectroscopy for the study of lipids on the other hand has been relatively sparse. Our treatment of this technique will therefore be brief. This limited use is related to the ease of recording spectra using the two methods. Until recently Raman spectra were obtained by means of photographic detection and it is only in the last year or two that an excellent recording instrument (the Cary Raman spectrophotometer) has become available. Although there are still some limitations with this technique it seems certain that in future many more studies of lipids will be made, particularly in aqueous solutions.

Theoretical considerations

Infra-red spectra arise from the interaction between matter and electromagnetic radiation of wavelength between about 1 to 50 μ (most commercial instruments cover the region from 2 to 15 μ but some recent instruments extend from 0·6 to 25 μ). The atoms of a molecule can vibrate in a number of modes, and for absorption of energy to occur it is essential that there should be a change in the dipole moment of a molecule during the vibration. The number of normal modes of vibration for a non-linear molecule is equal to $3n-6$ (where n = number of atoms in the molecule). Each normal mode of vibration can occur independently of the other modes, and the absorption band for each mode is known as its fundamental band or fundamental frequency. The fundamental frequencies are usually found in the 2–15 μ region. Most of the vibrational modes involve the very complicated motion of all the atoms, and the particular values of the frequencies are, therefore, highly characteristic for a particular molecule. In some cases the mode of vibration is highly localized in the molecule and involves the motions of atoms in a particular group giving rise to a characteristic group frequency. Empirically it has been shown that these frequencies are almost independent of the structure of the remainder of the molecules and hence afford a good diagnostic method for the presence of specific groupings. The environment of the group can modify the frequency slightly. This is illustrated in Table 7 with reference to the carbonyl group. It is thus possible to deduce from the wavelength of the carbonyl absorption band whether, for example, the environment of the carbonyl group is in a carboxylic acid or ester. Similar considerations apply to other groupings. Correlation charts are valuable for summarizing the empirical information relating frequency of band to the particular groups present and reference spectra are available. A list of absorption bands[1] useful for the application of infra-red spectroscopy to lipids taken from the excellent compilation of O'Connor [2] is given in Table 7.

Table 7. *Wavelength and wave number values for various functional groups*

Wavelength $\frac{\mu}{cm^{-1}}$	Functional group
	O—H stretching
2·75–2·80 μ (3636–3571 cm⁻¹)	Free —O—H
2·82–2·90 (3546–3448)	Bonded —O—H···O of single-bridged dimer
2·95–3·25 (3390–3077)	Bonded H···O—H···O— (with H on each O) of double-bridged polymer or cyclic 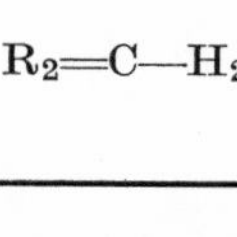 dimer
	C—H stretching
3·00–3·05 (3333–3279)	R≡C—H
3·22–2·25 (3105–3077)	R_2═C—H_2

[1] Note that $\tilde{\nu}$ (wavenumber, cm^{-1}) = 1/(wavelength, cm) = $1/\lambda$.

Table 7—*continued*

Wavelength μ cm^{-1}	Functional group
3·28–3·32 (3049–3012)	R_2═C—HR
3·40–3·45 (2941–2899)	R—C—H_3
3·42–3·50 (2924–2857)	R_2—C—H_2
3·45–3·48 (2899–2874)	R_3—CH
3·50–3·70 (2857–2703)	R—C(═O)—H
3·70 (2703)	C—H and bonded O—H···O combination band
	N—H stretching
2·85 and 2·95 (3509 and 3390)	Free N—H primary amide
3·00 and 3·15 (3333 and 3175)	Bonded N—H··· primary amide
2·90–2·95 (3448–3390)	Free N—H secondary amide
3·00–3·05 (3333–3279)	Bonded N—H··· secondary amide, single bridge (*trans*)
3·15–3·18 (3175–3144)	Bonded N—H··· secondary amide, single bridge (*cis*)
3·22–3·25 (3106–3077)	Bonded N—H··· secondary amide cyclic dimer
2·85 and 3·02 (3509–3311)	N—H primary amine
2·85–3·02 (3509–3311)	N—H secondary amine
2·95–3·12 (3390–3205)	N—H imines
3·20–3·30 (3125–3030)	$\overset{+}{N}$—H_3 amino acids
4·65 (2150)	$\overset{+}{N}$—H
	C—D stretching
4·64 2155	C—D
4·84 2066	C—D

Table 7—*continued*

Wavelength μ (cm⁻¹)	Functional group
	P—H, P—OH stretchings
4·05–4·25 (2469–2353)	P—H
3·70–3·90 (2703–2564)	P—OH (broad absorption)
	C=O and C=C, C≡C stretching vibrations
	Region 3·0 *to* 6·0 μ
	Aldehydes
5·75–5·80 (1739–1724)	RC(H)=O, saturated
5·83–5·90 (1715–1695)	PhC(H)=O, aryl
5·85–5·95 (1709–1681)	R—CH=CH—C(H)=O, α,β-unsaturated
	Ketones
5·80–5·85 (1724–1709)	RCH_2—C(=O)—CH_2R, saturated
6·00–6·05 (1667–1653)	R—CH=CH—C(=O)—R, α,β-unsaturated
5·63 (1776)	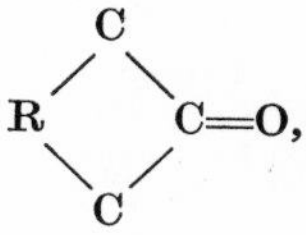 , 4-membered, saturated ring
5·73 (1745)	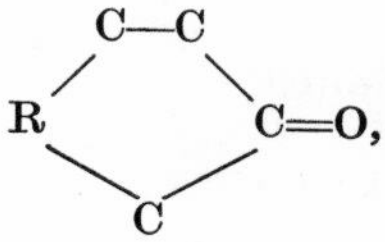 , 5-membered, saturated ring
5·81 (1721)	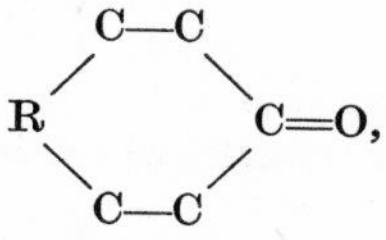 , 6-membered, saturated ring or

Table 7—*continued*

Wavelength μ / cm^{-1}	Functional group
	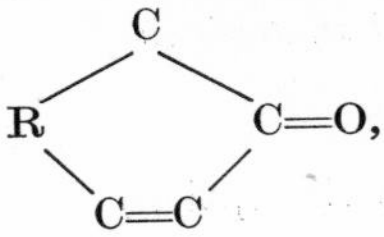 5-membered, α,β-unsaturated ring
5·95 (1681)	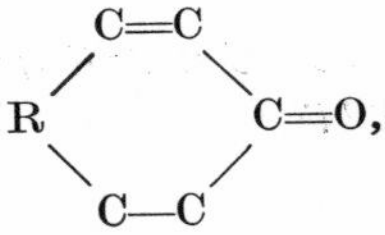 6-(or 7-) membered, α,β-unsaturated ring
	Acids
5·68 (1761)	O R—C—OH, saturated monomer
5·80–5·88 (1724–1701)	O···HO R—C—OH, O=C—R, saturated dimer
5·90–5·92 (1695–1689)	OH R—C=C—C=O, α,β-unsaturated
5·90–5·95 (1695–1681)	OH Ph—C=O, aryl
6·00–6·05 (1667–1653)	Chelated hydroxy-acids, some dicarboxylic acids
	Esters
5·65 (1770)	OCH_3 H_2—C=C—C=O, vinyl ester
5·75 (1739)	OCH_3 R—C=O, saturated
5·80–5·82 (1724–1718)	OCH_3 R—C=C—C=O, α,β-unsaturated, or R—COOPh, aryl
	C=C, C≡C stretching
6·0–6·1 (1667–1639)	C=C *cis* only (weak when internal in symmetrical molecules)

Table 7—*continued*

Wavelength μ cm^{-1}	Functional group
3·03 (3300)	HC≡CH
4·67–4·76 (2141–2101)	RC≡CH
4·44–4·58 (2252–2183)	RC≡CR
5·14 and 9·45 (1946–1058)	C═C═C
	C—H deformations, saturated groups *Region* 6 *to* 7μ
6·7–6·9 (1492–1449)	—C—H_2— group
6·8–7·0 (1471–1429)	—C—C—H_3 group, asymmetrical deformation
7·15–7·20 (1399–1389)	—C—(C—H_3)$_3$ group
7·20–7·25 (1389–1379)	—C—(C—H_3)$_2$ group
7·25–7·30 (1379–1370)	C—C—H_3 group symmetrical deformation
7·30–7·35 (1370–1361)	—C—(C—H_3)$_2$ group
7·45–7·50 (1342–1333)	—C—H— group
	C—O stretching and C—OH bending *Region* 7·7 *to* 10·0 μ *Alcohols*
8·3–8·9 (1205–1124)	Tertiary open-chain saturated
8·9–9·2 (1124–1087)	Secondary open-chain saturated
9·2–9·5 (1087–1053)	Primary open-chain saturated
8·3–8·9 (1205–1124)	Highly symmetrically-branched secondary
8·9–9·2 (1124–1087)	α-Unsaturated or cyclic tertiary
9·1–9·2 (1099–1087)	Secondary with branching on one α-carbon
9·2–9·5 (1087–1053)	Secondary, α-unsaturated or alicyclic 5- or 6-membered ring

Table 7—*continued*

Wavelength μ / cm^{-1}	Functional group
9·5–10·0 (1053–1000)	Secondary: di-unsaturated, α-branched and unsaturated, or 7- or 8-membered ring Primary: α-branched and/or unsaturated Tertiary: highly unsaturated
	Acids
7·75–7·80 (1290–1282)	C—O
8·40–8·45 (1190–1183)	C—O
	Esters
7·90–8·00 (1266–1250)	C—O
8·40–8·50 (1190–1177)	C—O
	Anhydrides
7·7–8·3 (1299–1205)	Cyclic
8·5–9·5 (1177–1053)	Open chain
	Phosphorus
(1300–1230)	P=O (hydrogen bonding can shift to lower frequencies) usually two bands are observed
9·52 (1050)	P—O—CH_3 aliphatic
	C—H deformation about a C=C and skeletal vibrations *Region* 10·0 *to* 15·0 μ *C—H bending*
10·05–10·15 (995–985)	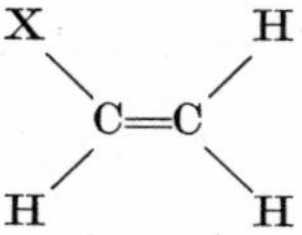
10·20–10·36 (980–965)	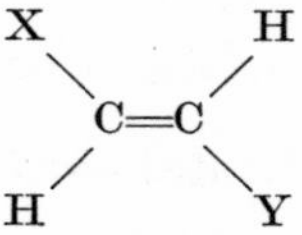 (*trans* only)

Table 7—*continued*

Wavelength μ (cm^{-1})	Functional group
10·90–11·05 (917–905)	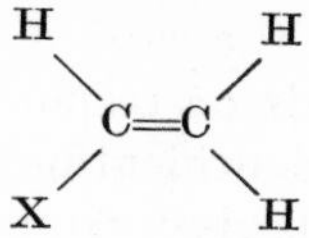
11·17–11·30 (895–885)	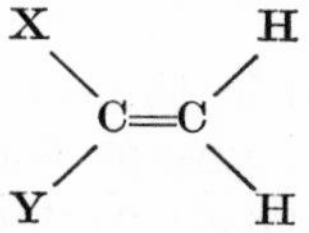
11·90–12·50 (840–800)	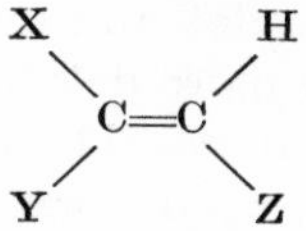
13·0 > 15·0 (769–667)	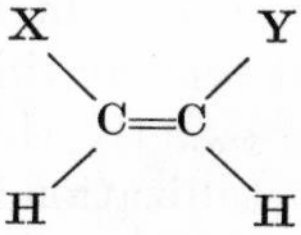 (*cis* only)
	Skeletal vibrations
9·75 and 11·55 (1026 and 866)	Cyclopropane
10·9 and 11·3 (917 and 885)	Cyclobutane
10·31 and 11·16 (885 and 896)	Cyclopentane
9·63 and 9·86 (1038 and 1014)	Cyclohexane
11·05 and 11·60 (905 and 862)	Cyclohexane
11·2 (893)	Epoxy-oxirane ring derived from internal R—C=C—R (*trans* only)
12·0 (833)	Epoxy-oxirane ring derived from internal R—C=C—R (*cis* only)
12·0 (833)	Hydroperoxide
12·95 (772)	Ethyl
13·0 (769)	CH_2 rocking on long carbon chain
13·5 (741)	*n*-Propyl
13·8 (725)	Hydroperoxide

An unknown substance can usually be identified by comparison with the spectra of molecules of known constitution. When a perfect match between spectra is obtained, identification is complete. This procedure can be carried out quite rapidly with infra-red absorption data arranged on punched cards by sorting through the cards for the particular card containing the main absorption bands corresponding to those of the unknown material. Even if complete identification is not possible by this means, usually two or three compounds giving somewhat similar spectra can be found.

When the substances are examined in the solution state the bands rising from the particular functional groups can usually be readily identified. However, when the materials are examined in the solid state the spectra are considerably more complex and many additional bands are observed. We shall discuss this in more detail later. In addition to this the occurrence of polymorphism considerably complicates the situation. As many as five or six polymorphic forms may be obtained for any one compound and as many as five or six different infra-red spectra may also be obtained. This means that for identification of known and unknown material both have to have exactly the same pretreatment before the spectra are obtained, e.g. crystallization from the same solvent at the same rate and at the same temperature. Orientation and partial polarization of the radiation within the spectrometer can cause intensity variations which require caution. Polarization data may also be obtainable on the solid state materials providing information about the orientation and packing of the lipid molecules in the solid state.

The infra-red spectra of compounds containing asymmetric carbon atoms are interesting. In solution and in the liquid state the spectra of enantiomorphs are identical. However, in the crystalline state the spectrum of the racemic compound can differ from that of the *d* or *l* rotatory isomers because of differences in the manner of packing in the crystal. (The spectra of diastereoisomers are different in all physical states.) The polymorphism of the isomers may also differ from that of the racemic material.

If we now consider scattered radiation instead of absorbed radiation, we find that this may be of three types, Tyndall, Rayleigh and Raman. The Raman scattered radiation differs from the other two in that the frequency of the radiation differs from that of the incident radiation. When the frequencies are higher than the incident radiation the lines are referred to as anti-Stokes lines and, if they are lower, Stokes lines. The difference in frequency between the incident radiation and a Stokes or anti-Stokes line is called the Raman frequency. The frequencies of the Raman lines correspond to the molecular vibrational frequencies.

The origin of the Raman effect is in the change of polarizability of a molecule during its vibration. Thus if α varies with Q_c, the normal co-ordinate of a vibration of frequency ν_c, then

$$\alpha = \alpha^0 + (\partial\alpha/\partial Q_c)_0 Q_c \tag{4.1}$$

where α^0 is the polarizability of the molecule when the nuclei are in the equilibrium positions and $(\partial\alpha/\partial Q_c)_0$ is the rate of change of α^0 with Q_c for infinitesimal nuclear displacements.

The quantity $(\partial\alpha/\partial Q_c)_0$ must be different from zero for the normal frequency ν_c to appear in the Raman effect, so that a normal vibration is active only if the nuclear displacements change the polarizability o the molecule.

Antisymmetrical vibrations usually give rise to strong infra-red absorption bands while symmetrical vibrations give rise to Raman lines. Infra-red and Raman spectroscopy give information which can supplement each other, e.g. if a molecule has a centre of symmetry no fundamental frequency can occur in *both* the infra-red and Raman spectrum.

An important property of the Raman effect is the polarization of the scattered radiation. Irrespective of the polarization of the incident light the Raman lines are observed to be partially polarized. With simple molecules measurement of the polarization of a Raman line can be of great assistance in identifying the associated mode of vibration, e.g. the interpretation of many of the characteristic group frequencies of complex molecules such as the CH-stretching bands of methyl and methylene groups are based on such measurements. The polarization of a Raman line is described by ρ, the depolarization factor, where

$$\rho = Is/Ip \tag{4.2}$$

and Is and Ip are the two intensities perpendicular and parallel to the exciting radiation respectively (ρ can have values from 0 to $\frac{6}{7}$).

If the exciting radiation is non-polarized the depolarization factor has a value of $\frac{6}{7}$ for all Raman lines associated with non-totally symmetrical vibrations, whilst for totally symmetrical vibrations ρ is less than this and may approach zero.

Instruments and techniques

Considerable progress has taken place in recent years with the production of commercial infra-red spectrometers. Nowadays most instruments are double beam in operation.

A typical modern infra-red spectrometer is the Unicam SP.100. The source of radiation is a water-cooled Nernst filament, the dispersion unit is a rocksalt prism Littrow monochromator with an off-axis paraboloid collimating mirror of 35 cm focus. The detector is a Golay pneumatic cell having a large receiving area and good mechanical robustness. The output of the detector is amplified by a simple and stable electronic amplifier and fed to a homodyne rectifier which gives a d.c. output proportional to the difference in intensity between sample and reference beam. The difference signal is fed to a servo mechanism which adjusts the star-wheel beam attenuator in the reference beam until the difference signal is reduced to zero. The percentage transmission is recorded linearly in wavenumbers (cm^{-1}) by means of marker pens. The optical system may be evacuated to prevent the effects of strong atmospheric absorption. Gratings are provided as accessories, thereby producing a prism-grating double monochromator of high resolving power and low stray light. The radiation first enters the grating monochromator through a curved entrance slit, is dispersed and then enters the prism monochromator through a wide intermediate slit. Radiation from the prism leaves through a straight exit slit and is condensed on to a Golay detector. The curvature of the entrance slit compensates for image curvature introduced by the prism monochromator.

Cell windows are usually made of rocksalt or potassium bromide. For gaseous samples, fairly long cells 1 to 20 cm may be used, and with a fixed-length cell the pressure of the gaseous sample may be varied to achieve a suitable optical density in the wavelength region of interest. Liquids may be examined for qualitative analysis by using rocksalt cells which vary in thickness from about 0·01 mm to several millimetres, or, quite frequently, by squeezing between rocksalt plates.

Solid and liquid samples may be examined in solution and this is most frequently used for quantitative analysis. Suitable solvents are a problem because of their absorption in the infra-red region. Water is not often used because of its high absorption and because most work is carried out with cells made with rocksalt windows. Carbon tetrachloride and carbon disulphide are used because they have considerable transparent regions. Other solvents used include acetone, methyl formate and nitromethane. A variable-path cell is of considerable convenience for balancing out the solvent absorption when using a double-beam spectrometer. Solid samples may be examined after melting between rocksalt plates or by making the sample in a medium such as Nujol or perfluorokerosine, or by pressing the sample into a plate with potassium bromide or potassium chloride. The use of low-temperature and high-temperature cells are also particularly valuable with lipid materials either to study their polymorphic behaviour or to confirm the identification of a compound by obtaining more than one spectrum and we shall discuss many applications of this. Beam-condensing units are now becoming commercially available and are useful for examining small samples of lipid material.

A method for attaining the infra-red spectra of small samples obtained by thin-layer chromatography has been described [4]. A circle of Kraft paper the same size as a normal potassium bromide disc, but having a small hole 2·4 × 7 mm at its centre, is placed in the press. The amount of sample is reduced to 50–100 μg and 20–30 mg of potassium bromide. The charge is placed in the hole and the disc pressed in the normal manner. The finished product consists of a potassium bromide window mounted in a paper circle. A corresponding mask for the reference beam is required.

There are some limitations on the experimental condition of the sample for Raman work. Most work is carried on with pure liquids or solutions. With the first, care must be taken to eliminate traces of suspended matter which increase the Rayleigh scattering. With the second, the intensity of the solute scattering is directly dependent on the concentration and low concentrations are difficult for measurement, although recent instrumental developments have helped somewhat here. One advantage of Raman studies over infra-red spectroscopy is the ability to study aqueous solutions. This is due to the relatively weak Raman spectrum obtained with water.

Recent Raman studies [5] have reported the peak heights relative to the 459 cm^{-1} line of carbon tetrachloride which is taken as 100 units. It is used as an internal standard. This circumvents a number of experimental difficulties since:

(*a*) the standard and sample are in a medium of the same refractive index.
(*b*) it eliminates the necessity of determining the density of the liquid.

Against this is the possibility of intermolecular interactions modifying the intensity of the standard but this can be either a series of measurements at different concentrations or by cross checking with differing secondary standard bands.

The use of an external standard involves the comparison of the emission intensity of the particular band by the standard in a matched sample tube under the same experimental conditions. This introduces complications due to the necessity for careful alignment of the tube and optics as well as the serious defect arising from using media of different refractive index.

QUANTITATIVE MEASUREMENTS

The basis of quantitative measurements with infra-red spectroscopy is similar to that of ultraviolet spectroscopy, namely the Beer–Lambert relationship. The determination of the concentration of two or more components is made in a similar way (see page 41). Examples of determinations of lipid components, e.g. cholesterol, triglycerides and phospholipids, are discussed later in this chapter.

Near infra-red spectroscopy

In addition to the fundamental region of the spectrum between 2 and 25 μ, the region from 0·8 to 3·6 μ is also useful, particularly for quantitative studies [6, 7]. Modern automatic recording spectrometers, such as

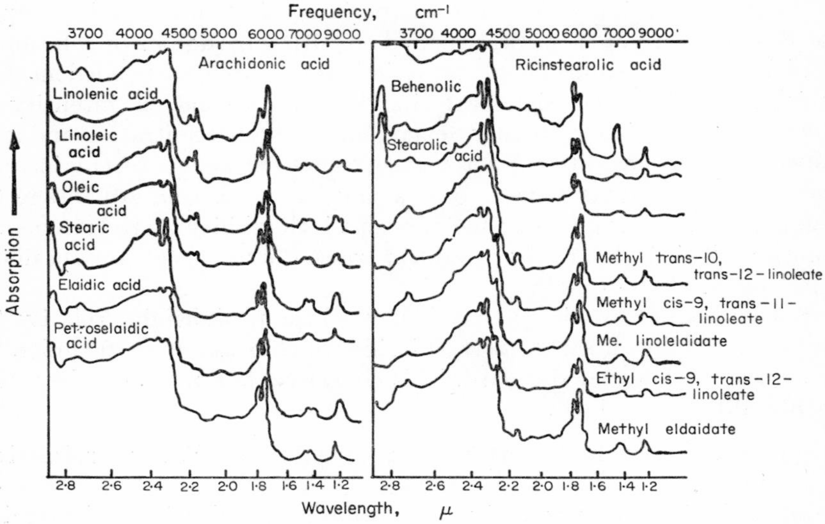

Fig. 19. Near infra-red spectra of a number of lipid materials. (Holman, R. T. and Edmondson, P. R. By courtesy of *Analyt. Chem.*, **28**, 1533, 1956.)

the Cary model 14 spectrophotometer, have made this region particularly accessible. Some of the advantages of the region are that whereas bands may overlap in the fundamental region, often separation of the bands now occurs. The bands arise from overtones of fundamental vibrations or due to combinations of vibrations. Thus, for example, a band at 1·7 μ is the first overtone of the CH-stretching vibration, whilst bands at 2·2 and 2·5 μ are combinations involving the CH stretching with other vibrational modes in the molecule. Another advantage is that quartz cells of known thickness may be used, and sample thicknesses varying from a fraction of a millimeter to 1 or 2 cm can be examined. This is particularly useful for quantitative studies. Bands arising from *cis* and terminal double bonds are also said to absorb, particularly in this region [8]. The *cis* double bond has been determined quantitatively using a band at 2·1 μ [9]. Other groups which can be studied to advantage in this region are the hydroperoxides – these show absorption bands at 1·46 and 2·07 μ whilst ordinary peroxides do not show absorption in this region [10]. Some typical near infra-red spectra are shown in Fig. 19.

Vibrational spectra of polymethylene chains

Many lipids contain polymethylene chains, so we shall consider the types of group vibration which couple to produce the vibrations of a complete polymethylene chain [11].

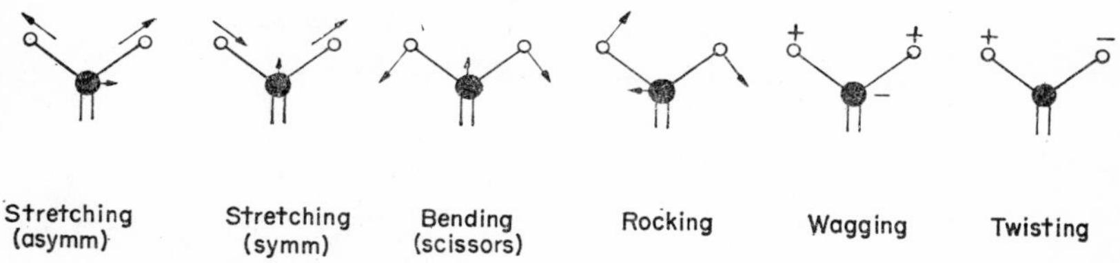

Fig. 20. The various vibrations of the CH_2 group.

The single CH_2 group of propane has six types of vibration (Fig. 20).

νCH (as.)	CH_2 asymmetric stretching (out of plane)	2926
νCH (s.)	CH_2 symmetric stretching (in plane)	2853
δCH_2	CH_2 bend or scissors	1460
ωCH_2	CH_2 wag	1336
tCH_2	CH_2 twist	1278
νCH_2	CH_2 rock	748

Ignoring vibrations of end groups, other vibrations occur:

$(n-1)$ C—C stretching modes (in plane)
$(n-2)$ C—C—C angle bending modes (in plane)
$(n-3)$ torsional vibrations about internal C—C bonds (out of plane)

If it is assumed that the polymethylene chain is in the planar *trans* configuration, certain simplifications arise. Because there is a plane of symmetry through the carbon chain the in-plane and out-of-plane vibrations cannot interact. Also, the two types of CH_2 stretching vibrations and CH_2 bending vibrations are unlikely to interact strongly. Because the frequency regions of the remaining types of vibrations are well separated, interaction is also expected to be slight. An example of the manner in which the CH_2 rocking vibrations couple, as expected theoretically and observed experimentally, is shown in Fig. 21. There is good qualitative agreement and about half the frequencies are infra-red active. Similar distributions have been obtained for other types of vibrations of the polymethylene chain. A number of factors in practice can affect the symmetry or otherwise of the observed distributions.

Within a particular distribution another selection rule is operative which determines the relative intensities of the spectroscopically active

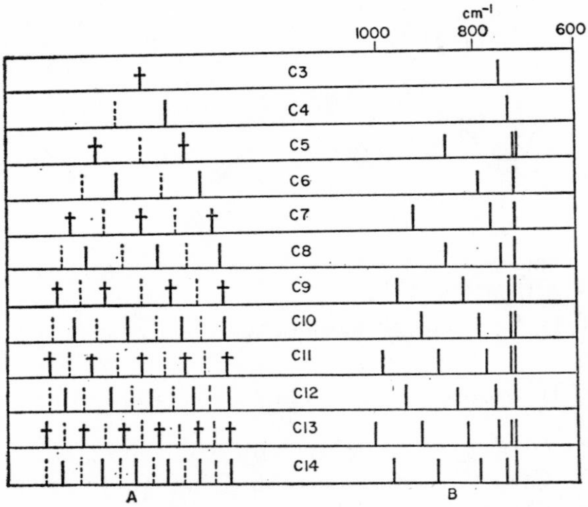

Fig. 21. An idealized distribution of frequencies for CH_2 rocking modes of *n*-paraffins, C_nH_{2n+2} (A), and the experimentally observed infra-red frequencies (B). (After N. Sheppard.[11])

bands. It is expected that as the number of methylene groups increase that the intensity will increase towards either the upper or lower limit of the progression, although this does not always occur. With an infinite chain, however, only those vibrations are spectroscopically active in which every unit cell along the chain vibrates in phase with its neighbours. The unit cell of a regular polymethylene chain consists of two polymethylene groups

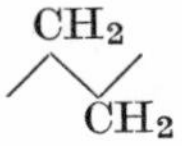

Because of the centre of symmetry within this repeating unit, often one limit of a particular CH_2 distribution is infra-red active while the other is Raman active.

We now summarize the data obtained on the different types of vibrations:

(a) CH_2 *stretching and* CH_2 *bending vibrations*
These three classes give rise to narrow frequency regions which cannot usually be separated into separate bands for short chains. With solid-state long-chain materials the bending frequency at about 1460 cm^{-1} is split into a doublet by the operation of interchain forces.

(b) CH_2 *rocking vibrations*
The lower frequency limit of the distribution is well defined and occurs at about 720 cm^{-1}. The band is split into a doublet with solid-state hydrocarbons when the chains are packed in the orthorhombic $\perp$ manner. The high frequency limit of the distribution lies above 1050 cm^{-1}.

(c) CH_2 *wagging vibrations*
Many long-chain compounds show a regular progression of absorption bands in the region from about 1380 to 1180 cm^{-1}. With the alkyl bromides the distribution has been traced to the CH_2 wagging vibration of ethyl bromide. Some discussion has centred upon this distribution as the bands have the same perpendicular polarization as the CH_2 rocking modes in the spectrum of a long-chain monocarboxylic acid. It has been argued that, as in the spectrum of an odd-numbered chain of an $X(CH_2)_nX$ molecule, every other CH_2 wagging frequency is predicted to have perpendicular polarization; it is this sub-set of frequencies which is most enhanced in intensity by interaction with polar end groups. A useful method for calculating the number of CH_2 groups in a long-chain molecule of type $X(CH_2)_nY$ is to double the number of observed bands in the CH_2 wagging progression. It is considered that every other band is weak and not usually observable.

(d) CH_2 *twisting vibrations*
There is disagreement about the range of frequencies covered by these vibrations. Analyses of the *n*-hydrocarbons lead to the range of 1300 to 1170 cm^{-1}, but 1200 to 930 cm^{-1} has also been suggested [12].

(e) C—C *stretch and* CH *rocking vibrations*
These vibrations are thought to occur in the range 1150 to 870 cm^{-1}. In many cases, particularly with short-chain molecules, there is consider able interaction between them. There is considerable discussion about their assignment [13].

An important matter for the consideration of lipids in liquid crystalline conditions is the extent of non-planarity of the polymethylene chains (see page 241). It is important, therefore, to consider how the infra-red spectrum is affected by internal rotation about any C—C bond. A single gauche configuration about any C—C bond of a polymethylene causes a loss of the plane of symmetry present when the chain is in the fully extended all-*trans* configuration. Much more interaction is now possible between the different types of group vibrations and therefore complicated spectra are expected. Information about the configurations of the non-planar isomers of the polymethylene halides [14] has been obtained but, as we shall see, there is less information available about the configuration of the methylene chains of lipids.

When spectra of polymethylene chains in the solid state are obtained a number of bands are observed to be split into doublets. This is particularly so when the chains are packed in the orthorhombic ⊥ manner (see Chapter 8). The band at 720 cm^{-1} associated with the CH_2 rocking mode is particularly prominent and is split by some 6 cm^{-1}. As many long-chain compounds tend to pack in this way the occurrence of a doublet is quite common. The doublet arises from interaction between the two chains present in the unit cell with hydrocarbons, or in the sub-cell with long-chain derivatives [15, 16]. When the chains have hexagonal packing only a single band at 720 cm^{-1} is observed. In this form there is effectively only one chain per primitive sub-cell and the inter-chain distance is increased compared with the orthorhombic ⊥ form. With triclinic packed chains T|| a single band is observed at 717 cm^{-1} consistent with the occurrence of one chain per unit or sub-cell.

Applications

MONOCARBOXYLIC ACIDS

The monocarboxylic acids have been studied to a considerable extent using infra-red spectroscopy. The vapour, solution, liquid and solid-state spectra of many of them have been studied and a great deal of information obtained [17–21]. Various topics have been studied, including the monomer–dimer relationship which may occur in the vapour and dilute solution, the hydrogen bonding taking place through the carboxyl groups, the polymer formation of the short-chain acids in the solid state, and the polymorphism of the longer-chain acids. There is such a vast amount of information available that only the main features of the spectral information can be discussed.

Formic and acetic acids

We discuss these acids separately from the higher acids since they are somewhat anomalous by comparison, although having certain features in common.

Table 8. *Band positions and intensities for carboxylic acids*[a] (CH_3—$(CH_2)_n$—CH_2—COOH)

Chain length (n)	BAND H (1466 cm^{-1})	I (1458 cm^{-1})	a (1440 cm^{-1})	b ν_{max}	b $\epsilon_{max}^{(a)}$	L ν_{max}	L $\epsilon_{max}^{(a)}$	c (1336 cm^{-1})	d ν_{max}	d ϵ_{max}
0	115[b]	—	—	1416	112	1385	45	38[i]	1284	83
1	54[cd]	61[e]	60[i]	1415	109	1383	32	34[f]	1278	113
3	76[c]	63	65[i]	1415	112	1381	37	36	1288	103
4	77[c]	74	65[i]	1414	113	1381	38	36	1281	113
5	83	82	65[i]	1414	114	1380	39	36	1278	105
6	91	84	68[i]	1413	115	1380	39	36[i]	1284	116
7	97	88	68[i]	1413	112	1379	39	36[i]	1278	107
9	112	93	73	1413	113	1379	40	36[i]	1281	110
11	134	113	80	1412	114	1379	42	39	1282	113
13	146	116	83	1413	113	1379	42	39	1280	111
14	159	125	90	1412	114	1379	44	41[i]	1282	115
15	162	131	90	1413	114	1378	44	41	1280	117
16	169	140	92	1412	116	1379	44	41	1280	117
17	180	148	90	1412	117	1378	45	40[i]	1280	120
18	187	156	85	1412	116	1378	46	42	1280	116

Table 8—*continued*

Chain length (*n*)	BAND e ν_{max}	e $\epsilon_{max}^{(a)}$	S ν_{max}	S $\epsilon_{max}^{(a)}$	f (934 ± 2 cm^{-1})	Y ν_{max}	Y $\epsilon_{max}^{(a)}$	Other bands[g]
0	1235	192	1079	48	74[j]	—	—	1425 (82); 1324 (42); 1134 (17); 994 (18); *849*[k] (33); 808[k] (22)
1	1218	108	1091	31	77	749	13	1305[in] (76); 1230[i] (76); 1141 (18); 1078 (24); 1045[i] (12); 890[i] (30); *855*[i] (15); 778 (25)
3	[h]	—	1098	31	77	732	19	1308[in] (65); 1262[l] (83); 1243[l] (86); 1212 (63); 1138 (16); 1075[i] (22); *860*[i] (20)
4	1235	89	1102	35	77	724	20	1295[in] (90); 1205 (55); 1180[i] (30); 1116 (27); *880*[i] (30); *822* (17); 765 (10)
5	1230	86	1105	32	80	723	24	1296[in] (90); 1202 (50); 1185[i] (28); 790 (12)
6	1234	82	1108	36	80	721	26	1265[i] (88); 1220[i] (75); 1200[i] (45); 1165[i] (28); 1132 (20); 1050[ip] (15); *860*[i] (15); *774* (12)
7	[h]	—	1108	30	75	721	27	1245[l] (76); 1227[l] (69); 1212[i] (62); 1198[i] (37); 1163[i] (24); 1060[p] (16); *860* (13); 762 (11); 738[ip] (14)
9	1235	81	1111	31	78	721	32	1300[in] (85); 1260[i] (80); 1220[i] (62); 1160[i] (22); 1070[p] (18); 765 (11); 740[im] (12)
11	1234	80	1113[i]	33	78	721	38	1080[ip] (20); *860* (16); *830* (14); 770 (12); 740[im] (15)

13	1238	82	1115	32	79	721	42	1092^{p} (26); *860*^{i} (24); 762 (14); 740^{im} (17)
14	1234	83	1115	33	81	721	43	1092^{p} (26); *860*^{i} (18); 770 (13); 740^{im} (15)
15	1234	83	1115	32	81	721	45	1092^{ip} (23); *870*^{i} (20); 740^{ip} (15)
16	1234	83	1115	33	82	721	48	1092^{ip} (27); *870*^{i} (20); 770^{i} (14); 740^{im} (18)
17	1235	84	1115	32	82	721	51	1095^{ip} (27); *875*^{i} (25); 765^{i} (14); 735^{im} (18)
18	1233	83	1116	35	79	721	54	1095^{ip} (32); 1060^{i} (20); 1022^{i} (18); *850*^{i} (17); 778 (12); 740^{im} (22)

(*a*) Bands H–c were measured in carbon tetrachloride solutions and bands d–Y in carbon disulphide. Unless otherwise indicated, the band positions are listed in the column heading and $\epsilon_{max}^{(a)}$ in the column.
(*b*) 1463 cm^{-1}.
(*c*) 1468 cm^{-1}.
(*d*) Note that band H is weaker than band I.
(*e*) 1460 cm^{-1}.
(*f*) 1340 cm^{-1}.
(*g*) The band positions are given first followed by $\epsilon_{max}^{(a)}$ in parenthesis. Bands indicated in italics are superimposed on strong solvent absorption bands and their positions and intensities are less certain.
(*h*) Anomalous.
(*i*) Inflection.
(*j*) 932 cm^{-1}.
(*k*) One of these bands may be a methylene rock.
(*l*) One of these bands may be the analog of band e.
(*m*) Tentatively identified with band X of methyl laurate.
(*n*) Tentatively identified with band O of methyl laurate.
(*p*) Tentatively identified with band T of methyl laurate.

The infra-red spectra of formic acid as vapour and in solution have received particular attention [17, 22]. By contrast with the higher carboxylic acids, which are known to be dimeric, the spectrum of formic acid in the liquid state has been interpreted to show that in this state the acid is in a polymeric, rather than a cyclic, dimer form [23]. Dielectric polarization studies indicate a significant contribution from polar configuration [24].

The spectrum of the solid also shows that the acid is in a polymeric form and reveals large crystal splitting consistent with the X-ray studies [23]. A complete study of formic acid and deuterated species in the vapour and crystal states has been made and many anomalies in previous assignments resolved [25]. However, there are still some uncertainties concerning the spectra of the crystal. Temperature-dependent bands are observed and some fairly large shifts. Some form of polymorphism may occur. In the spectrum of acetic acid the ν(C=O) band is at a low frequency [26]. This is consistent with the polymeric nature of this acid in the crystal.

The spectra of monocarboxylic acids have been studied between 1500–650 cm^{-1} in carbon tetrachloride and carbon disulphide solution and discussed using a concept of characteristic zones [27]. The zones are as shown:

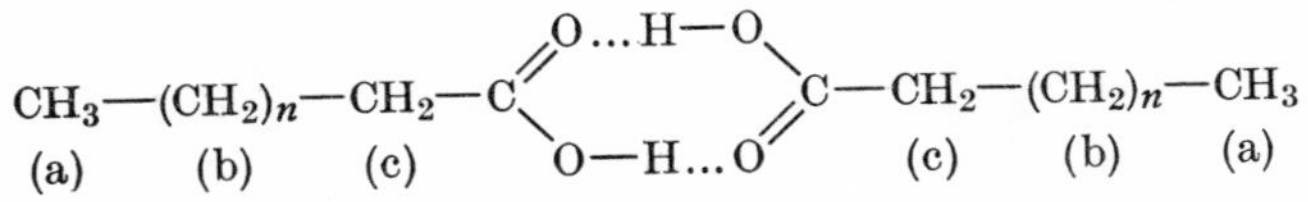

Using this zone concept, the following assignments of the carboxylic acid spectrum are made (see Fig. 22 and Table 8).

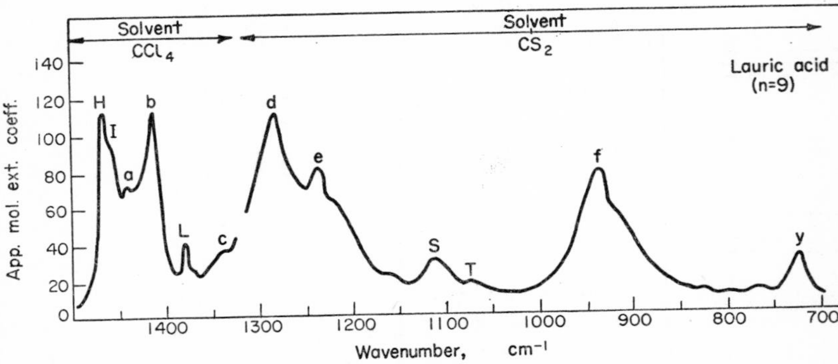

Fig. 22. Infra-red spectrum of lauric acid in solution. (Jones, R. N., *Canad. J. Chem.*, **40**, 321, 1962.)

ZONE A. Terminal methyl group. A band L is identified with the terminal methyl group and to the symmetrical CH deformation. The peak frequency is displaced progressively from 1385 to 1378 cm^{-1} as the chain length increases. This may arise from weak coupling with a skeletal mode.

ZONE B. The polymethylene chain. A band Y is associated with the CH_2 out-of-plane rocking mode and shifts progressively to 721 cm^{-1} with chain length. A band S shifts from 1086 to 1115 cm^{-1} for $n \geqslant 13$ whilst a band T appears as an inflection for $n = 6$, 11, 15–18 and is resolved for $n = 7$, 9, 13, 14. Its position is similar to that of the methyl esters and occurs near 1050 for $n = 6$. Other weak inflections in this region are associated with skeletal modes of various sub-units of the chain in *trans-trans*, *trans*, *gauche* and *gauche-gauche* conformations. A plot of the intensities of the Y and S bands as a function of n are shown in Fig. 23a and b for the acids and esters. The intensity data is very similar for the Y bands. The intensities of the S bands are not much affected by chain length.

ZONE C. A band at 1336 cm^{-1} is associated with a wagging mode of the α-methylene group.

Band a. This may be identified with a scissoring vibration of the α-methylene group.

Band b. A band occurs near 1416 cm^{-1} and is associated with the carboxylic dimer group.

Band c. This is possibly to be associated with the α-methylene wag.

Bands d and e. This is a doublet, probably associated with C—O stretching and OH in plane deformation coupled vibrations. The position of band d shifts in an unsystematic manner between 1276 and 1288 cm^{-1} for the short-chain compounds, for $n \geqslant 9$ it remains steady at 1281 ± 1 cm^{-1}. The weak band e is more variable in position but becomes steady at $n \geqslant 9$. The contour of the band is modulated in a characteristic way for each acid, and this may arise from coupled wagging and twisting vibrations of the methylene chain units. It may indicate that the polymethylene chains are predominantly in the *trans* configuration even in solution.

Band f. This band is out-of-plane deformation mode of the carboxylic acid dimer ring and it exhibits a pronounced asymmetry on the low-frequency side.

The intermediate-chain-length acids are interesting since they are all thought to occur in hydrogen-bonded dimeric ring forms, whilst the crystallization of the acids, at this chain length, is not completely dominated by the hydrocarbon chains. The spectra of these acids have

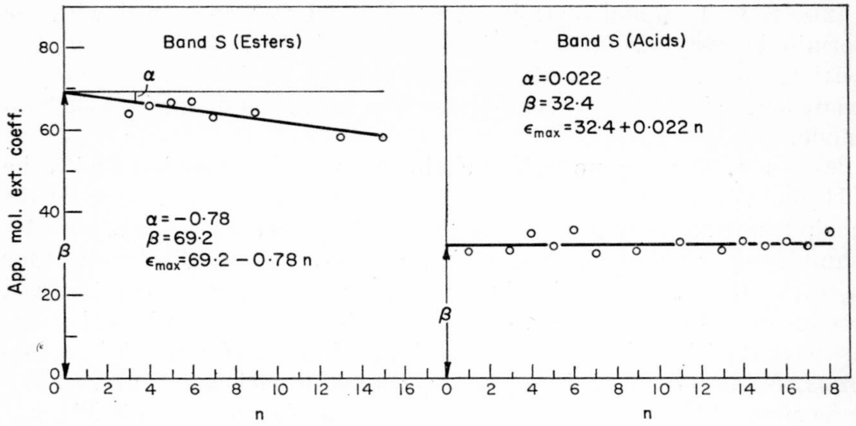

Fig. 23*a*. The variation of band S intensities as a function of chain length for esters and acids. (Jones, R. N., *Canad. J. Chem.*, **40**, 321, 1962.)

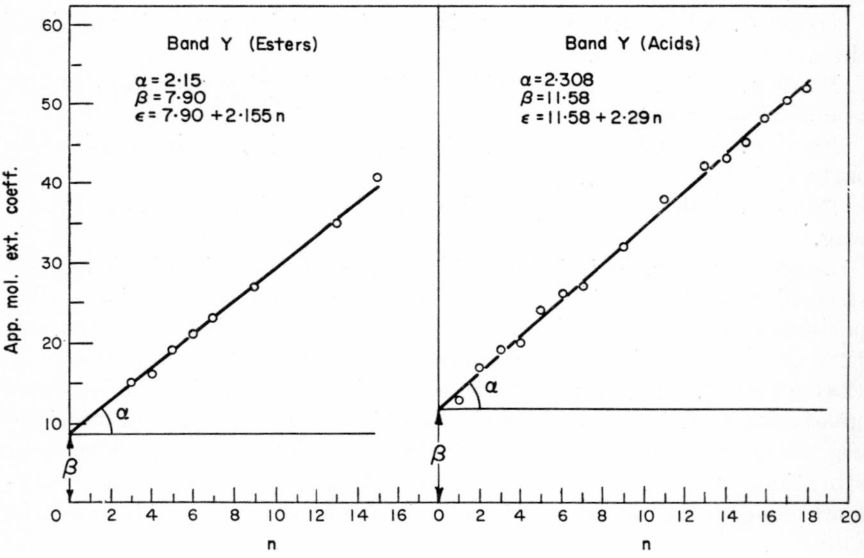

Fig. 23*b*. Variation of band Y intensities.

been examined in solution [28, 29] in the liquid and in the solid state [30]. The spectra of the acids in the liquid and crystalline state are given in Fig. 24, with assignments given in Fig. 25.

The dimeric carboxyl group gives rise to absorption bands at 1420 ± 20, 1300 ± 15 and 935 ± 15 cm^{-1}. The first two bands correspond to closely

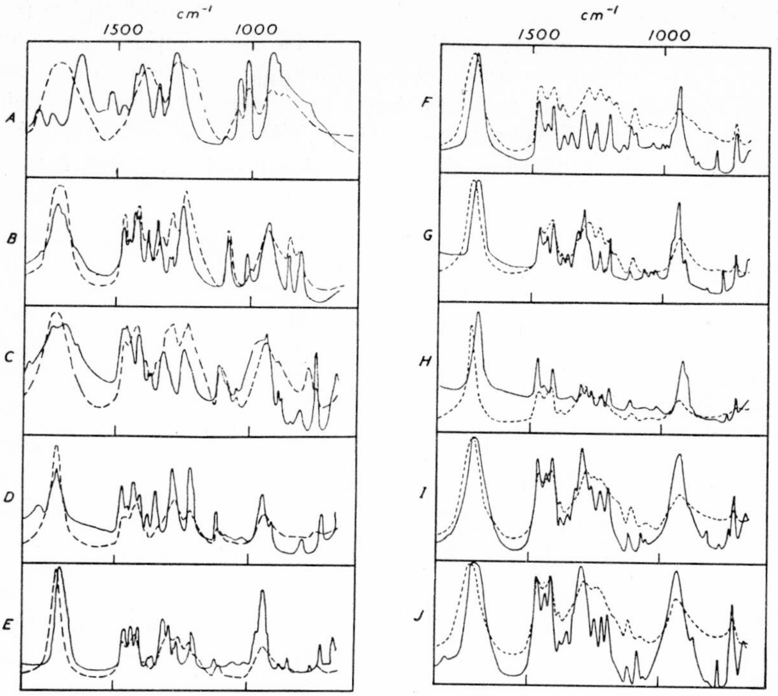

--- *Liquid.* —— *Solid.*

Acids: A, acetic; B, propionic; C, butyric; D, valeric; E, hexanoic; F, heptanoic; G, octanoic; H, nonanoic; I, decanoic; J, dodecanoic.

Fig. 24. Infra-red spectra of monocarboxylic acids, liquid and solid. Acids: acetic, propionic, butyric, valeric, hexanoic, heptanoic, octanoic, nonanoic, decanoic, dodecanoic.

coupled OH deformation and C—O stretching vibrations occur in the plane of the dimeric ring and the third band is caused by the out-of-plane OH deformation mode. A band near 680 cm^{-1} is associated with a

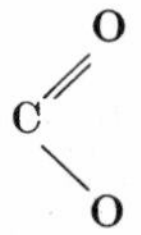

deformation mode.

Comparison between the spectra for the liquid and crystalline states of these acids shows that the region between 1350 and 700 cm^{-1} becomes much less defined for the liquid state, whilst, in general, crystallization results in only small shifts in the C═O frequencies (Table 9). Slight shifts and additional bands occur in the 3000–2500 cm^{-1} region (ν–OH region), as a result of crystallization, which are due to either perturbation effects of the crystalline field or to small changes in hydrogen bonding. The region between 700 and 1350 cm^{-1} also becomes much less defined for the liquid state. It is suggested that this is due to an increase in the number of possible rotational isomers in the liquid state, but it may be

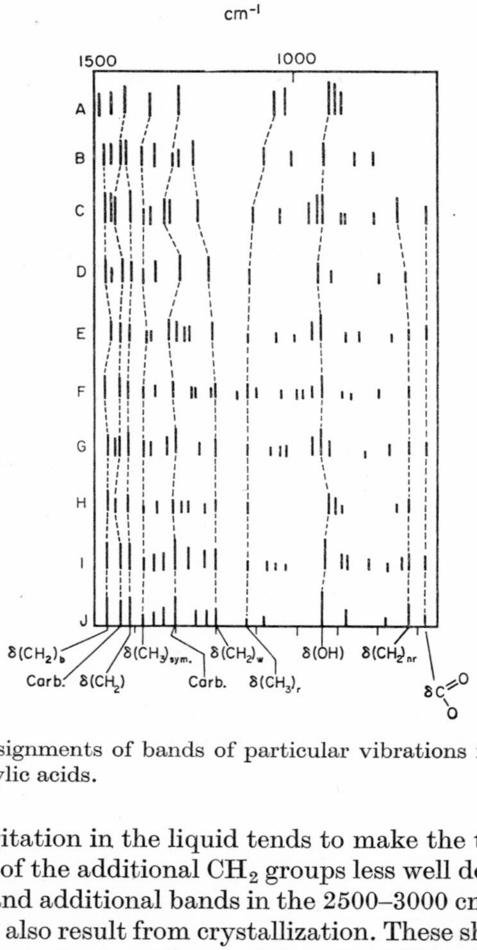

Fig. 25. Assignments of bands of particular vibrations for a series of monocarboxylic acids.

that thermal agitation in the liquid tends to make the twisting and the wagging modes of the additional CH_2 groups less well defined.

Slight shifts and additional bands in the 2500–3000 cm^{-1} ν–OH region (OH stretching) also result from crystallization. These shifts are thought to be due to perturbation effects of the crystalline field or to small changes in hydrogen-bond distances. The additional bands in the 3000 cm^{-1} region are considered to arise from combination of the OH-stretching frequency with lattice vibrations or with low frequencies associated with the dimeric ring. In the spectrum of hexanoic acid these bands are at approximately constant-frequency intervals of *ca.* 60 cm^{-1}. An alternative explanation for the extra peaks is in terms of summation bands due to appropriate combinations of fundamental vibrations of the

Table 9. *Wave numbers of* C=O *bands of monocarboxylic acids*

Acid	Liquid	Crystalline	$\Delta\nu$ (cm^{-1})	Acid	Liquid	Crystalline	$\Delta\nu$ (cm^{-1})
Acetic	1715	1654	−61	Heptanoic	1724	1710	−14
Propionic	1725	1730, 1710 (sh)	+5 ?	Octanoic	1722	1702	−20
Butyric	1729	1740, 1705	0	Decanoic	1716	1705	−11
Hexanoic	1721	1710	−11	Dodecanoic	1720	1705	−15

coupled carboxyl groups of the dimeric molecules. Series of bands in the 900–720 cm^{-1} region of the spectra of the acids are attributed to CH_2 rocking modes. The most characteristic series of bands in the 720–810 cm^{-1} region is listed in Table 10, which also shows the corresponding CH_2 rocking frequencies for normal paraffins in the crystalline state and for the dicarboxylic acids. It appears that probably all of these acids crystallize with the hydrocarbon chains predominantly in *trans* zig-zag configuration.

Table 10. *Frequencies* (cm^{-1}) *assigned to* $\delta[CH_2]_n$ *rocking vibrations*

n	Monocarboxylic acids $H{\cdot}[CH_2]_n{\cdot}CO_2H$	Dicarboxylic acids $HO_2C{\cdot}[CH_2]_n{-}CO_2H$	Paraffins $H{\cdot}[CH_2]_n{\cdot}H$
2	807	804	822
3	750	754	748
4	731	733	732
5	727	731	728
6	724	725	726
7	723	726	723
8	723	722	722
9	721	—	720
11	721	—	720

As the chain length of the monocarboxylic acids increase so do the bands in the 1380–1180 cm^{-1} region (Fig. 26).

A summary of the Raman data on monocarboxylic acids has been given by Kohlrausch [31]. Frequencies greater than 1500 cm^{-1} arising from the OH-stretching mode have been identified in the region 3100 to 2900 cm^{-1} and the Raman active C=O frequency of the dimer occurs near to 1650 cm^{-1}.

The long-chain acids are particularly interesting because of their solid state behaviour and their spectra can be particularly informative.

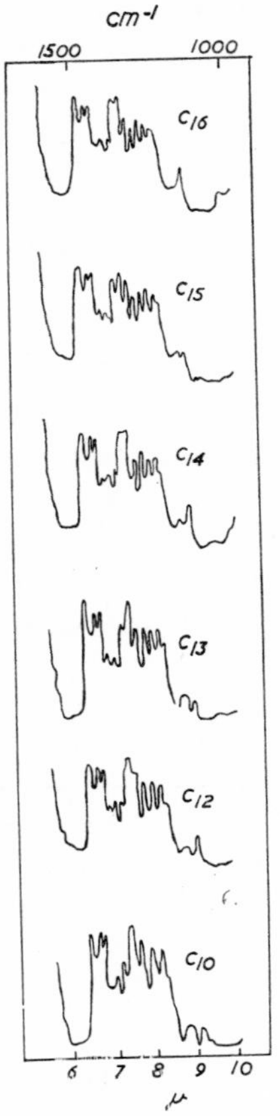

Fig. 26. Spectra of normal aliphatic acids in potassium bromide matrix showing the build up of a regular series of bands.

Long-chain acids, such as lauric and higher acids, show a regular series of bands in the 1350–1180 cm^{-1} region and the number and appearance of the bands can give information on the length of the chain involved. Lauric acid shows only three regularly spaced bands, the lowest frequency band is at 1195 cm^{-1}. With increase in chain length the number of bands increases by one for every two methylene groups in the length of the chain. With an even-acid the number of bands in the progression $= n/2$, whilst with an odd-acid the number of bands in the progression $= (n+1)/2$. Similar bands are shown by long-chain esters, paraffins and glycerides and are associated with CH_2 wagging modes [32, 33, 34, 35]. The virtual disappearance of the bands in the molten acids is said to be due to a continuous and random distribution of the $(CH_2)_n$ chains.

The long-chain acids exhibit polymorphism and spectral differences arise because of this [36, 37, 38, 39]. The even-numbered acids occur in three modifications, *A*, *B* and *C*, giving different long spacings decreasing in that order. A detailed description of the polymorphism is given in Chapter 8. The polymorphism of the odd-membered acids is more complex, the *C′*-form is always the first to separate from the molten acid and this changes some 10 or 20° C below the solidifying point into one or both of the forms *A′* and *B′*. The infra-red spectra of the even-acids show quite marked changes for the different polymorphic forms.

The spectral changes observed with temperature are shown in Fig. 27a and b for tridecanoic and pentadecanoic acids [39]. With the tridecanoic acid in its most stable *A′*-form only a single band is observed at 716 cm^{-1}, consistent with the triclinic T|| packing of the chains in this form. With pentadecanoic acid in its most stable *A′*-form there is a single band at 716 cm^{-1} for the *A′*-form which changes to a doublet at 727 and 719 cm^{-1}, consistent with the orthorhombic packing of this *B′*-form. This finally changes to a single band at 720 cm^{-1}, consistent with the near-hexagonal character of the *C′*-form near its melting point. The variation in the appearance of the bands in the 1380–1180 cm^{-1} region with the *C′*-form is thought to be related to the flexing and molecular mobility of the hydrocarbon chains which occur with this form. The appearance of the spectrum is analogous to that observed with other long-chain compounds such as the 1-monoglycerides and ethyl esters when in their hexagonal or α-crystalline form. It is in contrast to that observed with anhydrous sodium soaps, where all the fine detail in this region disappears some 100° C below the melting point. The spectra of the even acids, e.g. stearic acid in its *C*-form, show only a very slight shift and fall in intensity in the high-frequency component of the 720 cm^{-1} doublet. The lower-chain-length acids show a little more spectral change somewhat analogous to that observed with the odd-acids (cf. capric acid).

Polarization data have been obtained with the various polymorphic forms. This data helps to augment the X-ray data on the structure of the acids in these forms [40, 41]. One difficulty, however, in the application of the method arises with the triclinic crystals. This is because there are no rules for polarization of the absorption bands with such crystals.

Stearic acid and vaccenic acid have been studied in this way by means of a reflecting microscope attachment and polarized radiation. The latter is considered to crystallize in an orthorhombic system with the hydro-

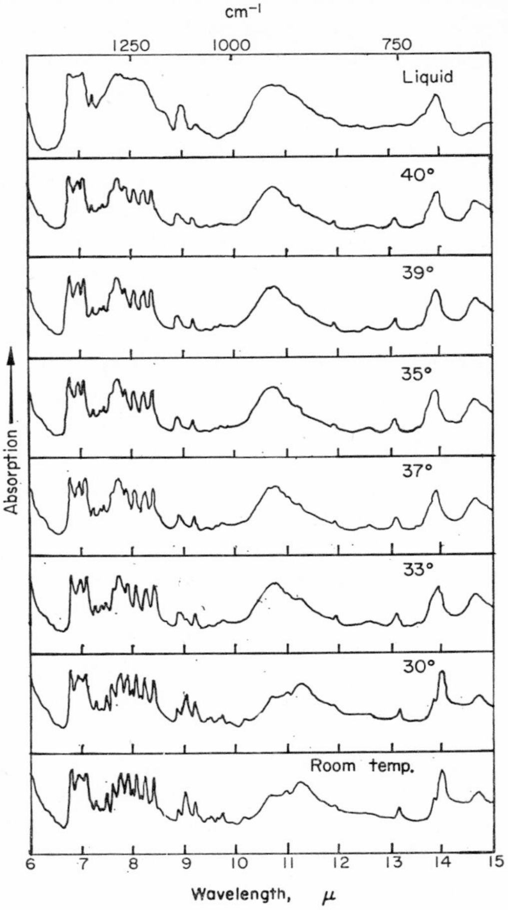

Fig. 27*a*. Infra-red spectral variations with temperature for tridecanoic acid.

carbon chains packed into an orthorhombic O⊥ sub-cell similar to polyethylene and the *C*-form of the saturated acids. A new polymorphic form is claimed to have been observed with octadecanoic acid [42].

Unsaturated acids

The unsaturated acids are particularly important components of biological materials. Certain features of the spectra are similar to those of the saturated acids, i.e. bands associated with the methylene group of the chain, the terminal methyl group and the carboxy and carbomethoxy groups are similar to those of the saturated acids and methyl

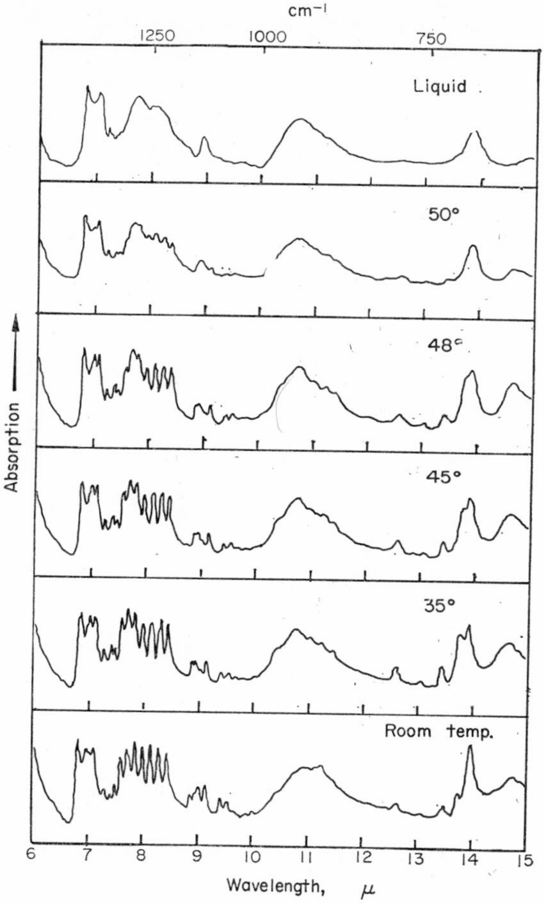

Fig. 27*b*. Infra-red spectral variations with temperature for pentadecanoic acid.

esters. Certain bands are, however, associated with the ethylenic group. These occur in the region 3000–3100 cm^{-1}, 1580–1650 cm^{-1} and 690–980 cm^{-1}, corresponding to stretching vibrations of the C═C—H group, stretching vibrations of C═C bonds and out-of-plane bending vibrations of the C═C—H carbon hydrogen bond respectively.

The possibility of using the spectra for analytical applications has been discussed. In the C—H stretching region a band at 3020 cm^{-1} increases with the number of *cis*-double bonds present, while the relative intensity of the methylene peak at 2920 cm^{-1} falls. These observations provide a basis for the evaluation of the degree of unsaturation. If d_A is the optical density at 3020 cm^{-1} and d_B the optical density at 2920 cm^{-1}, a plot of $d_B/(d_B - d_A)$ against the number of double bonds is approximately linear for oleic, linoleic, linolenic and arachidonic acids, while stearic and palmitic acids also fall on the same curve. Analytical working curves can be established for suitable mixtures of saturated and *cis*-unsaturated acids, and as the measurements are based on determinations of intensity

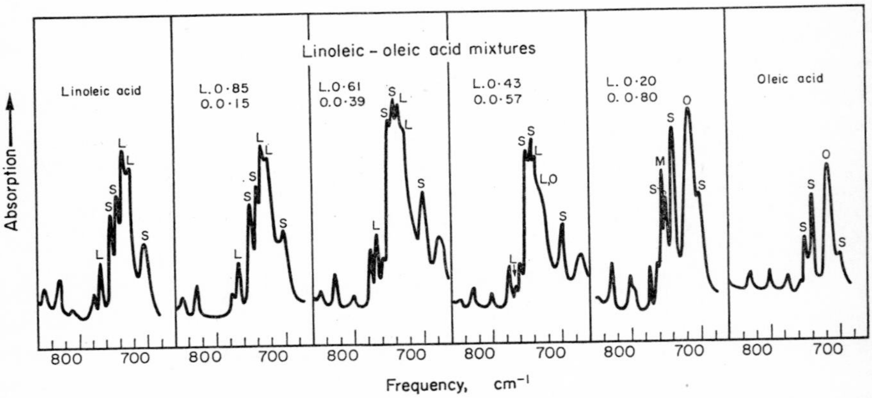

Fig. 28. Infra-red spectra of cooled solid films of mixtures of oleic and linoleic acids. Concentrations expressed in mole/fractions. (Sinclair, R. G., McKay, A. F., Myers, G. S. and Jones, R. N., *J. Amer. Chem. Soc.*, **74**, 2578, 1952.)

ratios the sample concentration or sample thickness is not required. A method based on this principle, in conjunction with an infra-red microscope, could permit the determination of the degree of unsaturation of suitable fatty-acid mixtures on microgram amounts. Divergencies from the linearity of the analytical working curve may be expected if the chain length varies considerably among the samples or if the acid mixtures contain appreciable quantities of *trans*-ethylenic linkages. Palmitic and stearic acids give almost coincident points, so small changes in chain length do not appear to affect the results seriously.

The problem of the identification and estimation of individual unsaturated acids in mixtures is more difficult.

The spectra of oleic, linoleic and linolenic acids are very similar, but it is possible, in solution and in liquid films, to obtain working curves for the analysis of mixtures of linoleic and linolenic acids from measurements of the ratios of the optical densities of the peaks at 1120 cm^{-1} in linoleic and 1067 cm^{-1} in linolenic acid. Small differences can also be observed between the liquid phase spectra of oleic and linoleic acids and between methyl linoleate and methyl linolenate, but these bands are all of low intensity and unsuitable for the analysis of mixtures.

The analysis of binary mixtures of unsaturated fatty acids may be possible using solid-phase low-temperature spectra. The spectra of oleic and linoleic acids differ considerably, especially between 660 and 760 cm^{-1}. The spectra of a series of mixtures of these two acids are shown in Fig. 28. The bands marked S are present in the spectrum of stearic acid. The three bands marked L diminish as the linoleic acid concentration decreases and the strong band O increases with the concentration of oleic acid.

It is suggested that mixtures of oleic and linoleic acids might be analysed by matching the solid-phase spectra with an atlas of the spectra of standard mixtures. Complications due to polymorphism formation may occur and should be watched carefully.

Ethylenic CH *bending vibration*

A strong band at 965–975 cm^{-1} is associated with the *trans*-substituted ethylene structure and is used to differentiate between *cis*- and *trans*-substituted unsaturated fatty acids and esters. The band occurs in elaidic acid. A band near 690 cm^{-1} has been associated with the vibration of the *cis* grouping, but this is less certain.

A band at 1435 cm^{-1} increases in intensity with the amount of unsaturation and has been tentatively assigned to a bending vibration of a methylene group adjacent to a double bond.

A great deal of work has taken place to provide a reliable method for estimating the amount of isolated *trans* content and the American Oil Chemists' Society have a tentative official method. The procedure applies to fatty acids if they contain 15% or more *trans* content. If the *trans* content is below this, the fatty acid is converted to the methyl ester. This eliminates overlapping absorption from the nearby carboxylic band.

The quantitative determination of *cis-trans* and *trans-trans* unsaturation has also been described. The *cis-trans* compounds in the presence or absence of *trans, trans* conjugation is determined directly by absorption at 10·55 μ. The *trans, trans* content is estimated directly from the absorption at 10·11 μ unless *cis-trans* isomers are present, when correction is needed for absorption due to this grouping.

A strong band at 965–975 cm^{-1} was first associated with a *trans* grouping in 1947 and later shown to arise from a CH deformation about a *trans*-C=C group. It was later observed that different substituents about the double bond gave rise to characteristic absorptions. These are shown in Table 11.

Conjugation of the unsaturated group is also characteristic. Thus *trans, trans* groupings are characterized by a band at 10·11 μ and *cis-trans* groupings by a doublet at 10·18 and 10·55 μ. These correlations are given in Table 11.

Table 11. *Correlations for various unsaturated groupings*

Unsaturated group	Wavelength μ	Wave number cm^{-1}
Isolated *trans*	10·34	967
cis-trans (conj.)	10·17	983
trans, trans (conj.)	10·12	988
cis-cis-trans (conj.)	10·11	989
cis-trans-trans (conj.)	10·09	991
trans, trans-trans (conj.)	10·06	994

The frequency of bands arising from the conjugation of a *cis* group has also been calculated and correlated with experimental data: *cis* 10·95 μ (913 cm^{-1}), *cis,cis* (conj.) 10·7 μ (934 cm^{-1}), *trans-cis* (conj.) 10·53 μ (950 cm^{-1}). All these bands are weak or very weak in intensity. The determination of *cis* absorption appears to be better carried out using the near infra-red region.

The spectra of the solid-state unsaturated acids in the 1350–1180 cm^{-1} region are informative. Whereas with the saturated acids a regular series of bands occur, for the *cis*-unsaturated acids the progression becomes irregular [43] (Fig. 29). With the *trans* acids, however, the region is more similar to the saturated acids, but here the band progression depends upon the chain segment next to the carboxyl group. This has been nicely illustrated by an examination of a number of octadecanoic acids with *trans*-double bonds in positions varying from the 6- through to the 11-position [44]. The bands in this region are shown in Fig. 30. They can be contrasted with the same region for the saturated acids from C_6 to C_{12}. Apparently the terminal chain segments do not give rise to regularly spaced medium-intensity bands. However, some weak bands occur between the main progression bands which might be caused by the terminal segments.

Polymorphism does not occur with these acids but it might be a complication in the application of this method to the determination of the position of the double bond in other acids. The frequency limit for the series is affected with these acids and the weak bands in the 1350–1300 cm^{-1} region are excluded because the spacings are irregular; positions do not change with chain length, and the polarization characteristics are different.

The hydroxyl groups of the hydroxy acids cause the packing of the molecules to be different from that observed with the normal acids.

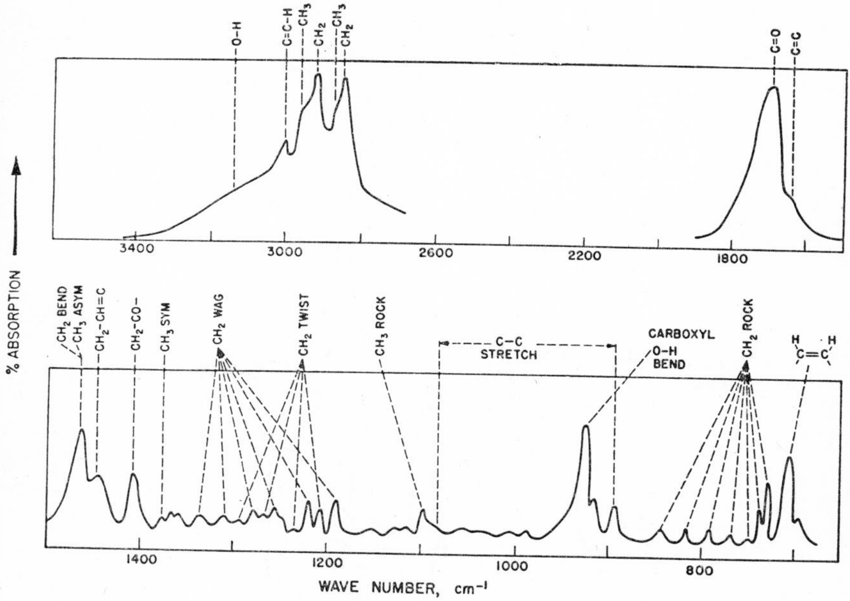

Fig. 29. Infra-red spectrum of a crystalline film of oleic acid at $-196°$C. (Jones, R. N. and Sandorfy, C. *Chemical Applications of Spectroscopy*, **9**, 1956.)

Hydrogen bonding also occurs. Susi has examined a number of dihydroxy acids [44]. All the acids show strong absorption around 3400 cm^{-1} and a series of bands of medium strength between 1000 and 1200 cm^{-1} corresponding to the OH-stretching vibrations and the C—O-stretching and/or deformation vibrations respectively. Only weak bands occur in the 1180–1350 cm^{-1} region with no apparent regularity. Whilst the position isomers of contiguously substituted dihydroxy stearic acids cannot be identified by clear-cut regularities as with the *trans*-mono-unsaturated acids there is enough spectral detail in the region between

1200 and 800 cm^{-1} to allow identification on a fingerprint basis. The high-melting and low-melting acids are distinguished in the 1000 and 1150 cm^{-1} region by the more complex structure of the low-melting members.

Branched chain acids

A series of monomethyl-substituted octadecanoic acids has been studied in the solid state [45, 46]. In the 1330 to 1180 cm^{-1} region, as the methyl

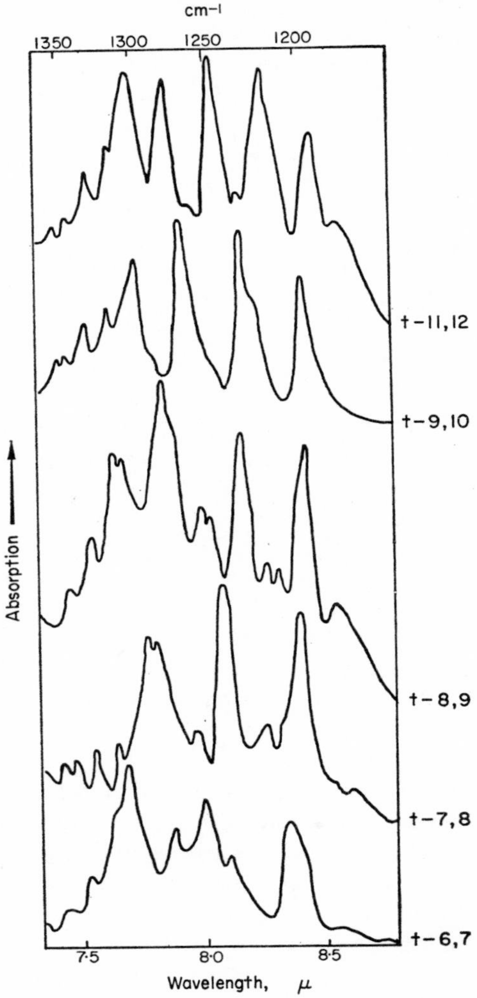

Fig. 30. 1175–1350 cm.$^{-1}$ region of transoctadecenoic acids. (Susi, H. By courtesy of *Analyt. Chem.*, **31**, 910, 1959.)

branch is moved towards the carboxyl group, irregularities are seen as many inflections in the band progression. The structures of the acids are dicussed in Chapter 8. Unusual sub-cells occur with these acids and crossed chains are also thought to occur.

ESTERS

The esters have been studied extensively in solution [29, 43], as liquids and in the solid state, and yet there are still uncertainties concerning the assignments of some bands in their spectra [29, 47, 48].

Particular features of the spectrum of the esters are the bands associated with the carbonyl C═O groups. The carbonyl frequencies of a large number of simple esters in the liquid condition show this to lie in the range 1750–1735 cm^{-1}. This enables the esters to be distinguished from the normal ketones as the carbonyl frequency is raised in the esters by the influence of the neighbouring oxygen atom. Jones and co-workers [49] have found that the carbonyl frequencies of over a hundred sterol acetates, propionates, etc., occur in the region 1742–1735 cm^{-1} regardless of the position of the ester group in the steroid nucleus.

The influence of $\alpha\beta$ unsaturation is to lower the carbonyl frequency whilst $\gamma\delta$ substitution has little, if any, effect. Conjugation with acetylenic links produce a greater shift to the range 1720–1708 cm^{-1}. With vinyl esters CO—O—C═C a marked enhancement of the carbonyl frequency occurs. Thus vinyl acetate absorbs at 1776 cm^{-1}. In α-diesters and α-keto esters the degree of interaction of the two adjacent CO groups is apparently very small. Some β-keto esters can undergo enolization and ethyl-α-methylacetoacetate and ethylacetoacetate show an additional band at 1650 cm^{-1} which is attributed to the ester carbonyl group after chelation to the enolic hydroxyl group.

The C–O stretching mode gives rise to strong bands in the 1300–100 cm^{-1} region in many compounds. Its precise frequency is sensitive to changes in the mass and the nature of the attached groups. The formates have a strong band in the 1250–1050 region, with methyl formate it is at 1214 cm^{-1}, ethyl formate at 1195 cm^{-1} and becoming 1185 cm^{-1} in the higher homologues. The acetates show a strong band in the range 1250–1230 cm^{-1} and it is near 1245 cm^{-1} in the small chain length acetates. A second, but weak, absorption occurs in the 1060–1000 cm^{-1} range. The frequencies of the CO-stretching mode of the series of simpler higher esters within each group are fairly constant. They are listed in Table 12.

Useful correlations for the spectra of a large number of aliphatic esters in the 15 to 40 μ region have been published [50].

In an analogous manner to the carboxylic acids the zone concept has

Table 12. C—O *frequency in various esters*

Class	C—O stretching frequency
Formates	1200–1180 cm^{-1}
Acetates	1250–1230 cm^{-1}
Propionates	1200–1150 cm^{-1}
Butyrates	1190 cm^{-1}
Isobutyrates	1200 cm^{-1}
Adipates	1175 cm^{-1}
Laurates	1163 cm^{-1}
Oleates	1172 cm^{-1}
Ricinoleate	1174 cm^{-1}
Stearate	1174 cm^{-1}
Sebacates	1172 cm^{-1}

been applied to the solution spectra of the methyl esters [27]. Four vibrational zones are discussed as shown:

$$\underset{(a)}{CH_3}—\underset{(b)}{(CH_2)_n}—\underset{(c)}{CH_2}—\underset{(d)}{COOCH_3}$$

Bands are marked in an analogous way to those of the carboxylic acids. Those marked H, I, L, S, T and Y are correlated with their counterparts in the spectra of the esters. This is illustrated with the spectrum of methyl laurate (Fig. 31). The variation of intensity of the Y and S bands, associated with the polymethylene chain, are given in Figs. 23a and b. The P, Q, R band system is considered to characterize the RCH_2COOCH_3 structure. Temperature variation has no pronounced effect upon the P, Q and R band contour over the range 30 to $-70°$ C. The three peaks are associated with a C—O skeletal motion coupled with an α-CH_2 deformation vibration. The evidence from the CH stretching region of the spectrum of methyl laurate is that the carbmethoxyl group exists wholly or predominantly in the conformation

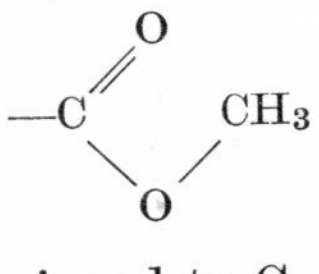

The bands S, T and U are assigned to C—C skeletal coupled with end group, C—C skeletal and C—O skeletal coupled with α-CH_2 deformation vibrations. As with the spectra of the acids, there are weak inflections near bands S and T. It is suggested that these are derived from complex underlying absorption associated with skeletal modes of various sub-units of the chain in *trans-trans*, *trans-gauche* and *gauche-gauche* con-

LIBRARY

Hazel McCallion

Academic Learning Centre

Customer ID: 21761010805747OO

Due: 14/11/2008,23:59

Title: High-performance liquid chromatography and lipids : a practical guide

ID: 31761021201629

Due: 14/11/2008,23:59

Title: Lipid analysis ; isolation, separation, identification, and structural analysis of lipids

ID: 31761033760372

Due: 14/11/2008,23:59

Title: Lipide chemistry. With contributing ... by Frank B. N. Gurd [and] Irving Z...

... lipids by spectroscopic ...

Due: 14/11/2008,23:59

Total items: 6

10/31/2008 3:04 PM

Thank you, have a ni...

LIBRARY

Thank you have a nice day

10/31/2008 3:04 PM
Total items: 6

Due: 14/11/2008,23:59

techniques including thin layer and gas liquid chromatography

ID:31761021240429
Due: 14/11/2008,23:59

Title: The lipids, their chemistry and biochemistry

ID:31761033895590
Due: 14/11/2008,23:59

Title: The lipids, their chemistry and biochemistry

ID:31761021512926

formations. The spectra of a number of methyl esters showing the bands P, Q, R, S, T and U are shown in Fig. 32. The band positions and intensities for a series of methyl esters are given in Table 13.

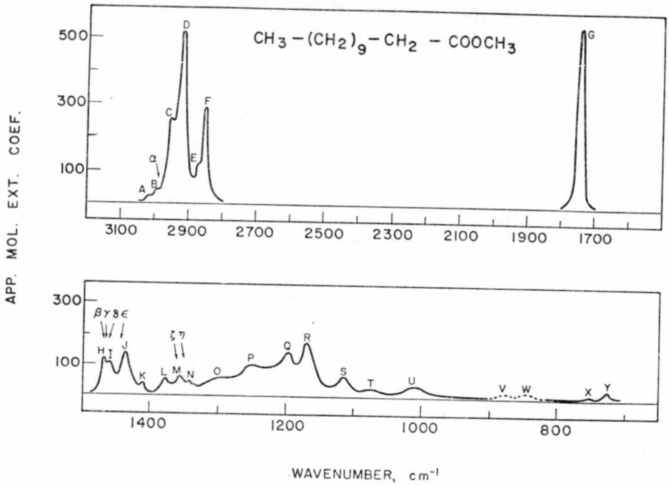

Fig. 31. Spectrum of methyl laurate. (Jones, R. N. *Canad. J. Chem.*, **40**, 301, 1962.)

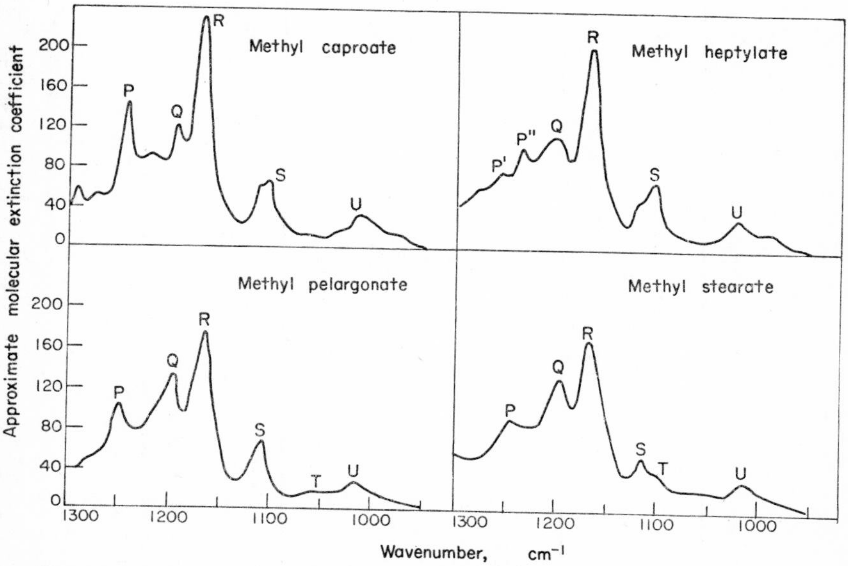

Fig. 32. Spectra of methyl esters showing bands in the 1000–1250 cm.$^{-1}$ region. (*Canad. J. Chem.*, **40**, 321, 1962.)

Table 13. *Band positions and intensities for methyl esters*[a] (CH_3—$(CH_2)_n$—CH_2—$COOCH_3$)

Chain length	BAND								
	H	I	J	K	L		M	P	
(n)	(1467 cm^{-1})	(1458 cm^{-1})	(1436 cm^{-1})	(1419 cm^{-1})	ν_{max}	$\epsilon_{max}^{(a)}$	(1362 cm^{-1})	ν_{max}	$\epsilon_{max}^{(a)}$
0	—	92[bc]	117	35[ei]	1382	26	118	—	—
3	71[d]	72	127	33	1380	43	54	1244	140
4	73[d]	75	131	33	1380	44	56	1234	102
5	77[d]	81	126	34	1379	47	57	1250	98
6	90	87	130	34	1378	48	59	1248	103
7	97	93	133	35	1378	48	60	1244	105
9	113	107	136	36	1378	51	62	1245	97
13	145	125	144	36[i]	1378	54	67	1244	98
15	164	143	149	36[i]	1377	58	69	1244	95

(*a*) Bands H–M were measured in carbon tetrachloride and bands N–Y in carbon disulphide. Unless otherwise indicated the band positions are listed in the column heading, and $\epsilon_{max}^{(a)}$ in the column.
(*b*) 1456 cm^{-1}.
(*c*) Band H not observed.
(*d*) Note that Band H is weaker than Band I.
(*e*) 1425 cm^{-1}.

Chain length (n)	Q		R		S		U		Y		Other bands[f]
	ν_{max}	$\epsilon_{max}^{(a)}$	ν_{max}	$\epsilon_{max}^{(a)}$	ν_{max}	$\epsilon_{max}^{(a)}$	ν_{max}	$\epsilon_{max}^{(a)}$	ν_{max}	$\epsilon_{max}^{(a)}$	
0	1198	245	1175	195	1086	72	1023	63	—	—	1328[i] (32); 1272 (50); 968 (16); 955[i] (8); *850* (37); 807 (20)
3	1192	120	1169	232	1100	64	1015	36	733	15	1350[i] (40); 1318 (48); 1287 (48); 1268 (52); 1217 (90); 1110 (60); 970[i] (14); 934 (5); 918 (7); 902 (7); *864*[g] (15); 770 (6); 745[ij] (6)
4	1198	112	1167	204	1102	66	1022	33	726	16	1318 (44); 1276[i] (60); 1256 (77); 1118[i] (48); 992 (20); 763 (7)
5	1198	132	1166	192	1105	67	1020	26	724	19	1318[i] (42); 1299[k] (48); 1225[i] (92); 860[g] (13)
6	1196	134	1165	176	1107	66	1020	27	723	21	1303[k] (44); 1050[l] (19); 995[i] (20); 875[g] (9); 832[h] (8); 762 (8); 748[j] (6)
7	1198	138	1167	168	1110	63	1016	28	721	23	1064[l] (23); 898 (7); *864*[g] (11); *832*[h] (13)
9	1196	137	1169	162	1112	64	1016	30	721	27	
13	1196	138	1169	170	1115	58	1016	29	721	35	1300[ik] (55); 1090[il] (25); 990[i] (20); *874*[g] (12); *836*[h] (11); 762[i] (10)
15	1196	136	1168	171	1115	57	1015	31	721	41	1300[k] (55); 1090[il] (35); 1070[i] (25); 900[i] (25); *865*[g] (11); *835*[h] (10); 765[i] (9)

(*f*) The band positions are given first followed by $\epsilon_{max}^{(a)}$ in parenthesis. Bands indicated in italics are superimposed on strong solvent absorption bands and their positions and intensities are less certain.
(*g*) Tentatively identified with Band V of methyl laurate.
(*h*) Tentatively identified with Band W of methyl laurate.
(*i*) Inflection.
(*j*) Tentatively identified with band X of methyl laurate.
(*k*) Tentatively identified with band O of methyl laurate.
(*l*) Tentatively identified with band T of methyl laurate.

By using deuterated derivatives a detailed assignment of methyl laurate has been obtained [51] and is given in Table 14.

Table 14. *Summary of band assignments for methyl laurate*

Band[a]	ν_{max}	$\epsilon_{max}^{(a)}$	ASSIGNMENT Group	Mode
A	[3020] cm^{-1}	16	—$COOCH_3$	asym. C—H stretch (a')
B	2995	40	—$COOCH_3$	asym. C—H stretch (a'')
α	2955	—	—$COOCH_3$	sym. C—H stretch
C	2950	260	CH_3—	asym. C—H stretch
D	2922	520	—$(CH_2)_9$—	asym. C—H stretch
E	[2870]	120	CH_3—	sym. C—H stretch
F	2852	290	—$(CH_2)_9$—	sym. C—H stretch
G	1742	550	—$COOCH_3$	C═O stretch
H	1465	113 {Band β	—$(CH_2)_9$—	C—H scissor
		Band γ	CH_3—	asym. C—H bend
I	1458	107 Band δ	—$COOCH_3$	asym. C—H bend (a'')
ε	1440	—	—$(CH_2)_9$—	C—H scissor or wag
J	1436	135	—$COOCH_3$	sym. C—H bend
K	1419	36	α-CH_2—	C—H scissor
L	1378	51	CH_3—	sym. C—H bend
	1368	—	—$(CH_2)_9$—	C—H wag or twist
M	1362	62	α-CH_2—	C—H wag
η	1352	—	—$(CH_2)_9$—	C—H wag or twist
N	[1340]	40	—$(CH_2)_9$	C—H wag or twist
O	1305	50	—$(CO_2)_9$—	C—H twist (or wag ?)
P	1248	97	—CH_2—$COOCH_3$	C—C skeletal coupled with α-CH_2— deformation
Q	1196	135	—CH_2—$COOCH_3$	C—C skeletal coupled with α-CH_2— deformation
R	1169	162	—CH_2—$COOCH_3$	C—C skeletal coupled with α-CH_2— deformation
S	1112	64	—$(CH_2)_9$—	C—C skeletal coupled with end groups
T	1074	25	—	C—C skeletal
U	1015	33	—CH_2—$COOCH_3$	C—C skeletal coupled with α-CH_2— deformation
V	875	—	—$COOCH_3$	Methyl rock ?
W	845	—	—$COOCH_3$	Methyl rock ?
X	755	8	—$(CH_2)_9$—	C—H rock
Y	722	27	—$(CH_2)_9$—	C—H rock

(*a*) Points of inflection are designated by square brackets. Greek letters identify bands that are not observed in the methyl laurate spectrum but are presumed to be present from the analysis of the spectra of the deuterated derivatives.

It has been noted that the band at 720 cm^{-1} requires the presence of at least four *trans*-linked methylene groups. As this band increases linearly with chain length for many polymethylene compounds it has been inferred that in the liquid state the chains exist predominantly in conformation sets in which at least four consecutive methylenes are linked in a *trans*-grouping. Each section will then contribute a set of bands to the vibrational pattern determined by its chain length. The superposition of bands from the units of different length could produce the broad-band systems observed (see the discussion in Chapter 8 on the shape of hydrocarbon chains in the liquid state). The infra-red and Raman spectrum of polymethylene compounds in the liquid state is said to agree in the main rather well with an assignment based on a vibrational analysis of the all-*trans*-methylene chain.

The spectra of a large number of ethyl esters have been examined in solution, liquid and the solid state [29, 35].

The ethyl esters have a band at 1042 cm^{-1} which is not observed with the methyl esters and enables them to be distinguished. The long-chain ethyl esters exhibit polymorphism and the infra-red spectra of the different forms have been studied.

The *cis*- and *trans*-isomers of the ethyl esters have been studied using Raman spectroscopy [52]. Some values for the ethyl esters are given in Table 15.

Table 15. *Raman data for some ethyl esters*

Oleate	Elaidate	Linoleate	β-Linoleate	Linolelaidate	Linolenate
	962 (1)	953 (1)	952 (1)		954 (0)
974 (3d)		972 (5d)	973 (4d)	977 (1)	972 (2)
1267 (7d)	1269 (1)	1264 (7d)	1264 (7d)	1261 (2d)	1250 (1)
		1643 (6d)	1643 (5d)	1656 (10p)	1265 (6d)
1655 (8p)	1669 (8p)	1658 (10p)	1657 (10p)	1668 (5d)	1656 (9p)
3009 (6p)	3008 (3p)	3012 (5p)	3012 (5p)	3009 (2p)	3013 (8p)

The ethylenic bond in all compounds of the type RCH=CHR′ gives rise to a frequency near 1650 cm^{-1} for *cis* compounds. The frequency is 10 to 20 cm^{-1} less than for the *trans* compound.

The use of Raman spectra for examining C=C-stretching bands may be very useful as these bands are often very much more intense than those observed in the infra-red spectrum.

ALCOHOLS

A considerable number of studies of alcohols have been published dealing with various aspects of their spectra. The band arising from the OH group and its variation of position and intensity as a function of concentration and change of state has received particular attention [53, 54]. The frequency range for the unbonded OH-stretching vibration is

Table 16. *Range of band positions for alcohols*

Primary alcohols	~1050 cm^{-1} (s)	1350–1260 cm^{-1} (s)
Secondary alcohols	~1100 cm^{-1} (s)	1350–1260 cm^{-1} (s)
Tertiary alcohols	~1150 cm^{-1} (s)	1410–1310 cm^{-1} (s)

3650–3590 cm^{-1}, but this shifts on hydrogen bonding with intermolecular hydrogen bonds to 3550–3450 cm^{-1} for single-bridge compounds and to 3400–3200 cm^{-1} when polymeric association occurs.

Absorption bands in the low-frequency region of the spectrum arise from C—O-stretching and from the OH-deformation mode. Two bands

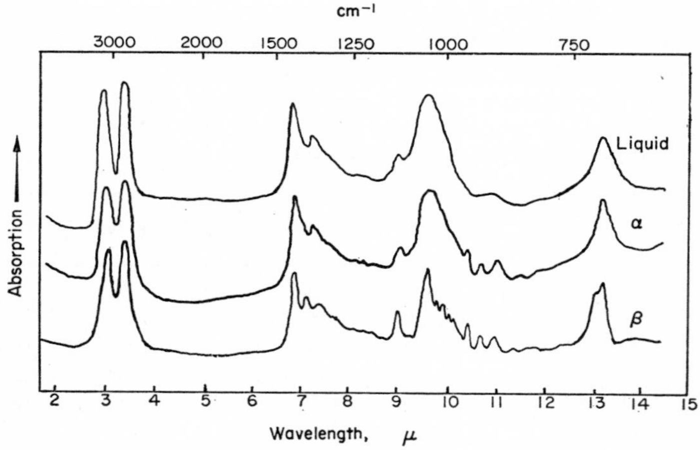

Fig. 33. The polymorphic forms of *n*-cetyl-alcohol.

occur covering a wide frequency range which may be associated with these vibrations, but both are affected by hydrogen bonding. Coupling effects makes it difficult to assign the bands. The range of absorption of these bands are given in Table 16.

The spectra of a number of long-chain alcohols of primary, secondary and tertiary type in the solid state have been examined [55]. The regular series of bands arising from the polymethylene chain in the 1190 to 1380 cm^{-1} region are observed. With the primary alcohols the spacings are given by $\Delta n = 19 \pm 1$ cm^{-1}.

The primary alcohols examined show a doublet in the 720 cm^{-1} region whilst the secondary alcohols show only a single band. This is presumably due to a difference in the mode of hydrocarbon packing in the two cases.

The polymorphism of some long-chain alcohols has been studied using infra-red spectroscopy and the spectra of the polymorphic forms of *n*-cetyl alcohol are shown in Fig. 33. By rapid scanning of the region near 720 cm^{-1} as the temperature was varied the transitions from one form to another have been followed [35].

ANHYDROUS SOAPS

We do not intend to discuss in detail the spectra of soap systems, but in view of an analogy with some phospholipid systems we include a brief account of the effect of temperature on anhydrous sodium stearate and palmitate.

Several changes of state occur when an anhydrous sodium soap is heated from room temperature to the m.p. [56, 57, 58]; e.g., dilatometric measurements over this temperature range [57] show two gross irregularities in the density–temperature curve at about 105–120° and 200° C, with minor breaks at other temperatures. With anhydrous sodium palmitate, five phase transitions have been observed between the crystalline state and the isotropic melt. An X-ray examination of this soap [58] shows that the long spacings vary with temperature but suggests that the phases can be grouped into two basic structures, named the waxy and neat phase, both being thought to be liquid–crystalline.

The infra-red spectra of sodium palmitate at different temperatures [59] are shown in Fig. 34. As the temperature approaches 100° C the distribution of bands in the 1250 cm^{-1} region become less well-resolved, particularly the bands at the high-frequency end of the distribution. This is interpreted to mean that the hydrocarbon chains are beginning to flex and twist. (This will produce some rotational isomerism, each isomer having its own frequency in this region, producing a smearing-out of the spectrum.) This interpretation is supported by the fact that the band at 719 cm^{-1} also decreases slightly in intensity. (This band is associated with the in-phase motion of all the CH_2 groups, so that twisting of parts of the chain will reduce the intensity of this band.) On further heating to about 120–130° C this band decreases considerably in intensity, indicating that many more methylene groups are spinning freely about the C—C bonds. All the fine structure in the 1250 cm^{-1}

region vanishes, whilst bands assigned to other CH_2 rocking modes also become diffuse or disappear. Bands assigned to methyl rocking modes decrease in intensity but remain prominent. There is little, if any, movement in frequency of the carboxylate bands at 1560, 1415 or 695 cm^{-1} but the intensity of the 695 cm^{-1} band decreases.

Above 120–130° C the spectrum of the soap is, in fact, entirely 'liquid-like' in character. The changes observed in the spectra are analogous to

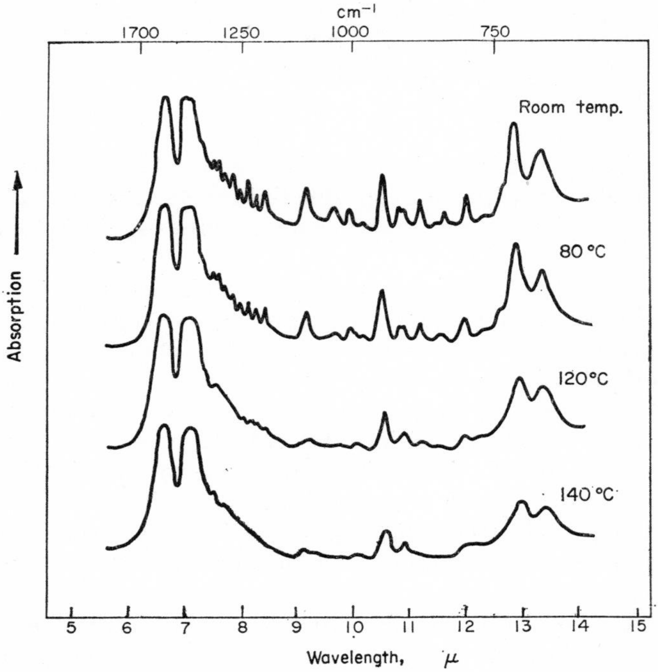

Fig. 34. The infra-red spectra of anhydrous sodium palmitate at different temperatures.

those observed in the spectra of, e.g. long-chain monocarboxylic acids, when the transition from the crystalline to liquid state occurs. Yet this transition occurs some 180° C below the 'true' m.p. of the soap. It seems clear that at this temperature the hydrocarbon chains are in a 'liquid state'. We can conclude that the soap is only prevented from completely melting by the strong bond between the highly polar sodium metal and carboxylate groups. The spectra clearly demonstrate the appearance of the 'liquid–crystalline' phase of soaps. X-ray data on this phase support this interpretation, since the long spacings are sharp whilst the short spacings are diffuse. The spectral evidence showed clearly for the first time that all the phase changes above 110° C occur with the hydrocarbon chains in a liquid-like condition.

Little change is observed on further heating of the soap up to 200° C, except that the bands at 719 and 695 cm^{-1} decrease further in intensity and the relative intensity of the 1460 and 1415 cm^{-1} band alters. The 1415 cm^{-1} band then becomes of greater intensity.

On cooling of the soap all these spectral changes are observed in reverse order and all the fine detail in the spectra return.

Analogous spectral changes on heating sodium stearate are observed. These changes can obviously be correlated with the variation of other properties of the soaps at these temperatures, such as flow, yield and mobility [60]. The increased cohesion and plasticity and fibre-forming properties observed above 110° C are doubtless due to the fluidity of the hydrocarbon chains at this temperature. The spectra of phospholipids at different temperatures have also been examined and are discussed on page 119.

GLYCERIDES

Glycerides are, in the main, usually difficult materials to characterize because of the variety of possible isomers which can occur. Infra-red spectroscopy has, however, been shown to be a versatile analytical tool with wide applications in this field of investigation. While the greater part of the early infra-red spectroscopic work was carried out with the material in solution in either carbon tetrachloride or chloroform, recent studies have shown that much greater qualitative information may be obtained, especially about the configuration of glycerides, by obtaining the spectra of the materials in the crystalline state. This introduces complications arising from the occurrence of polymorphism, i.e. the existence of more than one crystalline form for the same glyceride. However, these complications themselves can be turned to good account, and the spectra may be used to provide information about the crystalline nature of the glyceride.

Triglycerides, diglycerides and monoglycerides have been examined [61–67] and their spectra are given.

Triglycerides

O'Connor *et al.* [68] have given the spectra from 2–12 μ of a number of triglycerides obtained from solutions in chloroform and have assigned the main bands to vibrations of the functional groups present. These bands also occur in the spectra of the liquid. Table 17 shows the frequencies of the main bands for long-chain triglycerides. The carbonyl band has been used, combined with thin-layer chromatography, to provide a quantitative technique for triglycerides in serum lipids. The bands in these spectra are generally broad and smeared into each other.

The spectrum of the randomly oriented crystalline material includes these major bands arising from the functional groups, but splitting of bands and shifts also occur. A discussion of the nomenclature used to designate the polymorphic form of glycerides is given in Chapter 8.

Table 17. *Assignment of major triglyceride bands*

Probable assignment:	
C—H stretching (CH_2 and CH_3)	3030–2967 cm^{-1}
C=O stretching (COOR)	1751–1733 cm^{-1}
C—H bending (CH_2/CH_3 groups)	1464–1453 cm^{-1}
C—H bend (symmetrical deform of CH_3)	1383–1361 cm^{-1}
C—H in plane wagging or rocking of CH_2 groups	1261–1250 cm^{-1}
C—O stretching (COOR)	1179–1166 cm^{-1}
CH_2 rocking mode	730–717 cm^{-1}

Saturated triglycerides

The spectra of the saturated triglycerides are found to vary according to the polymorphic form in which they occur. The variety of spectra obtained with a single saturated triglyceride in its various polymorphic forms is illustrated for trimargarin in Fig. 35. The major differences between these spectra are similar to those shown by 'even-acid' saturated triglycerides, such as tristearin. Among other spectral differences a single band occurs at 720 cm^{-1} in the spectrum of the α_L-form; a doublet at 719 and 727 cm^{-1} in the spectrum of the $\beta'/_L$-form; and a single band at 717 cm^{-1} in the spectrum of the β_L-form corresponding to the main CH_2 rocking mode of the methylene groups. The lowest form, designated sub-α_L, is obtained by quenching the liquid glyceride to $-70°$ C and running the spectrum at this temperature. The transition sub-α_L–α_L is observed to be a reversible one. The main CH_2 rocking mode in the spectrum of the sub-α_L-form is also a doublet at 719 and 727 cm^{-1}. These variations have been discussed in terms of the packing of the hydrocarbon chains present in the crystals, hexagonal in the α_L-form, orthorhombic O$\perp$ in the $\beta'/_L$-form, and triclinic T$\|$ in the β_L-form. The packing of the hydrocarbon chains in the sub-α_L-form is also deduced to be probably orthorhombic O$\perp$. For characterization purposes the most suitable form is considered to be the α_L-polymorphic form, which for triglycerides of greater molecular weight than trilaurin, is the form usually obtained by solidification at room temperature from the melt. It is therefore fairly

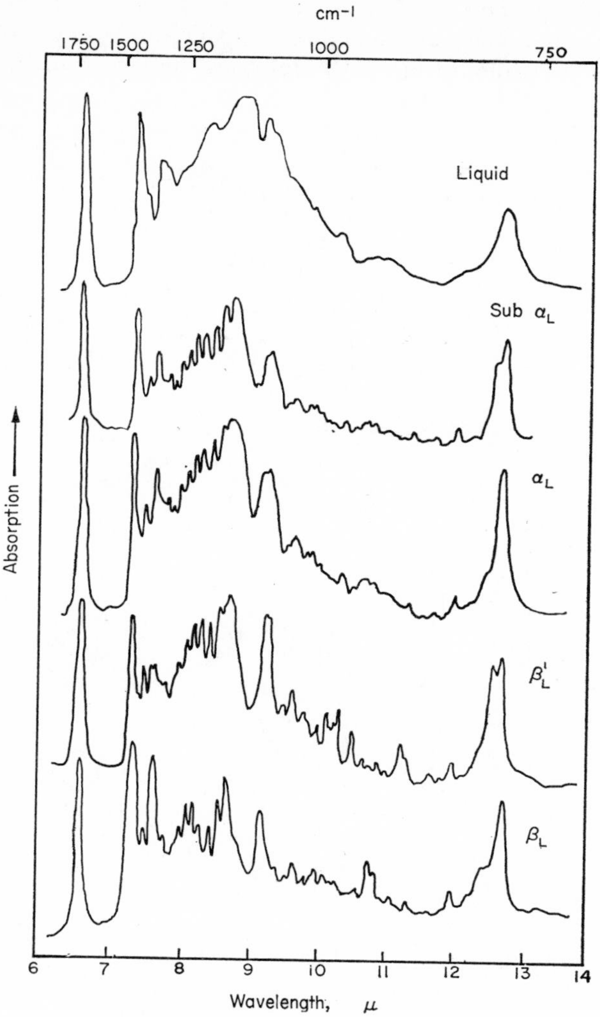

Fig. 35. The polymorphic forms of trimargarin.

easily and conveniently obtained. The spectra of the remaining forms are obtained by suitable thermal treatment or by crystallization from solvent followed by KCl disc or Nujol mull preparation.

The spectra of a series of saturated triglycerides are shown in Fig. 36. In each case the glyceride is in the α_L-polymorphic form. The number of bands in the 1250 cm^{-1} region increases with increasing chain length as with other long-chain derivatives. The frequencies of these bands are given in Table 18. The number of bands for an even number of carbon atoms in the chain is usually equal to half the number of carbon atoms in the chain $\frac{1}{2}n$, while for an odd number of carbon atoms it is usually

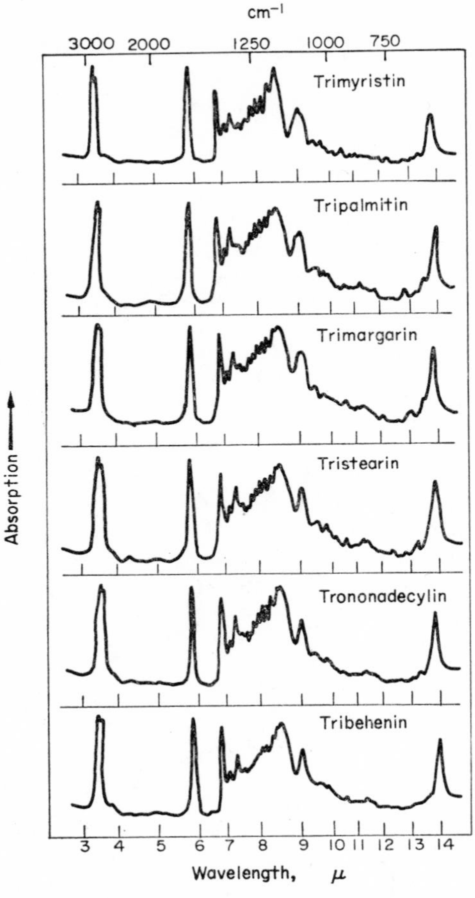

Fig. 36. Infra-red spectra of triglycerides in the α_L-form.

equal to half of the number of carbon atoms plus one $\frac{1}{2}(n+1)$. While the number of bands in the spectrum of a triglyceride with an odd-numbered chain is the same as in the spectrum of the next higher even-numbered chain, all the bands are shifted in frequency. The frequency difference between the band of highest frequency and its next lower neighbour is always less than the frequency difference between the other bands. These bands are analogous to those observed with anhydrous sodium soaps, fatty acids and esters.

To differentiate saturated triglycerides of mixed chain length is a little more difficult since a number of complications can occur. With glycerides such as 1-palmitodistearin the number of bands in the 1250 cm^{-1} region of the α_L-form is the same as that in tristearin while with 1-stearodipalmitin the number of bands is the same as in the spectrum of tripalmitin. With some glycerides, however, the α_L-form is not stable, while with other glycerides the most stable form is a β'_L-form rather than a β_L-form (cf. the spectra of 2-stearodipalmitin (PSP) and 2-palmitodistearin (SPS)). In the spectrum of a triglyceride of considerable difference in chain length, e.g. 1,2-diaceto-3-palmitin, the band at 1379 cm^{-1} is of strong intensity corresponding to the methyl groups present, and the CH_2 rocking mode is a single band at 718 cm^{-1}, indicating that the hydrocarbon chains are probably triclinically packed in this form as in the β_L-form of other saturated triglycerides.

Table 18. *Frequencies of bands in the* 1250 *cm^{-1} region for a series of glycerides*

Saturated triglycerides (α_L-form)	Frequency of bands in the 1250 region (cm^{-1})
Trimyristin	1344, 1329, 1300, 1276, 1252, 1229, 1200
Tripalmitin	1342, 1331, 1308, 1285, 1265, 1240, 1222, 1199
Trimargarin	1334, 1318, 1299, 1276, 1260, 1235, 1219, 1198
Tristearin	1341, 1330, 1308, 1289, 1270, 1255, 1232, 1216, 1193
Trinonadecylin	1346, 1335, 1323, 1302, 1285, 1266, 1248, 1230, 1213, 1194
Tribehenin	1339, 1323, 1310, 1293, 1279, 1265, 1252, 1233, 1222, 1205, 1189

Saturated diglycerides (β_L-form)	Frequency of bands in the 1250 region (cm^{-1})
1,3-Dilaurin	1328, 1310, 1298, 1266, 1235, 1211,
1,3-Dimyristin	1347, 1329, 1306, 1279, 1258, 1231, 1209
1,3-Dipalmitin	1346, 1332, 1310, 1290, 1266, 1245, 1224, 1205
1,3-Distearin	1340, 1328, 1309, 1292, 1271, 1255, 1231, 1214, 1198

Table 18—*continued*

Saturated diglycerides (α_L-form)	Frequency of bands in the 1250 region (cm^{-1})
1,2-Dilaurin	1349, 1329, 1299, 1270, 1239, 1210,
1,2-Dimyristin	1347, 1333, 1306, 1281, 1259, 1231, 1205
1,2-Dipalmitin	1343, 1331, 1308, 1286, 1265, 1240, 1221, 1199
1,2-Distearin	1342, 1328, 1307, 1290, 1269, 1253, 1232, 1213, 1192

Monoglycerides (β_L-form)	Frequency of bands in the 1250 region (cm^{-1})
1-Mono-olein	1333, 1294, 1255, 1213
1-Monocaprylin	1327, 1283, 1231
1-Monocaprin	1329, 1293, 1256, 1221
1-Monolaurin	1337, 1302, 1275, 1242, 1215
1-Monomyristin	1332, 1306, 1284, 1258, 1230, 1205
1-Monopalmitin	1339, 1314, 1293, 1271, 1248, 1227, 1202
1-Monostearin	1332, 1312, 1297, 1277, 1258, 1233, 1219, 198

Unsaturated triglycerides

The unsaturated triglycerides can be divided into those containing *cis* groups and those containing *trans* groups, although glycerides containing both these groups can occur. There is little difficulty in differentiating these two main types since the presence of the *trans* group is clearly shown by the band at 963 cm^{-1}. This band occurs in the spectrum of material in the liquid state, in solution, or in the crystalline state. The spectra obtained from the polymorphic forms of trielaidin designated α_L and β_L are shown in Fig. 37. The strong band attributable to the *trans* group in the molecule is apparent in all the spectra. The relative intensities of the bands in the 1250 cm^{-1} region in the spectra change in a manner analogous to that observed with saturated triglycerides.

The presence of a *cis* group is usually indicated by the presence of a weak band near 1660 cm^{-1}. The band attributable to the bending vibration of the hydrogen atoms in the *cis* group, however, is not constant in frequency and is very sensitive to crystal structure. As with the saturated triglycerides a variety of spectra can be obtained, depending on the particular crystalline form in which the material can exist. (Most unsaturated natural lipids exist predominantly in the *cis* form but can change to a mixture of *cis* and *trans* forms on partial hydrogenation.)

Where possible, it is preferable to obtain more than one spectrum with these glycerides. Examination of the 1250 cm^{-1} region of the spectrum of the α_L-form provides information about the chain length. The spectrum of the most stable form, usually obtained by slow crystallization from solvent, is also informative, e.g. the most stable form of 2-oleo type

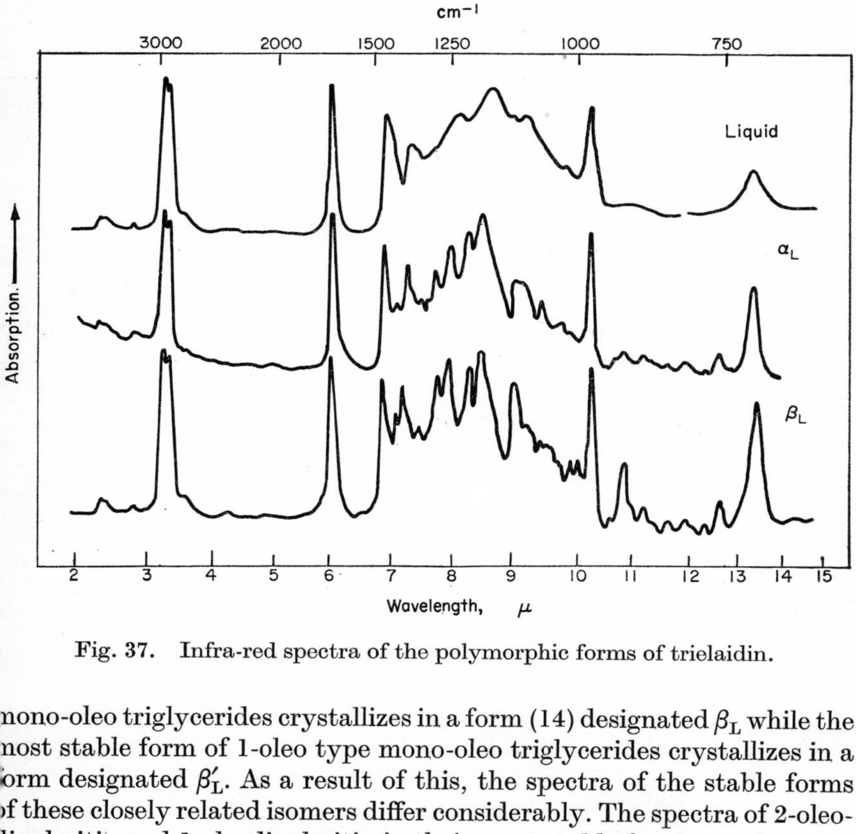

Fig. 37. Infra-red spectra of the polymorphic forms of trielaidin.

mono-oleo triglycerides crystallizes in a form (14) designated β_L while the most stable form of 1-oleo type mono-oleo triglycerides crystallizes in a form designated β'_L. As a result of this, the spectra of the stable forms of these closely related isomers differ considerably. The spectra of 2-oleodipalmitin and 1-oleodipalmitin in their most stable forms are shown in Fig. 38.

The main CH_2 rocking vibration in the spectrum of the 2-oleo isomer is single at 717 cm^{-1} while that of the 1-oleo isomer is a doublet at 729 and 719 cm^{-1}. The spectrum of the 2-oleo isomer also shows a strong band at 690 cm^{-1} attributed to a vibration of the *cis* group. A strong band does not occur in this region of the spectrum of the 1-oleo isomer. A sub-α_L-form showing a doublet at 719 and 727 cm^{-1} is also observed witl these glycerides. (This is particularly clear in the spectra of 1-oleo distearin at 0° C.) This large difference observed between the spectra oi the 1- and 2-oleo isomers is very useful and has already been used tc determine the major glyceride present in cocoa butter and kokur butter. Spectra of other natural fats, such as illipe butter, have also beer obtained. The major glyceride in all these natural fats, except lard appear to have the same 2-oleo type of configuration. Unusual variation:

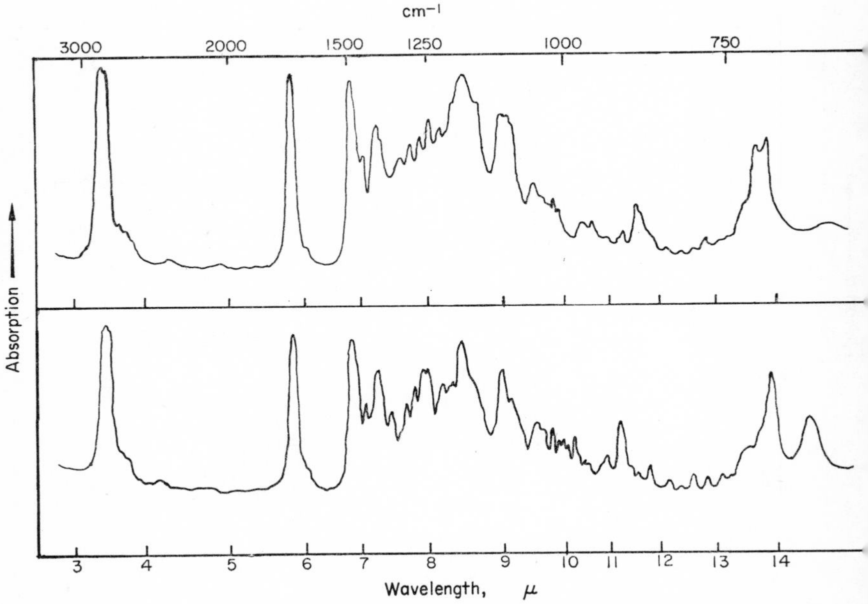

Fig. 38. Infra-red spectra of 1-oleo-dipalmitin and 2-oleo-dipalmitin.

may occur when mixed crystal formation occurs. This is particularl observed with mixtures of 2-oleo- and 1-oleodistearin. Mixtures of equa amounts of these glycerides, crystallized slowly from solvent anc dispersed in Nujol, give rise to a spectrum quite different from that o either glyceride and corresponds to a definite mixed crystal formation

Spectra obtained from the polymorphic forms of triolein are shown i Fig. 39. The strong band near 690 cm^{-1} and the band at 1660 cm^{-1} attributable to the presence of the *cis* group, are apparent. In th spectrum of the α_L-form the band is single at 723 cm^{-1}, and in th spectrum of the $\beta'/_L$-form it is split into two components at 729 anc 722 cm^{-1} while in the spectrum of the β_L-form it is single at 722 cm^{-1}

This is closely analogous to the variation of this band observed in the spectrum of the saturated triglycerides. It is suggested that perhaps the chains, or parts of the chains, will pack predominantly in a similar manner to that observed with saturated triglycerides despite the presence of the *cis* groupings in the chain.

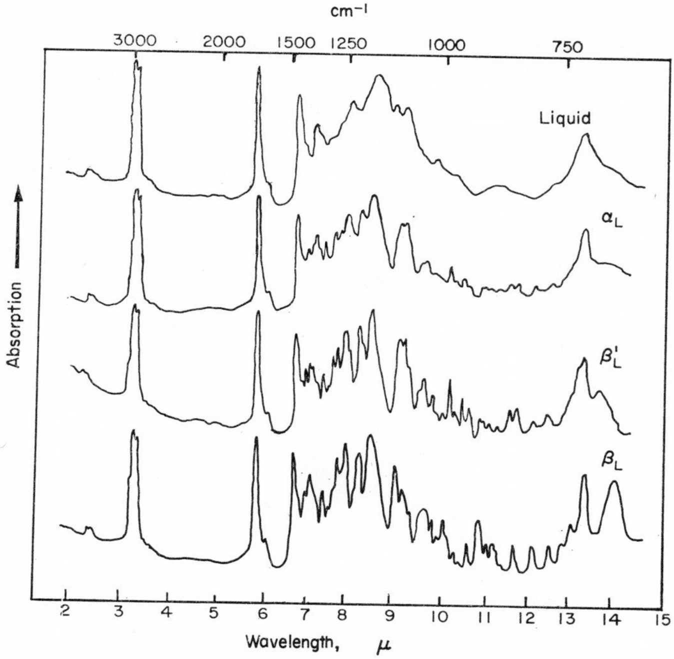

Fig. 39. Infra-red spectra of the polymorphic forms of triolein.

Diglycerides

Diglycerides may also exist in two isomeric forms, depending on the position of the chain on the glycerol residue. Thus 1,3- and 1,2-type glycerides occur.

Characterization of the two types is usually fairly simple since the spectra of crystalline forms of these two types of glyceride differ considerably as a consequence of the different modes of packing adopted by the hydrocarbon chains. The 1,3-type of diglyceride, such as distearin and dipalmitin, appears to crystallize in two very similar forms (probably with triclinic packed chains) while the 1,2-type glyceride appears to crystallize in two forms, with X-ray short spacings different in type from those of the 1,3-diglycerides. The spectrum of a diglyceride, such as distearin in its most stable form after crystallizing from solvent and dispersing in Nujol, affords a very convenient way to differentiate between the 1,2- and 1,3-diglyceride isomers. The 1,3-type of glyceride from the melt gives rise to a spectrum nearly identical with that obtained

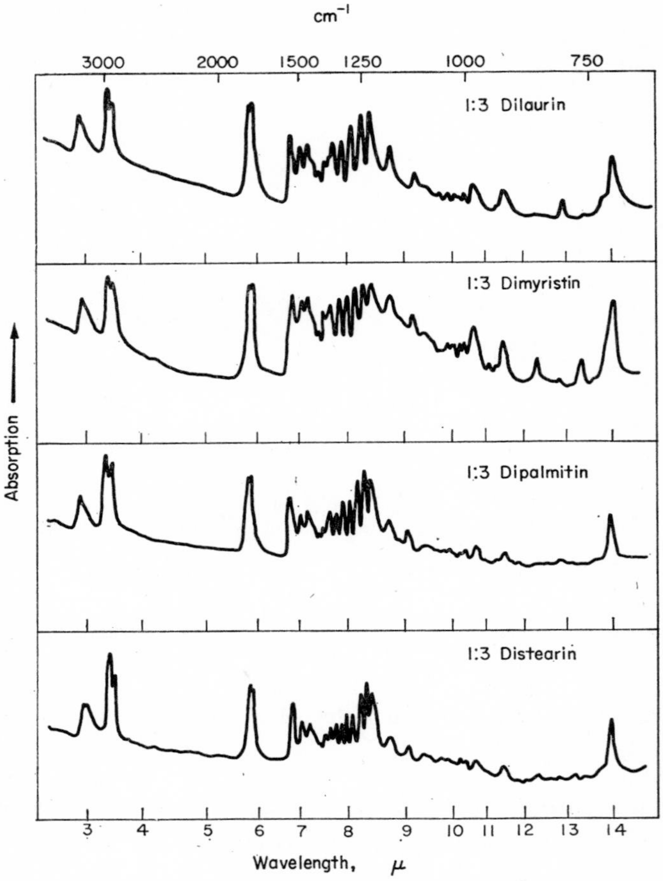

Fig. 40. Infra-red spectra of the β_L-polymorphic forms of some 1:3-diglycerides.

by dispersing the solvent-crystallized material in Nujol, i.e. it exists in two β_L-type forms. These glycerides do not appear to crystallize in an α_L-form. The spectra of a series of 1,3-diglycerides are shown in Fig. 40. Information about the chain length can be deduced from the 1250 cm^{-1} region. The frequencies of the bands are given in Table 18.

The 1,2- and 1,3-diglycerides have been examined in solution in the fundamental region and the configurations in solution deduced. The diglycerides are considered to have three predominant configurations, one internally hydrogen bonded and two involving no hydrogen bonds.

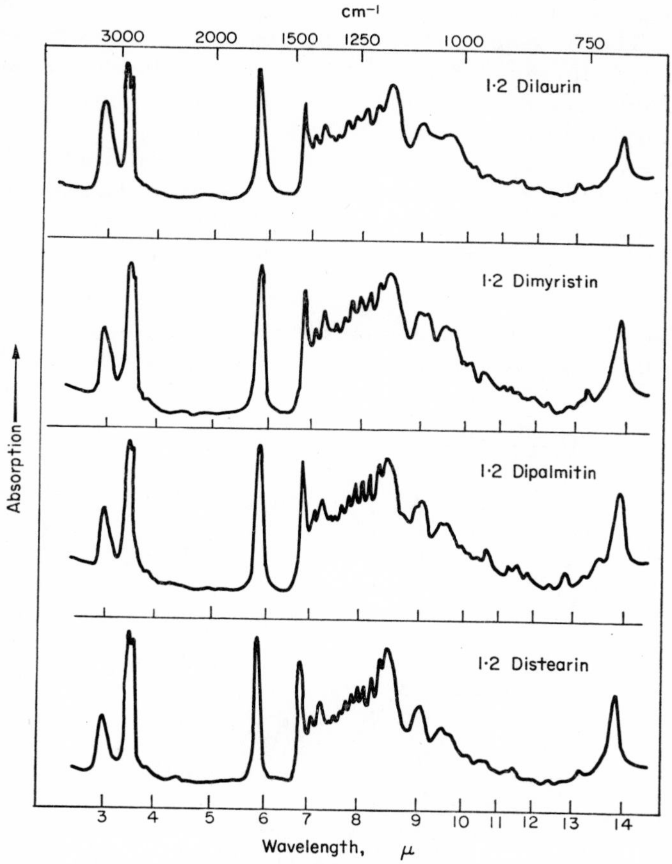

Fig. 41. Infra-red spectra of 1,2-diglycerides in the α_L-form.

The hydrogen-bonded form of the 1,3-diglyceride is considered to have a *trans*, *gauche* configuration and the other forms a *trans*, *trans* configuration around the glyceride backbone. With the 1,2-diglyceride the hydrogen-bonded structure appears to be in a *trans*, *trans* configuration. It should be noted that not all 1,3-diglycerides crystallize in the β_L-form, e.g. 1-aceto-3-palmitin crystallizes (20) in a β_L'-form, and its spectrum is very different from that observed with, say, 1,3-dipalmitin. In particular, the main CH_2 rocking mode near 720 cm^{-1} consists of a doublet.

The spectra of the two polymorphic forms (designated $\alpha_L \equiv \alpha_M$ and $\beta'_L \equiv \beta_M$) of the 1,2-diglycerides have marked spectral differences. In the spectrum of the α_L-form the main CH_2 rocking mode is single at 720 cm^{-1}, while in the spectrum of the β'_L-form a doublet occurs at 727 cm^{-1} and 719 cm^{-1}. This may imply that the hydrocarbon chains are predominantly packed in the hexagonal and orthorhombically packed $O\perp$ manner respectively. The spectra of a series of 1,2-diglycerides in the α_L-polymorphic form are shown in Fig. 41.

Information about the chain length can be deduced from the bands in the 1250 cm^{-1} region of the spectra. The number of bands observed is equal to half the number of carbon atoms in the chain, $\frac{1}{2}n$ for the 'even carbon' diglycerides. The frequencies of the bands are given in Table 18.

Monoglycerides

Monoglycerides can be of two main types, depending on where the chain is attached to the glycerol residue. If the chain is attached in either the

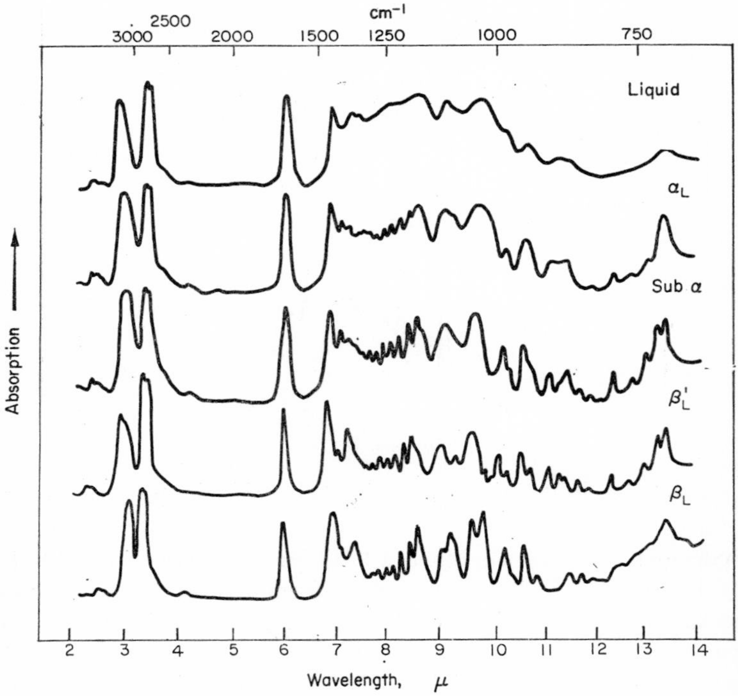

Fig. 42. The polymorphic forms of 1-monopalmitin.

1- or 3-positions, the glyceride is designated a 1-monoglyceride, since these positions are equivalent. The spectra of the monoglycerides in the liquid state show the bands to be broad and tending to smear into each other.

A means of differentiating the two types of monoglyceride follows from the fact that different thermal treatment of the 1-monoglycerides gives rise to different spectra, corresponding with the different polymorphic

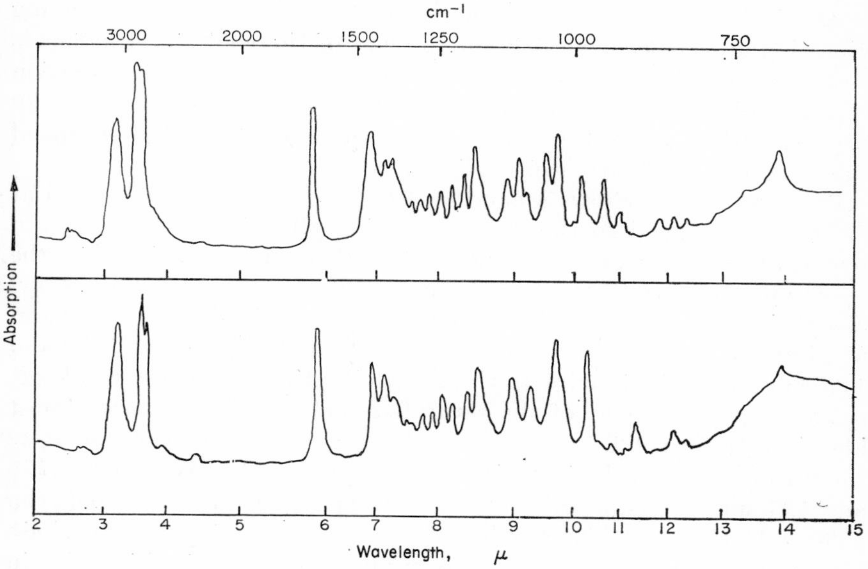

Fig. 43. The infra-red spectra of 1-monomyristin (top) and 2-monomyristin (bottom).

forms in which the 1-monoglycerides can occur. The 2-monoglycerides exist in only one polymorphic form.

The spectra of a series of 1-monoglycerides in the stable β_L-form are shown in Fig. 42. The major differences between the spectra lie in the 1250 cm^{-1} region. The frequencies of these bands are given in Table 18.

The spectrum of the crystalline form of a 2-monoglyceride is quite distinct from that of the 1-monoglyceride; and this simplifies characterization of the two types (Fig. 43). The practical use of the spectra obtained with the crystalline form of 1-monoglycerides has been demonstrated by Kuhrt *et al.* [69] who showed that monoglycerides were formed to an appreciable extent when monoglyceride-free fat was used to make bread.

CHOLESTEROL ESTERS

The infra-red spectra of a number of pure cholesterol esters of long-chain fatty acids have been reported [70]. The spectral data enables differentiation to be made between the saturated and the unsaturated cholesteryl esters and also to determine the nature of the fatty acid present. All the solution and solid-state spectra of cholesterol and its esters show two bands at 840 and 800 cm^{-1} due to the C—H bending vibration adjacent to the 5,6 double bond of the cholesterol molecule and a very weak band at 1667 cm^{-1} assigned to the stretching vibration of the double bond. Strong absorption bands at 2941, 1470 and 1370 cm^{-1} are due to the CH groups of the methylene and methyl groups of the cholesteryl and fatty-acid radicals.

Cholesterol itself shows a band at 3600 cm^{-1} and a broader band at 3330 cm^{-1} assigned to the O·H stretching vibration of the free and bound hydroxyl group. A strong band at 1050 cm^{-1} is assigned to the C—O vibrations of the hydroxyl group. With the esters, the hydroxyl absorptions near 3330 and 1050 cm^{-1} disappear and a strong sharp band at 1730 cm^{-1}, due to the ester group, occurs. The peaks at 1250 and 1175 cm^{-1} are associated with the C—O vibrations of the ester linkage.

The solution spectra of the saturated cholesteryl esters are almost identical. In the solid state, however, the spectra of the saturated esters show an increase in the intensity and sharpness of bands at 1430, 1175 and 725 cm^{-1}. Also, a series of regularly spaced bands occur between 1330 and 1185 cm^{-1}. The number of bands is proportional to the chain length of the compound. Some weaker bands also occur in this region in the spectra of the laurate. Only one band occurs at 722 cm^{-1} for solid cholesteryl laurate, whereas there is a doublet in this region for the higher homologues. This may be an indication of a difference in the chain packing. Spectral changes with temperature (Fig. 44) show that the onset of the liquid crystalline state of these esters takes place in an analogous way to the phospholipids (cf. pages 119 and 122).

The unsaturated esters are distinguished from the saturated compounds by the presence of a small peak at 1135 cm^{-1}, whilst several weak bands in the 1110 cm^{-1} region can be used to differentiate the unsaturated esters from each other. Cholesteryl oleate has a small band at 1120 cm^{-1} and an inflection at 1105 cm^{-1}, the linolenate has an inflection at 1120 cm^{-1} and a definite peak at 1105 cm^{-1}. The linoleate shows only a shoulder at each of these two wavelengths. All three compounds have a peak at 1136 cm^{-1} which increases with unsaturation, and a peak at

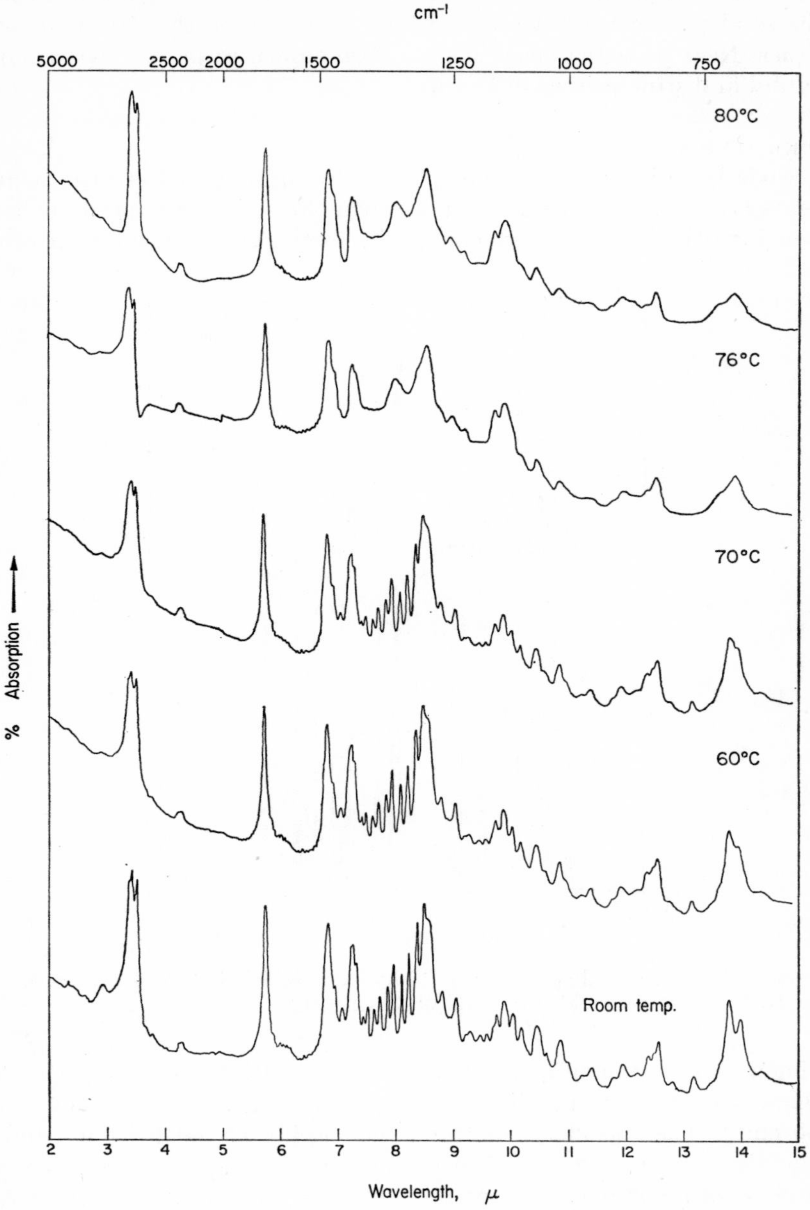

Fig. 44. Infra-red spectra of cholesteryl stearate at different temperatures.

1085 cm^{-1} which decreases in intensity with increasing unsaturation. The solid-state spectra are useful for distinguishing the various homologues. Near infra-red spectra have been shown to be not particularly helpful in distinguishing the various esters.

STEROIDS

Steroids have been extensively studied by infra-red spectral measurements [71, 72]. The spectra of more than three thousand steroids have been investigated and they can all be distinguished from each other

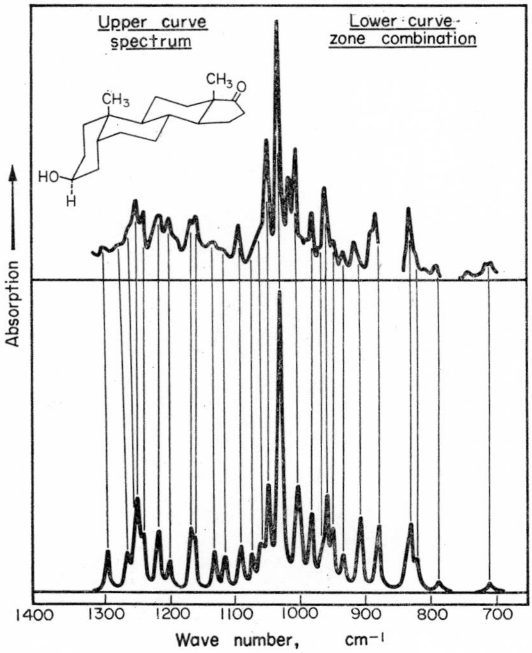

Fig. 45. Infra-red spectrum of 3β-hydroxy-etiocholan-17-one. (Jones, R. N. *Ist. Superiore di Sanita,* **2** (3), 514, 1959.)

using a combination of qualitative and quantitative measurements. The region used for empirical identification work lies between 1350 and 650 cm^{-1}. The specificity of this region is illustrated for four stereoisomeric hydroxy-ketones. With such large molecules assignment of bands is difficult if not impossible. The concept of zone patterns has again been applied to spectra obtained on an absolute intensity basis of molecular extinction coefficients. A characteristic zone pattern is set up for each functional group consisting of a Lorentz curve form and a half-band width of 7 cm^{-1}. By analysing many spectra the position of certain characteristic groups can be determined [73]. These individual bands correspond in position to the bands in the pattern and the height of the curve is taken from the extinction coefficient of the absorption peak of the simple mono-substituted steroid. Fig. 45 shows how the construction of a zone pattern is compared with the experimental spectrum.

PHOSPHOLIPIDS

The infra-red spectra of a number of phospholipids have been published but there are many unsatisfactory gaps and discrepancies in the data. Some of the discrepancies are due to the fact that the materials under examination were impure, or that acyl migration had occurred during the preparation. In other cases the occurrence of polymorphism has confused the situation so that different spectra have been reported for the same material. As yet, there is no detailed analysis of the effect of crystallinity on their infra-red spectra.

Here we discuss the spectra of the main phospholipid types obtained with the materials in solution and then discuss the more informative but more confusing spectra of the solid-state material.

We can make the following observations about the similarities and differences we expect of the main phospholipids. All the spectra of the cephalins, lecithins, plasmalogens and the main glycerol derivatives will show bands arising from the glyceryl residue. If they are long-chain derivatives then bands arising from the vibrations of the polymethylene chain will also occur. The remaining common feature is the presence of a phosphate group. Vibrations of this grouping usually occur as follows: (*a*) P=O stretching, vibration absorption at 1350–1250 cm^{-1} (v.s.), sometimes a doublet and hydrogen bonding can shift the band to lower frequencies with an increase in intensity; (*b*) POC vibration, absorption about 1050–980 cm^{-1} (v.s.), usually two bands are observed; (*c*) POH vibration absorption in the region 2700–2560 cm^{-1}.

To summarize the expected major difference between the phospholipid classes, we note that the phosphatidyl ethanolamines and phosphatidyl serines contain an NH_2 or $^{+}NH_3$ grouping, the lecithins contain an $N(CH_3)_3$ grouping, the sphingolipids contain an amide grouping and the plasmalogens do not contain an ester (C=O) grouping. These differences themselves are sufficient, using the solution spectra, to distinguish these main classes. The spectra of a lecithin in CS_2 solution, a sphingomyelin as a solid film and a cephalin in CS_2 solution are shown in Fig. 46. The region from 1670–1390 cm^{-1} is obscured by CS_2 absorption. It is easy to see that the ester band (C=O) near 1740–1720 cm^{-1} occurs in the spectra of the cephalins and lecithins but not with the sphingolipid. The sphingolipid has bands at 1640 and 1540 cm^{-1}. Also bands occur at 970 cm^{-1} in the spectra of the lecithin and sphingomyelin but not with the cephalin.

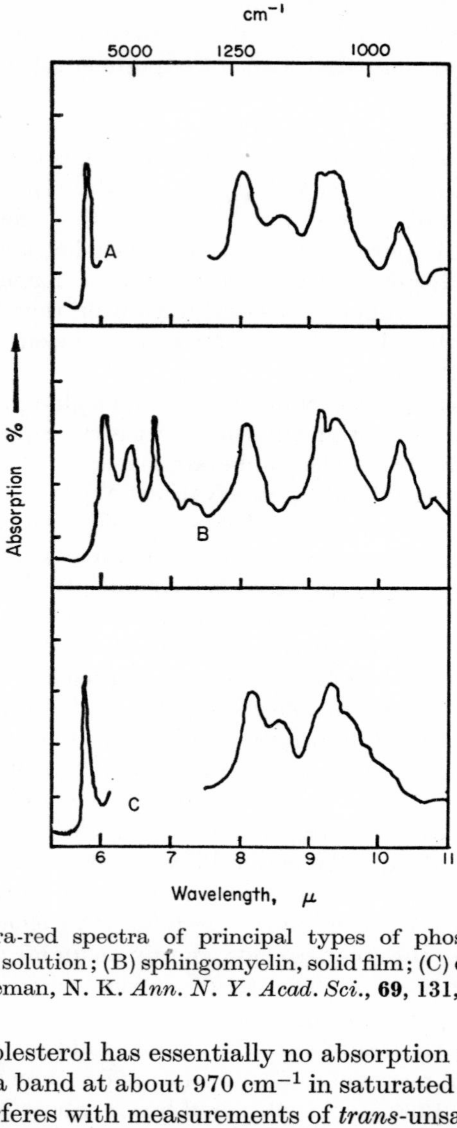

Fig. 46. Infra-red spectra of principal types of phosphatides: (A) lecithin in CS_2 solution; (B) sphingomyelin, solid film; (C) cephalin in CS_2 solution. (Freeman, N. K. *Ann. N. Y. Acad. Sci.*, **69**, 131, 1957.)

(Unesterified cholesterol has essentially no absorption near 1720 cm^{-1}.) The presence of a band at about 970 cm^{-1} in saturated and unsaturated compounds interferes with measurements of *trans*-unsaturated content. Differences have been observed in the region of the P=O stretching frequency between the phosphatidyl ethanolamines (strong band 1227 cm^{-1}) and the phosphatidyl serines (1220–1180 cm^{-1}).

Such differences have been used to analyse total serum lipid extract [74]. The spectrum of such an extract is shown in Fig. 47, and analysis

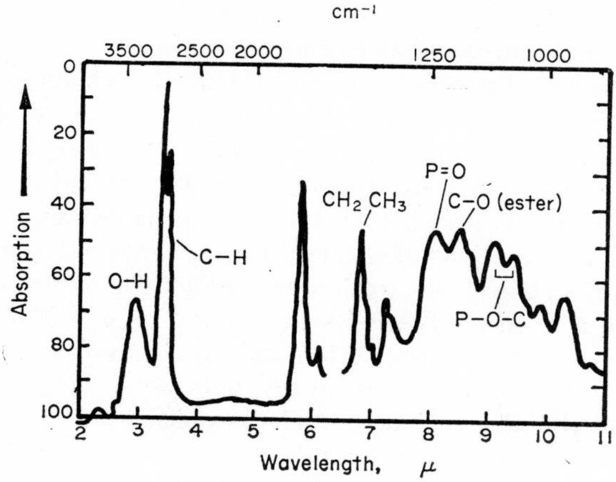

Fig. 47. Infra-red spectrum of total lipid extract from 1 ml of serum. (Freeman, N. K. *Ann. N. Y. Acad. Sci.*, **69**, 131, 1957.)

made in terms of total esterified fatty acids, total cholesterol and total phosphatides. Equations are set up of the form

$$\begin{matrix}1724\text{ cm}^{-1}\\ A^{(5\cdot 8\mu)}\end{matrix} = \begin{pmatrix}1724\text{ cm}^{-1}\\ \alpha_{EFA}^{(5\cdot 8\mu)}\times C_{EFA}\end{pmatrix} + \begin{pmatrix}1724\text{ cm}^{-1}\\ \alpha_{TC}^{(5\cdot 8\mu)}\times C_{TC}\end{pmatrix} + \begin{pmatrix}1724\text{ cm}^{-1}\\ \alpha_{RP}^{(5\cdot 8\mu)}\times C_{RP}\end{pmatrix} \quad (4.3)$$

$$\begin{matrix}1380\text{ cm}^{-1}\\ A^{(7\cdot 25\mu)}\end{matrix} = \begin{pmatrix}1380\text{ cm}^{-1}\\ \alpha_{EFA}^{(7\cdot 25\mu)}\times C_{EFA}\end{pmatrix} + \begin{pmatrix}1380\text{ cm}^{-1}\\ \alpha_{TC}^{(7\cdot 25\mu)}\times C_{TC}\end{pmatrix} + \begin{pmatrix}1380\text{ cm}^{-1}\\ \alpha_{RP}^{(7\cdot 25\mu)}\times C_{RP}\end{pmatrix} \quad (4.4)$$

$$\begin{matrix}1093\text{ cm}^{-1}\\ A^{(9\cdot 15\mu)}\end{matrix} = \begin{pmatrix}1093\text{ cm}^{-1}\\ \alpha_{EFA}^{(9\cdot 15\mu)}\times C_{EFA}\end{pmatrix} + \begin{pmatrix}1093\text{ cm}^{-1}\\ \alpha_{TC}^{(9\cdot 15\mu)}\times C_{TC}\end{pmatrix} + \begin{pmatrix}1093\text{ cm}^{-1}\\ \alpha_{RP}^{(9\cdot 15\mu)}\times C_{RP}\end{pmatrix} \quad (4.5)$$

where EFA is the esterified fatty acids, TC total cholesterol, RP residual phosphatides (i.e. total phosphatides – EFA in phosphatides), α is the absorbance/g/l in the cell used, and C is the concentration g/l. These simultaneous equations can be solved for the concentrations. By making various assumptions and approximations the equations are further reduced so that by intensity measurement at these three frequencies the concentration of esterified fatty acids, cholesterol and residual phosphatides can be determined.

It has been conjectured that such analyses on a routine basis could be very valuable in clinical laboratories.

By using chromatography and infra-red spectroscopy, serum phospholipids have been analysed [75]. The extracted lipids are separated into five fractions by successive elution from a silicic acid–celite column with methylene chloride, acetone, 35% methanol, 65% methylene chloride (two fractions) and methanol. The phospholipids are contained in the last three fractions. Using reference compounds the amounts of cephalin, lecithin and sphingomyelin have been determined.

A method has also been developed for estimating cholesterol esters and triglycerides simultaneously in serum lipids [76]. This involves separating the phospholipids from the total lipid mixture by a simple bath adsorption on silicic acid. Cholesterol esters and triglycerides are the main constituents in the non-adsorbed lipid and measurements are made on this mixture. The analysis of the two components is based on the fact that the ester carbonyl absorption frequency for cholesteryl esters is different from that of triglycerides by about 14 cm^{-1}. For this analysis it is necessary to have the resolution and precision of a grating spectrophotometer. Pure triolein and pure cholesteryl oleate are used as standards and the absorption coefficients obtained at the two selected frequencies. The oleate absorbs at 1730 cm^{-1} and the triolein at 1745 $cm^{-2}1$. There are two requirements for this method: (*a*) the silicic adsorption must separate out all the phospholipids and none of the components to be measured; (*b*) the contribution of other non-adsorbed lipids must be small enough to be manageable. The non-adsorbed lipid material contains unesterified cholesterol and unesterified fatty acids. The cholesterol molecule has no carbonyl group, whilst the absorption arising from the free fatty acids can be made less than 5%. The acetone solvent must also be completely removed from the lipid.

Spectral studies have been made with sphingomyelin [77] and show the existence of a *trans*-configuration of the double bond in sphingomyelin, *N*-lignocerylsphingosine and cerebroside using the band at 970 cm^{-1}. After hydrogenation this band disappears with the latter two compounds and is diminished with the sphingomyelin. With the sphingomyelin another band also occurs in this region. It is suggested that lecithin may be quantitatively determined when present in mixtures with sphingomyelin.

The infra-red spectra of a number of natural phospholipids have been examined by Rouser *et al.* [78] and some of their spectra are shown in Fig. 48. These show the spectra of a brain lecithin, phosphatidyl ethanolamine and sphingomyelin, a synthetic saturated dimyristoyl phosphatidyl ethanolamine and a partially hydrogenated phosphatidyl ethanolamine. These workers pointed out that the spectra of the natural phosphatidyl ethanolamine is quite different from that of the synthetic

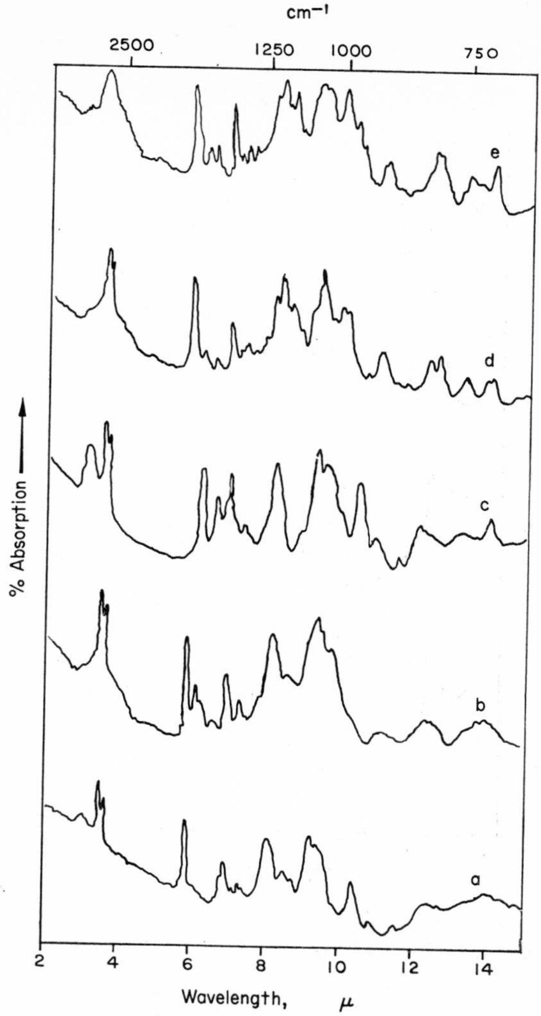

Fig. 48. Infra-red spectra of a series of phospholipids. (*a*) Infra-red spectrum of beef brain lecithin isolated from a silicic acid–silicate–water column. (*b*) Infra-red spectrum of beef brain phosphatidyl ethanolamine isolated from a DEAE cellulose column. (*c*) Infra-red spectrum of brain sphingomyelin isolated from a silicic acid–silicate–water column. (*d*) Infra-red spectrum of synthetic dimyristoyl-phosphatidyl ethanolamine. (*e*) Infra-red spectrum of partially hydrogenated phosphatidyl ethanolamine. (Phosphatidyl ethanolamine of soybean was isolated from a DEAE column, hydrogenated over a palladium catalyst.) (Rouser, G., Kritchevsky, G., Heller, D. and Lieber, E. *J. Amer. Oil Chemists' Soc.*, **40**, 425, 1963.)

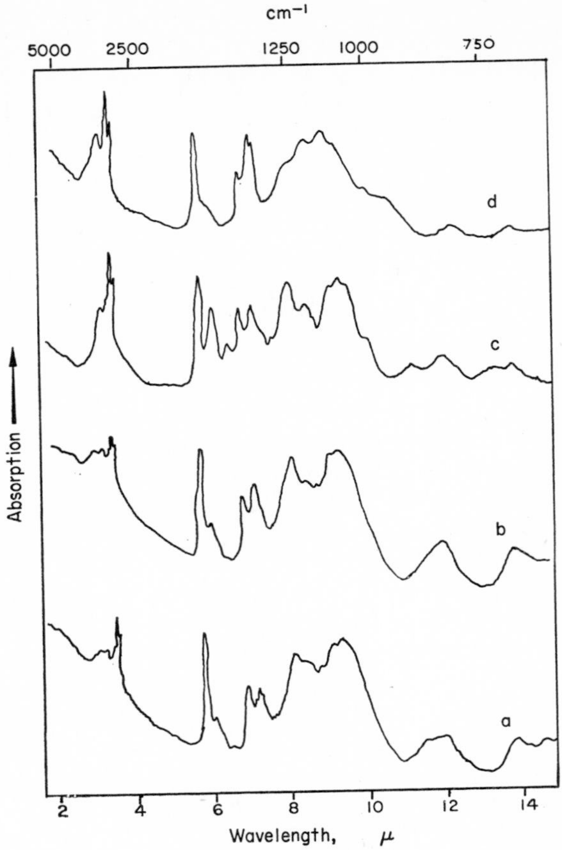

Fig. 49. Infra-red spectra of acidic lipids in KBr discs. (*a*) Infra-red spectrum of cardiolipin isolated from beef heart mitochondria by DEAE cellulose column chromatography. The sample was evaporated directly from a mixture of chloroform–acetic acid containing ammonium acetate. (*b*) Infra-red spectrum of the same preparation of cardiolipin shown in previous figure after addition of excess concentrated aqueous ammonia to convert to the ammonium form. (*c*) The infra-red spectrum of beef brain phosphatidyl serine isolated from a DEAE cellulose column (eluted with chloroform–acetic acid 3:1 containing ammonium acetate). The sample was in the ammonium form. (*d*) Infra-red spectrum of beef brain phosphatidic acid isolated first from DEAE cellulose and then from a silicic acid–silicate–water column. The preparation was predominantly in the ammonium form. (Rouser, G., Kritchevsky, G., Heller, D. and Lieber, E. *J. Amer. Oil Chemists' Soc.* **40**, 425, 1963.)

material and suggested that hydrogenation of the natural material may be a useful technique to adopt in order to aid identification. They also commented that their spectra of the dimyristoyl phosphatidyl ethanolamine was different from that of other workers. It was also observed with the natural phospholipids that differences in chain length, unsaturation and even the presence of an α,β-unsaturated ether link did not cause appreciable changes in the spectra. The spectra of acidic lipids were also studied and it was noted that the free acid and the salt form give different spectra. The spectra of some ammonium salts of cardiolipin, phosphatidyl serine and phosphatidic acid are shown in Fig. 49. These workers also suggested that infra-red spectroscopy is useful for characterizing the hydrolysis products of lipids. The sample is hydrolysed and separated into water-soluble and organic solvent-soluble fractions and the weight of these determined. The solutions are then chromatographed and their spectra obtained. If possible this is compared with that of a model substance. The infra-red spectra of a number of ceramides and cerebrosides are shown in Fig. 50.

The spectra of a number of synthetic phospholipids have also been published [79]. The spectra of two isomeric lecithins containing one stearic acid and one oleic acid chain in different positions were shown to be completely identical and to show much less structure than that of the mixed acid fully saturated lecithin. This behaviour is also observed with phosphatidyl ethanolamines, and also with the serine-containing glycerophosphatides and lysolecithins.

The reason for this contrast between the spectra of the natural, the unsaturated phospholipids and the saturated phospholipids became clear as a result of investigating the spectral variation observed with temperature [80].

A pure DL-dipalmitoyl-α-cephalin[1] was crystallized from chloroform and made into a KBr disc. The spectrum at room temperature (Fig. 51) corresponds to that of an *A′*-form. At low temperature, $-186°$ C, the spectrum shows a great deal of fine structure, e.g. the band near 720 cm^{-1} associated with the CH_2 rocking mode is split into a doublet. At room temperature some of this fine structure has disappeared and now only a single band occurs at 720 cm^{-1}. As the temperature increases up to about 100 to 120° C all the remaining fine structure disappears and the spectrum resembles that of a liquid rather than a solid, although the 'true' melting point of the lipid is some 195° C. This is analogous to the behaviour observed with sodium soaps and the interpretation is the same, i.e. as the temperature increases the hydrocarbon moiety begins to flex and twist until melting of the chain occurs. The ionic end-groups

[1] 2,3-dipalmitoyl-DL-1-phosphatidyl ethanolamine.

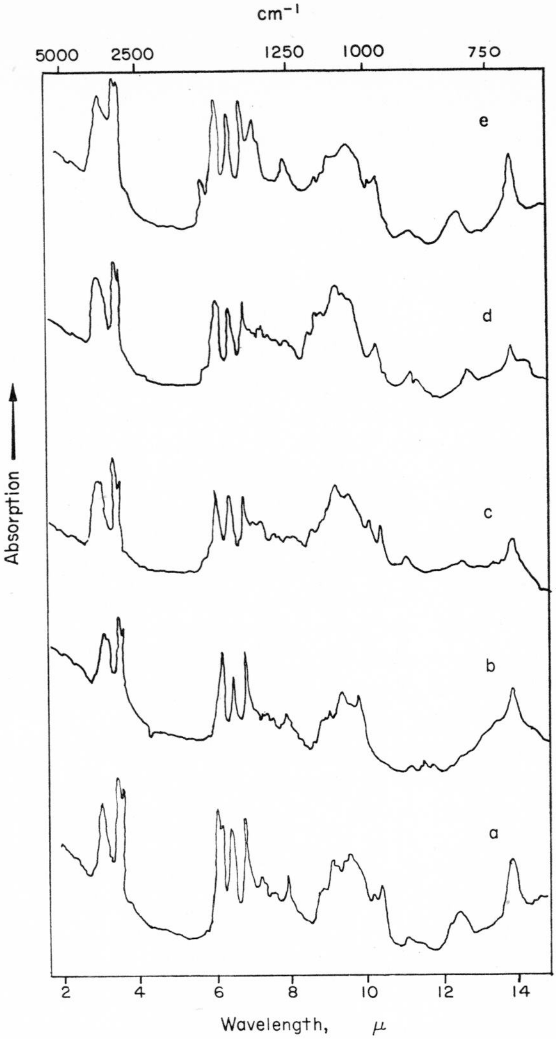

Fig. 50. Infra-red spectra of ceramides and cerebrosides in KBr discs. (*a*) Infra-red spectrum of ceramide prepared by enzymic degradation of sphingomyelin. (*b*) Infra-red spectrum of yeast cerebrin. The sample was eluted from a Florisil column with chloroform–methanol 4 : 1. (*c*) Infra-red spectrum of cerebroside isolated from the spleen lipids of a patient with Gaucher's disease. (*d*) Infra-red spectrum of beef brain cerebroside isolated by column chromatography on magnesium silicate and DEAE cellulose. (*e*) Infra-red spectrum of ceramide after heating with 0·05 N HCl for 6 hr in a sealed tube at 100° C. (Rouser, G., Kritchevsky, G., Heller, D. and Lieber, E. *J. Amer. Oil Chemists' Soc.*, **40**, 425, 1963.)

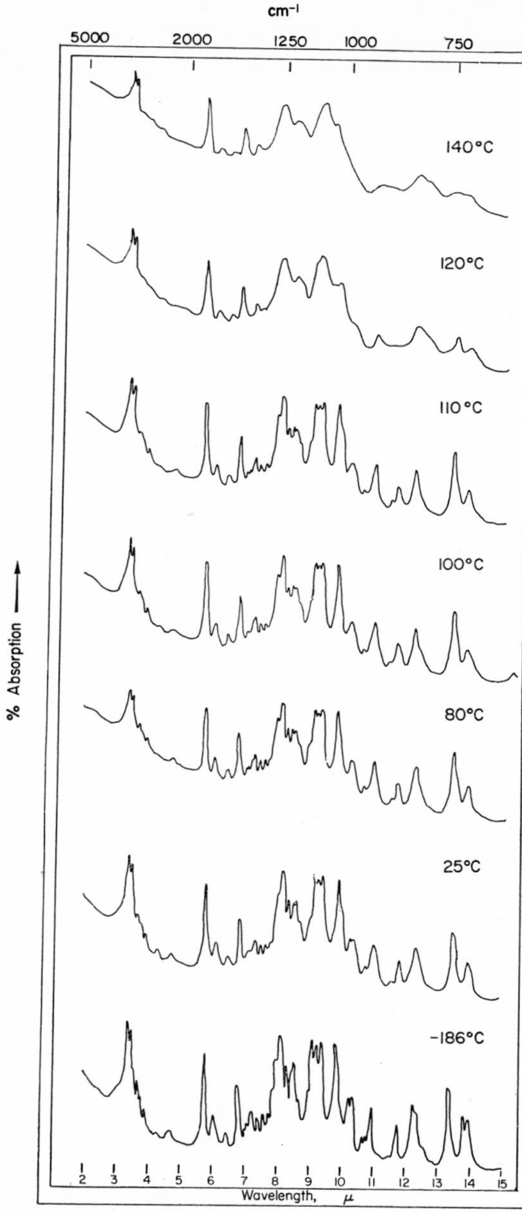

Fig. 51. Infra-red spectra of 2,3 dipalmitoyl-DL-1-phosphatidyl ethanolamine at different temperatures.

retain the crystalline character of the material until the 'true' melting point is reached. This interpretation is consistent with the decrease observed in the X-ray long spacings and the fact that the short spacings form diffuse haloes at ~ 4·5 Å when the temperature is above about 100° C.

This observation has a number of implications because the phospholipids containing both saturated and unsaturated chains will have the corresponding transition temperature at a lower temperature and it is clear that with phospholipids containing chains of this type that the hydrocarbon chains can be in an essentially liquid condition at room temperature despite the fact that the lipid has a 'true' melting point of some 200° C. This is the reason why the spectra obtained at room temperature of a variety of natural lipids of this type show no significant difference between related isomers. (This liquidity of the hydrocarbon chains well below the melting point of the lipid is probably the reason why synthetic membranes prepared from natural phospholipids are quite different under the electron microscope from those prepared with phospholipids containing saturated fatty acids.) This liquid character of the chains in the natural phospholipids is clearly of considerable importance for the function of these lipids in the biological systems, and when water is present will determine the particular type of phase which can exist at any particular temperature and be in turn related to permeability processes.

We can make some further interesting speculations related to this. If we consider a phospholipid containing saturated and unsaturated fatty acids, but where there is a *trans* grouping present rather than a *cis* grouping, we should expect the transition temperature for melting of the hydrocarbon chains to be a little higher but not quite as high as with the corresponding fully saturated phospholipid. If this is true, it will probably also be the case in the presence of water. However, if, as has been suggested, the unit membrane exists rather critically on the borderline of a phase transition, sensitive to temperature and below which permeability processes are affected, then the presence of lipids of this type in a membrane could give rise to important physiological effects. This is clearly speculative at this time and many more studies are required to confirm this point. The presence of linoleic or linolenic acids in the membrane phospholipids will presumably further lower the transition temperature.

It is also clear that, in order to determine whether differences occur between related isomers containing unsaturated and saturated fatty-acid chains, it is necessary to cool the phospholipid below the transition temperature when the hydrocarbon chains crystallize.

This has been done with a L-2-oleoyl-3-stearoyl-α-lecithin. At room temperature the spectrum of the material in a KBr disc shows that the hydrocarbon chains are in a liquid-like condition. On cooling the disc slowly down to liquid nitrogen temperature the spectrum sharpens and shows considerable fine structure (see Fig. 52). On raising the temperature

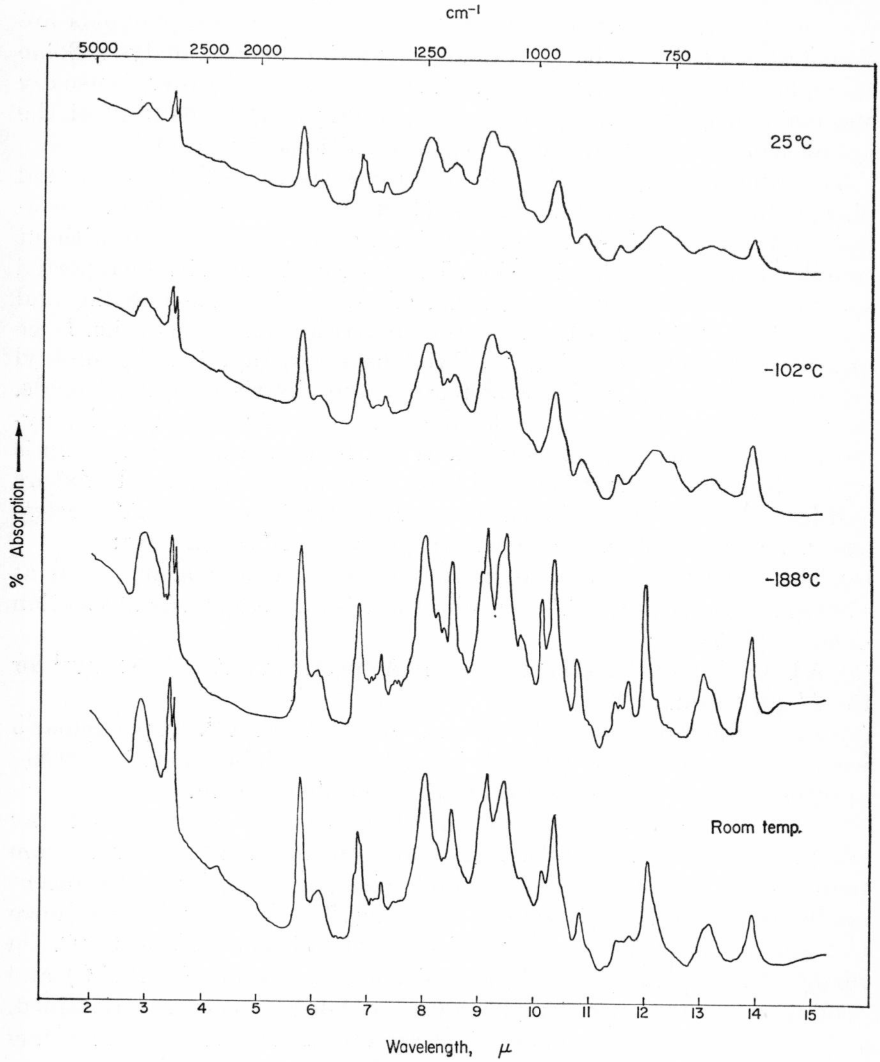

Fig. 52. Infra-red spectra of 2-oleoyl-3-stearoyl-L-1-phosphatidyl choline at room temperature, liquid nitrogen temperature and after warming again up to room temperature. (Descending order.)

to room temperature some of this fine structure disappears. However, it does not revert to the original spectrum until a temperature between 40 to 50° C is reached. Further work is at present being carried out to ascertain whether the original liquid-like state of the phospholipid is due to the transition temperature being exceeded during the preparation of the KBr disc.[1] Transition temperatures of phospholipids are shown up very clearly by the use of differential thermal analysis. Some examples of this are shown in Fig. 53. It can be seen that there is usually one main melting temperature corresponding to the 'melting' of the hydrocarbon chains but other thermal transitions also occur.

The literature concerning the infra-red spectra of the saturated phospholipids examined in the solid state shows considerable confusion [78, 81]. This has been previously commented upon without completely resolving the situation. There are differences in the reported spectra of the same compound, e.g. of L-dimyristoyl-α-cephalin, and unexplained differences between the spectra of homologues, i.e. large unexplained spectral differences exist between, say, the dipalmitoyl cephalin compared with the distearoyl and dimyristoyl compounds. Some of these differences are attributed to the occurrence of two polymorphic forms for these materials. When DL-dipalmitoyl-α-cephalin is crystallized in two different ways from a chloroform–methanol mixture and from ethanol two different spectra, referred to as A and A′ spectra, occur. The major differences between the A and A′ spectra are:

(*a*) The ester carbonyl band in the A-spectrum is a sharp band at 1739 cm^{-1} whilst in the A′-spectrum there is an asymmetric absorption band at 1725 cm^{-1}.

(*b*) A band occurs at 1563 cm^{-1} for the A-spectrum but at 1550 cm^{-1} for the A′-spectrum.

(*c*) Many differences occur between 1050 and 670 cm^{-1}. In particular a weak band occurs at 745 cm^{-1} with the A-spectrum but there is a strong absorption band at this frequency with the A′-spectrum.

That this arises from polymorphism has now been confirmed by X-ray study. Only one polymorphic form had been reported to occur at room temperature with these phospholipids (see page 295) but more recent studies now show the existence of two forms. The A-form has been shown to transform irreversibly to the A′-form when it is heated to 90° C. On further heating to above the transition temperature (~ 120° C) and cooling to room temperature, however, an A-type spectrum is obtained.

If the saturated phospholipid is heated to above its reported melting

[1] In view of the occurrence in nature of the unsaturated acid in the 2-position it is of some importance to determine whether this transition temperature differs from that of the isomer with the unsaturated acid in the 1-position.

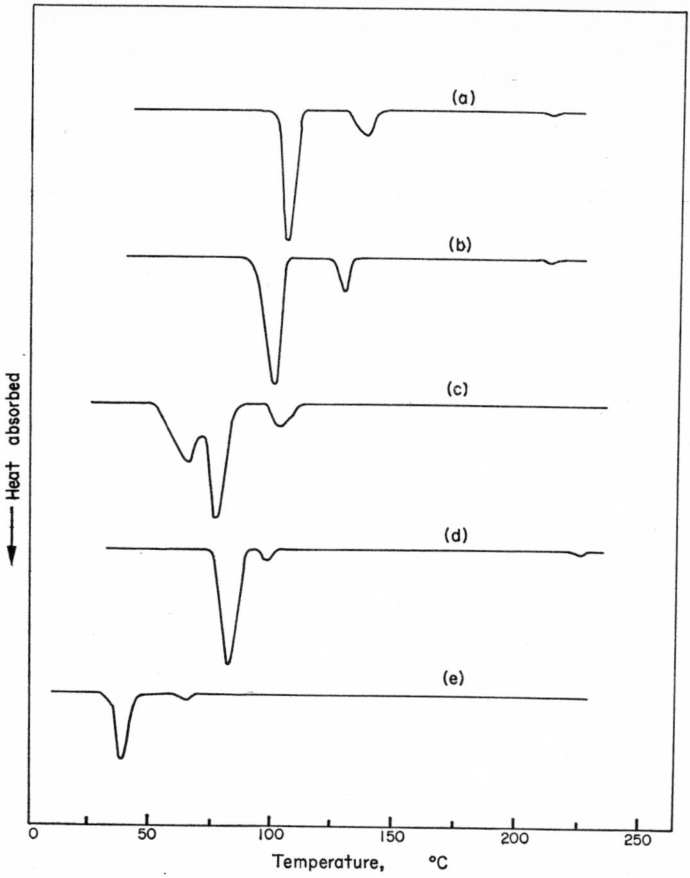

Fig. 53. Differential thermal analysis of phospholipids.
(*a*) 2,3-dimyristoyl-DL-1-phosphatidyl ethanolamine.
(*b*) 2,3-dielaidoyl-DL-1-phosphatidyl ethanolamine.
(*c*) 2-oleoyl-3-stearoyl-DL-1-phosphatidyl ethanolamine.
(*d*) 2,3-distearoyl-DL-1-phosphatidyl choline.
(*e*) 2-oleoyl-3-stearoyl-DL-1-phosphatidyl choline.

point (say 220° C) and cooled to room temperature a different spectrum is obtained which is convenient in the 1250 cm^{-1} region for determining the length of the hydrocarbon chains present (Fig. 54). The spectral variations with temperature show that the chains of the A′-form are probably packed in the orthorhombic (O ⊥) arrangement at the lowest temperature but become less tightly packed as the temperature increases.

It has been suggested [82] that absorption in the 2500–2700 cm^{-1}

region can be associated with P—OH stretching vibrations of the phosphatidyl ethanolamines when in the solid state. The small band observed near 2100–2300 cm^{-1} may also be related to vibrations of the

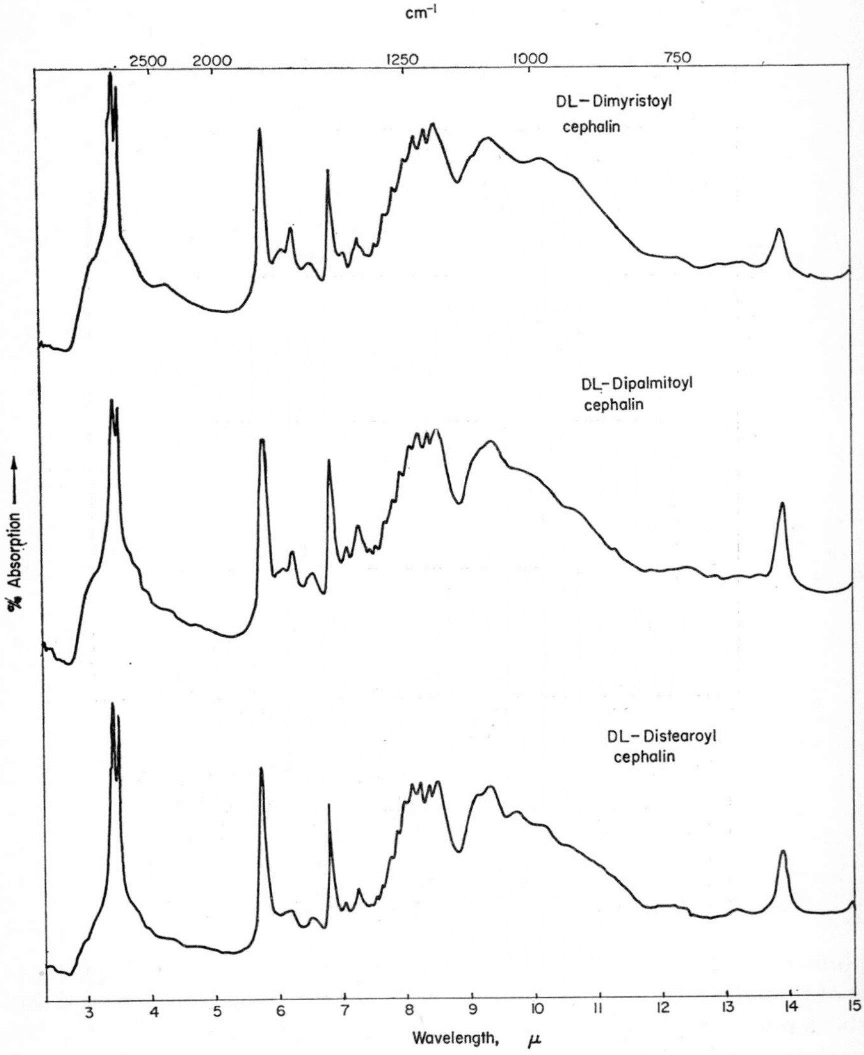

Fig. 54. Infra-red spectra of some saturated 2,3-DL-phosphatidyl ethanolamines. Spectra are obtained by heating the phospholipid above the 'true' melting point and allowing to cool to room temperature. The number of bands in the 1250 cm^{-1} region is related to the chain length.

P—OH group but it should be pointed out that a weak band near 2100 cm^{-1} is often observed where NH_3^+ groupings occur in a molecule. It was concluded that this is an indication that these molecules do not exist in a zwitter-ion form in contrast to the lecithins. The frequencies of absorption of the NH_2 stretching and deformation vibrations of the

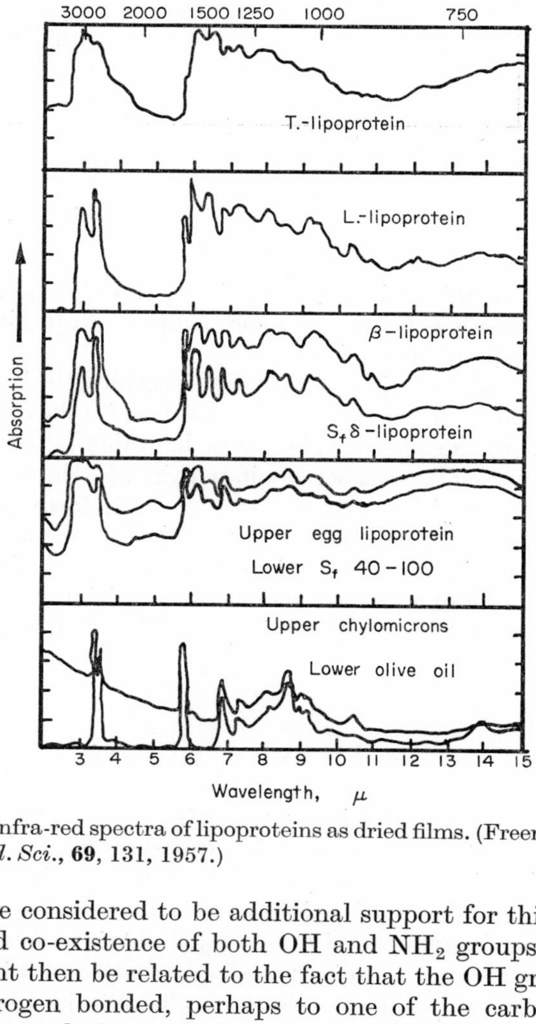

Fig. 55. Infra-red spectra of lipoproteins as dried films. (Freeman, N. K. *N. Y. Acad. Sci.*, **69**, 131, 1957.)

cephalins were considered to be additional support for this conclusion. The suggested co-existence of both OH and NH_2 groups in the same molecule might then be related to the fact that the OH group could be strongly hydrogen bonded, perhaps to one of the carbonyl groups. However, this conclusion is by no means certain and it could be argued to the contrary that the evidence favours a zwitter-ion structure and the presence of an NH_3^+ grouping. Single crystal X-ray studies will probably

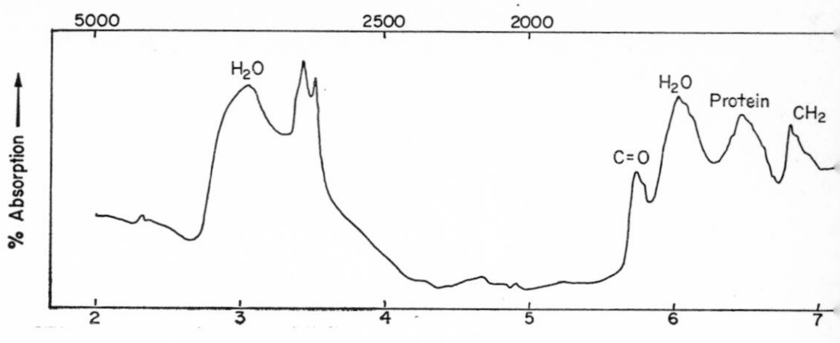

Fig. 56. Infra-red spec

be necessary to confirm these speculations. The high melting points of the phospholipids do suggest that ionic groups occur linking molecule to molecule throughout the lattice.

It seems probable that, just as with the glycerides, the infra-red spectra of the phospholipids in the solid state will reveal (*a*) the type of phospholipid present, (*b*) the polymorphic form in which it occurs as well as information on the hydrocarbon chain packing, (*c*) the chain length and any unsaturation which is present, such as *cis* or *trans* grouping, (*d*) in some cases the positions of the fatty acids in the phospholipid, i.e. whether they are in the 1,2- or 1,3-positions on the glycerol moiety, (*e*) as the spectrum of a racemic material may differ from that of the D- or L-optical isomer when examined in the solid state information on this may also be possible.

LIPOPROTEINS

The absorption of infra-red radiation by water is very strong and so lipoproteins have usually been examined in the dry or nearly dry condition. One method used is to evaporate lipoprotein solutions on to a silver chloride plate and to examine the spectra of the dried films. Another method is to freeze-dry the intact lipoprotein with potassium bromide and press the powdered mixture into a pellet.

The spectra of a number of lipoproteins obtained from ultra-centrifugally isolated serum samples have been compared with model substances [83]. The molecular species were characterized by their rate of flotation in a given medium and under a specified field of centrifugal force. The spectra of some of these lipoproteins are shown in Fig. 55, corresponding to increasing flotation rates. The order is one of increasing

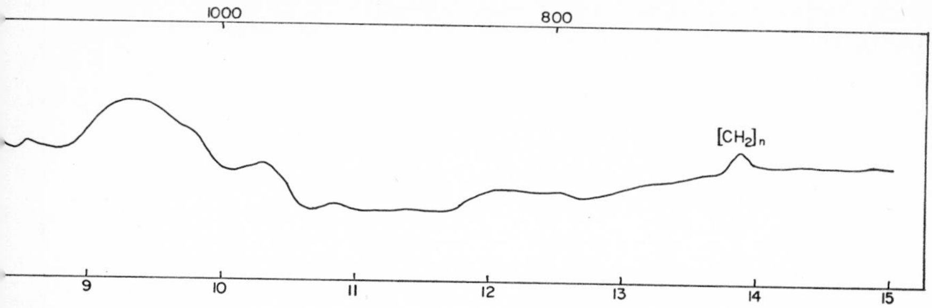

n sheath of pig optic nerve.

lipid content. The various prominent bands have been assigned as follows: ~ 1730 cm^{-1} ester carbonyl, arising from glycerides, cholesteryl esters, and some phospholipids including lecithin, 2940–2860 cm^{-1} – the absorption bands of the CH groups from fatty-acid chains and cholesterol. The principal protein bands are at 3330 cm^{-1} – the NH stretch 1640 cm^{-1} – C=O stretch – and the band at 1540 cm^{-1} assigned to monosubstituted amides. The L-, T- and S_F6-lipoproteins are normal serum constituents. A comparison between the spectra of lipoproteins obtained in different ways is possible. β_1-Lipoprotein and S_F6-lipoprotein spectra are very similar.

Fractionation of the lipoprotein with solvents separates the protein and lipids. The spectra of some of the lipoprotein fragments from egg lipoprotein after successive extraction are shown in Fig. 55. These have been compared with those of some reference materials and it has been shown that fat predominates in the extracted mixture. Acetone soluble material from S_F6-lipoprotein gives cholesterol whilst the acetone insoluble material from human serum contains mainly lecithin.

A study of myelin sheath is at present in progress [84] and a typical spectrum is shown in Fig. 56. This shows the strong absorption due to the water present but also bands which may be tentatively related to the phospholipid material and the assignments are indicated in the figure. It appears from the spectrum that the hydrocarbon chains are in a liquid-like condition. This is consistent with the observed X-ray short spacing at about 4·6 Å. This does not necessarily preclude some order among the chains. (The amount of order present in liquid hydrocarbons is discussed on page 241.) A band near 1540 cm^{-1} may perhaps be related to protein material present but additional studies are needed to confirm this.

Further studies using D_2O and also studies at different temperatures should provide additional useful information. There is also the possibility that polarized infra-red radiation may be useful in helping to confirm the opinions reached from optical, X-ray and electron diffraction studies on the spatial arrangements of the phospholipids.

REFERENCES

1. WHEELER, D. H. (1954) *Progress in Chemistry of Lipids*, Vol. II. Pergamon Press, London.
2. O'CONNOR, R. T. (1956) *J. Amer. Oil Chemists' Soc.*, **33**, 1.
3. BARCELO, M. J. and BELLANATO, J. (1953) *Anal. real. soc. españ. Fis Quim.*, **49**, 557.
4. DONGES, K. and STAIB, W. (1962) *J. Chromatog.*, **8**, 25.
5. NOACK, K. and JONES, R. N. (1961) *Canad. J. Chem.*, **39**, 2201.
6. KAYE, W. (1954) *Spectrochim. Acta*, **6**, 257.
7. HOLMAN, R. T. and EDMONDSON, P. R. (1956) *Analyt. Chem.*, **28**, 1533.
8. HOLMAN, R. T., ENER, S. and EDMONDSON, P. R. (1959) *Biochem. Biophys. Res. Comm.*, **80**, 72.
9. GODDU, R. F. (1957) *Analyt. Chem.*, **29**, 1790.
10. HOLMAN, R. T., NICKELL, C., PRIVETT, O. S. and EDMONDSON, P. R. (1958) *J. Amer. Oil Chemists' Soc.*, **35**, 422.
11. SHEPPARD, N. (1955) *Molecular Spectroscopy*, p. 145. Institute of Petroleum.
12. TSCHAMLER, H. (1954) *J. Chem. Phys.*, **22**, 1845.
13. SHEPPARD, N. (1959) 'Rotational Isomerism' in *Advances in Spectroscopy* (ed. H. W. Thompson). Interscience.
14. BROWN, J. K. and SHEPPARD, N. (1955) *Proc. Roy. Soc.*, **231A**, 555.
15. CHAPMAN, D. (1957) *J. Chem. Soc.*, 4489.
16. STEIN, R. S. and SUTHERLAND, G. B. B. M. (1954) *J. Chem. Phys.*, **22**, 1993.
17. HERMAN, R. C. and HOFSTADTER, R. (1938) *J. Chem. Phys.*, **6**, 534; (1939) **7**, 460.
18. DAVIES, M. M. and SUTHERLAND, G. B. B. M. (1938) *J. Chem. Phys.*, **6**, 755.
19. BATUEV, M. I. (1948) *Compt. rend. Acad. Sci. U.R.S.S.*, **59**, 1117.
20. FLETT, M. ST. C. (1951) *J. Chem. Soc.*, 962.
21. HADZI, D. and SHEPPARD, N. (1953) *Proc. Roy. Soc.*, **216A**, 247.
22. DAVIES, M. M. and THOMAS, O. (1950) *Discuss. Faraday Soc.*, **9**, 335.
23. CHAPMAN, D. (1956) *J. Chem. Soc.*, 225.
24. JOHNSON, J. F. and COLE, R. H. (1951) *J. Amer. Chem. Soc.*, **73**, 4536.
25. MIYAZAWA, T. and PITZER, K. S. (1959) *J. Chem. Phys.*, **30**, (4), 1076.
26. BRATOZ, S., HADZI, D. and SHEPPARD, N. (1956) *Spectrochim. Acta*, **8**, 249.

27. JONES, R. N. (1962) *Canad. J. Chem.*, **40**, 321.
28. SHREVE, O. D., HEETHER, M. R., KNIGHT, H. B. and SWERN, D. (1950) *Analyt. Chem.*, **22**, 1498.
29. O'CONNOR, R. T., FIELD, E. T. and SINGLETON, W. S. (1951) *J. Amer. Oil Chemists' Soc.*, **28**, 154.
30. CORISH, P. J. and CHAPMAN, D. (1957) *J. Chem. Soc.*, 1746.
31. KOHLRAUSCH, K. W. F. (1943) *Ramanspektren Leipzig.* Becker & Erler.
32. JONES, R. N., MCKAY, A. F. and SINCLAIR, R. G. (1952) *J. Amer. Chem. Soc.*, **74**, 2575.
33. MEIKLEJOHN, R. A., MEYER, R. J., ARONOVIC, S. M., SCHUETTE, H. A. and MELOCK, V. W. (1957) *Analyt. Chem.*, **29**, 329.
34. PRIMAS, H. and GUNTHARD, H. H. (1953) *Helv. Chim. Acta*, **36**, 1659.
35. CHAPMAN, D. (1957) *Spectrochim. Acta*, **11**, 609.
36. SINCLAIR, R. G., MCKAY, A. F. and JONES, R. N. (1952) *J. Amer. Chem. Soc.*, **74**, 2570.
37. BELLAMY, L. J. (1954) *The Infra-red Spectra of Complex Molecules.* Methuen, London.
38. VON SYDOW, E. (1955) *Acta Chem. Scand.*, **9**, 1119.
39. CHAPMAN, D. (1962) *J. Chem. Soc.*, 2310.
40. SUSI, H. (1959) *Spectrochim. Acta*, **12**, 1063.
41. SUSI, H. (1960) *J. Amer. Oil Chemists' Soc.*, **37**, 431.
42. HOLLAND, R. F. and NEILSEN, J. R. (1963) *Acta Cryst.*, **16**, 902.
43. SINCLAIR, R. G., MCKAY, A. F., MYERS, G. S. and JONES, R. N. (1952) *J. Amer. Chem. Soc.*, **74**, 2578.
44. SUSI, H. (1959) *Analyt. Chem.*, **31**, 910.
45. FISCHMEISTER, I. (1962) *Arkiv. Kemi*, **20**, 353.
46. FISCHMEISTER, I. (1962) *Arkiv. Kemi*, **20**, 385.
47. THOMPSON, H. W. and TORKINGTON, P. (1954) *J. Chem. Soc.*, 640.
48. JONES, R. N. and HERLING, F. (1954) *J. Org. Chem.*, **19**, 1252.
49. JONES, R. N., HUMPHRIES, P., HERLING, F. and DOBRINER, K. (1951) *J. Amer. Chem. Soc.*, **73**, 3215.
50. LUCIER, J. J. and BENTLEY, F. F. (1964) *Spectrochim. Acta*, **20**, 1.
51. JONES, R. N. (1962) *Canad. J. Chem.*, **40**, 301.
52. YVERNAULT, T. (1946) *Oleagineux*, **1**, 189.
53. SUTHERLAND, G. B. B. M. (1950) *Discuss. Faraday Soc.*, **9**, 274.
54. PLYLER, E. K. (1952) *J. Res. Nat. Bur. Stand.*, **48**, 281.
55. BRINI-FRITZ, M. (1957) *Bull. Soc. chim. France*, 516.
56. VOLD, M. J. and VOLD, R. D. (1939) *J. Amer. Chem. Soc.*, **61**, 808.
57. VOLD, M. J., MACOMBER, M. and VOLD, R. D. (1941) *J. Amer. Chem. Soc.*, **63**, 168.
58. NORDSIECK, H., ROSEVEAR, S. D. and FERGUSON, R. H. (1948) *J. Chem. Phys.*, **16**, 175.
59. CHAPMAN, D. (1958) *J. Chem. Soc.*, 784.
60. SOUTHAM, F. W. and PUDDINGTON, I. E. (1947) *Canad. J. Res.*, **25**, 125.

61. CHAPMAN, D. (1955) *Nature*, **176**, 216.
62. CHAPMAN, D. (1956) *J. Chem. Soc.*, **55**.
63. CHAPMAN, D. (1956) *J. Chem. Soc.*, 2522.
64. CHAPMAN, D. (1957) *J. Chem. Soc.*, 2715.
65. CHAPMAN, D. (1958) *J. Chem. Soc.*, 4680.
66. CHAPMAN, D. (1958) *J. Chem. Soc.*, 3186.
67. CHAPMAN, D. (1960) *J. Amer. Oil Chemists' Soc.*, **37**, 73.
68. O'CONNOR, R. T., DU PRE, E. F., and FEUGE, R. O. (1955) *J. Amer. Oil Chemists' Soc.*, **32**, 88.
69. KUHRT, N. H., WELCH, E. A., BLUM, W. P., PERRY, E. S. and WEBER, W. H. (1952) *J. Amer. Oil Chemists' Soc.*, **29**, 261.
70. LABARRERE, J. A., CHIPAULT, J. R. and LUNDBERG, W. O. (1958) *J. Analyt. Chem.* (*U.S.S.R.*), **30**, 1466.
71. JONES, R. N. (1958) *Trans. Roy. Soc. Canada*, Sect. III, **52**, 9.
72. ROBERTS, G., GALLAGHER, B. S. and JONES, R. N. (1958) *Infra-red Absorption Spectra of Steroids an Atlas.* Interscience, New York.
73. JONES, R. N. (1959) *Inst. Superiore Sanita*, **2**, 514.
74. FREEMAN, N. K. (1957) *Ann. N.Y. Acad. Sci.*, **69**, 131.
75. NELSON, G. J. and FREEMAN, N. K. (1959) *J. Biol. Chem.*, **234**, 1375.
76. FREEMAN, N. K. (in course of publication).
77. MARINETTI, G. and STOTZ, E. (1954) *J. Amer. Chem. Soc.*, **76**, 1347.
78. ROUSER, G., KRITCHEVSKY, G., HELLER, D. and LIEBER, E. (1963) *J. Amer. Oil Chemists' Soc.*, **40**, 425.
79. DE HAAS, G. H. and VAN DEENEN, L. L. M. (1961) *Rec. Trav. chim.*, **80**, 95; DE HAAS, G. H. Thesis, Utrecht University.
80. BYRNE, P. and CHAPMAN, D. (1964) *Nature* **202**, 987.
81. VAN VEEN, A. and VERKADE, P. E. (1960) *Rec. Trac. Chim.*, **79**, 1085.
82. BELLAMY, L. J. and BEECHER, L. (1953) *J. Chem. Soc.*, 728.
83. FREEMAN, N. K., LINDGREN, F. T., NG, Y. C. and NICHOLS, A. V. (1953) *J. Biol. Chem.*, **203**, 293.
84. CHAPMAN, D. (unpublished results).

5. Mass spectroscopy

Although mass spectroscopy has been known for some forty years it is only recently that its analytical uses in chemistry, and in particular in organic and biochemistry, have become of significance [1, 2]. The instrumental developments since 1940 have made the potential of the technique more apparent and in particular the development of heated inlet systems has made it possible for a large number of molecules, previously thought to have too little vapour pressure, to be available for investigation. This has led directly to the adoption of the technique for the study of lipids [3]. Whilst mass spectroscopy is still in its early stages of development compared with infra-red and nuclear magnetic resonance spectroscopy it is clear that there will be considerable extension to its uses and that there will be many more applications to the field of lipids.

Theoretical considerations

Mass spectra are obtained by bombarding the molecules of a compound in the vapour phase at low pressure with electrons of low energy. If the electrons have sufficient energy to cause ionization the molecular or parent-ion is formed.

$$M + e^- \rightarrow M^+ + 2e^- \qquad (5.1)$$

As the energy of the bombarding electrons is increased the probability of ionization increases and the parent ion can be formed with excess energy in its electronic and vibrational degrees of freedom. This excess energy of the molecule ion may be sufficient to equal the dissociation energy in one of the ion's degrees of freedom and a fragment ion will be formed. At greater electron energies further ions are produced. At electron energies of about 25–30 eV, two electrons can be removed from the molecule and doubly charged parent and fragment ions may be formed. The nature of the ions and their relative abundance depend upon the structure of the molecule being bombarded. In general, two compounds of different structure give different fragment patterns. As the relative intensities of the ions produced change less above 50 eV it is common to plot spectra for chemical analysis at bombarding voltages about 75 eV. At this electron energy the total probability of ionization is high and so there is good sensitivity of detection.

Under the usual conditions of operation few negatively charged parent ions are formed, and usually only positive ions are measured. The mass of the positively charged parent ion gives the molecular weight of the sample and its formula gives the molecular formula. These ions often stand out prominently at the high mass end of the spectrum free from interference by other ions. In some mass spectra, however, the parent ion has very small intensity and may even be undetectable. If no parent ions are detected, the rate of decomposition is too high for detection. The rate of decomposition increases with increase in molecular size within an homologous series as a greater number of reaction paths are then available. The parent ions are usually formed with little kinetic energy so that their masses can sometimes be measured accurately in a single focusing type mass spectrometer.

It is not yet possible to calculate the mass spectrum of a complex molecule but there have been a number of attempts to discuss the modes of formation of fragment ions. The large difference in mass of the nuclei and the ionizing electron means that the energy given to the nuclei is much less than that given to the electrons in the molecule. If an ionizing electron is near enough to one of these valence electrons it can be ejected, leaving the parent ion. Further electronic rearrangement can occur before any change in the nuclei positions takes place. As the mass spectrometer does not analyse neutral fragments, to predict the spectrum it is necessary to know not only at which bonds the ions are likely to break but which of the fragments will retain the positive charge. It has been suggested that the excitation of the parent ion is nearly thermal in nature and that the 'weak point' can wander about in a molecule. It is known that fragmentation may be delayed for as long as 10^{-5} sec, which is very much greater than the vibrational periods of the nuclei. Dissociation is considered to occur when the electronic configuration to enable it to take place most easily is reached. The ions redistribute their energy among the various vibrational modes by rapid radiationless transitions between the various electronic states.

As well as fragments being detected which can be described by assuming simple cleavage of bonds in the parent ion, other fragments occur which arise from atomic rearrangement at the moment of fragmentation. Such rearrangement is known to occur to a certain extent in almost all spectra of molecules containing two or more carbon atoms and is very common where migration of hydrogen atoms is involved. It is also common with unsaturated hydrocarbons and the spectra of various isomers of the same molecular formula are found to be almost identical.

The ions produced in an ion source are accelerated by a potential of a few thousand volts between two plates and deflected by a magnetic field H after passing through a slit. The magnetic field focuses the ion beam on to a collector through a further slit. The signal is amplified, usually with an electrometer d.c. amplifier and sometimes a vibrating-reed amplifier or electron multiplier.

The radius of the path described by the ion of mass M and of charge e depends upon the accelerating potential V and the magnetic field H. The potential energy eV of the ion will equal the kinetic energy after full acceleration where v is the velocity.

$$eV = \tfrac{1}{2}Mv^2 \qquad (5.2)$$

In the field H the ion experiences a centripetal force Hev which is balanced by a centrifugal force Mv^2/r.

$$Hev = \frac{Mv^2}{r} \qquad (5.3)$$

therefore

$$r = \frac{Mv}{eH} \qquad (5.4)$$

and hence

$$\frac{M}{e} = \frac{H^2 r^2}{2v} \qquad (5.5)$$

Usually r is kept fixed and by varying H (or V) ions of differing M/e are allowed to reach the detector. The signal recorded always refers to a mass to charge ratio and not to an absolute mass.

Between the ion source and the collector the pressure is kept low, of the order of 10^{-7} mm Hg, using mechanical backing pumps and diffusion pumps.

Experimental techniques

A block diagram of a typical mass spectrometer is shown in Fig. 57. This is a single-focusing instrument. We shall now briefly describe the various components of the spectrometer. Further details may be found elsewhere [1, 2].

INLET SYSTEM

For the study of high molecular weight organic compounds a heated inlet system is required which can operate up to 300° C. For structural analysis there should be no thermal decomposition of the sample in the inlet system. One type of commercial inlet system [4] is shown in Fig. 58.

Means are provided for introducing gaseous, liquid or solid samples in a variety of ways:

(*a*) Admission of a vapourized liquid or solid sample through the hot valve system via the heated three-way metal valve, glass reservoir, sintered disc leak and glass inlet pipe. The whole system can be heated to 350° C and all metal surfaces except the seatings of the valves are coated with glass to minimize catalytic decomposition of the sample.

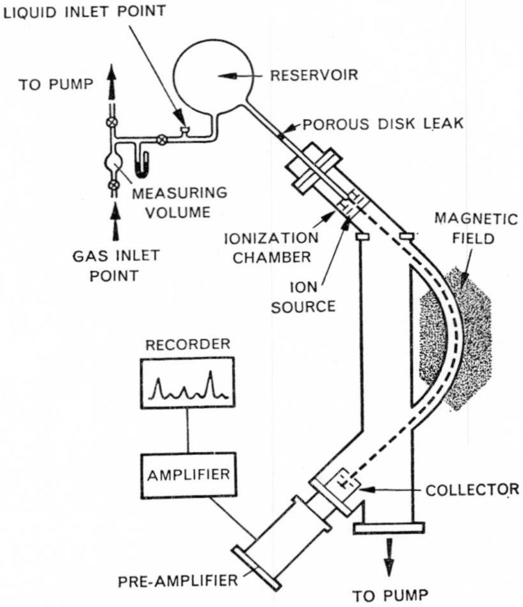

Fig. 57. Mass spectrometer. Diagram of basic features of instrument.

This system is suitable for compounds which can be heated without decomposing to a temperature where the vapour pressure is greater than 0·1 torr.

(*b*) Admission of a sample through the gallium-covered sintered disc. This system is entirely of glass, employing magnetically-operated glass ball valves, and can also be heated to 350° C. Liquids are introduced by placing them in a capillary, the end of which is pushed through the gallium to make contact with the sinter. Solids can be introduced in a similar way, though less reliably, by placing a small amount on the end of a glass rod.

(*c*) Admission of a gas or volatile liquid through a conventional cold inlet system. This is particularly useful for reference compounds for mass measurement.

(*d*) Introduction of otherwise intractable solid samples directly into the ionization chamber on the end of a probe. The sample is carried on a filament which is heated electrically to volatilize the sample. The probe

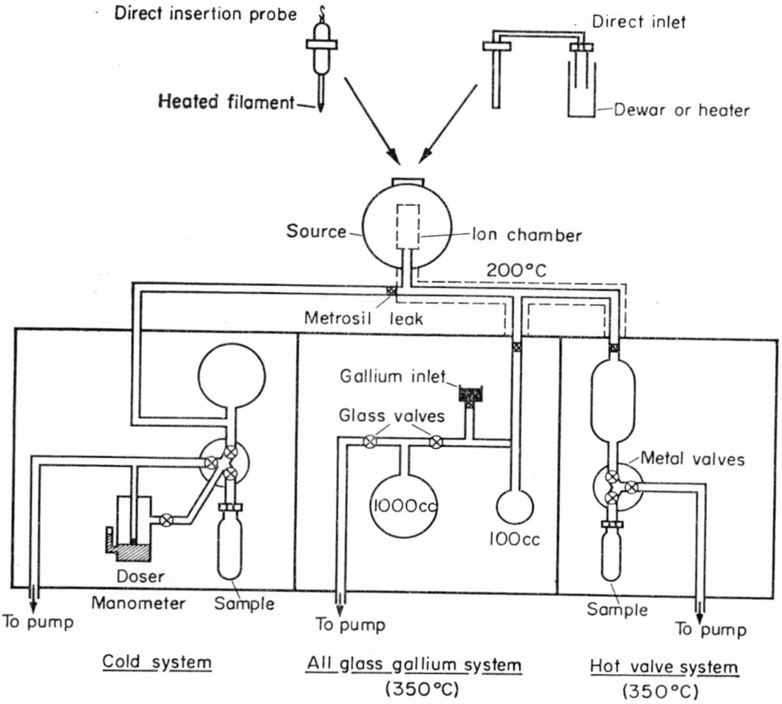

Fig. 58. Schematic diagram of sample handling system. (Elliott, R. M., Craig, R. D. and Errock, G. A., Associated Electrical Industries Ltd. *Proc. Int. Instrument and Measurement Conf., Stockholm, Sweden*, 1960.)

is inserted through a flange in the source housing as indicated. (See discussion on glyceride spectra.)

(*e*) Direct evaporation of the sample into the spectrometer from a tube which is attached to the flange mentioned above. This system is intended primarily for the identification of gases and vapours evolved from solids.

ION SOURCE

The ionization of the molecules can be achieved by a number of different ways. With organic molecules the method of electron bombardment is the most common. The sample in the vapour state enters the ionization chamber through a hole in the back of the chamber and passes through a collimated electron beam. Positive ions are produced. A small positive potential between the back wall of the ion source and the first accelerator plate pushes the ions towards the accelerating region and also attracts any negative ions which have been formed and discharges these at the repeller plate. The positive ions are further accelerated and pass through an exit slit towards the collector. The intensity of the electron beam is kept constant over the whole scan of the spectrum. The intensity of the recorded peaks is directly proportional to the electron current.

RECORDING

The ions arrive at a collector or electron multiplier and after amplification are recorded, using either an oscillograph or pen-and-ink recorder. The time needed to scan the spectrum is determined mainly by the response time of the recording system. The intensity ratios of the signals produced are very large but have to be recorded with equal accuracy, because of the importance of some peaks of low intensity.

RESOLVING POWER

With a single focusing magnetic deflection mass spectrometer the resolution increases with both the radius of the deflection path and also

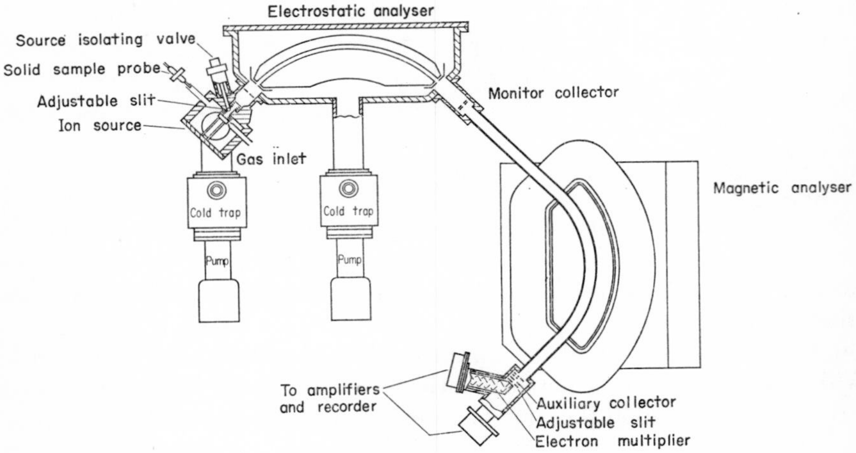

Fig. 59. Schematic diagram of MS9 mass spectrometer. (Elliott, R. M., Craig, R. D. and Errock, G. A., Associated Electrical Industries Ltd. *Proc. Int. Instrument and Measurement Conf., Stockholm, Sweden*, 1960.)

the acceleration potential. The definition of the term 'resolution' can be stated in different ways. One definition considers resolution as $M/\Delta M$ with the specification that two ion beams M, $M + \Delta M$ of equal intensity be recorded as two peaks between which the recorder trace returns to less than 2% of the intensity of peak M. Considerable increase in resolving power can be achieved by eliminating the kinetic energy gained by the ions during the acceleration. This can be carried out using an electrostatic analyser before the ions enter the magnetic field. Instruments using electrostatic and magnetic fields and obtaining both velocity and direction focusing are described as double focusing mass spectrometers. The resolution obtained with such instruments is of the order of several thousands or higher. The use of such an instrument enables the empirical formula of the various ions to be determined. The commercial apparatus of this sort is available and has been used with many organic molecules. A schematic diagram of this instrument is shown in Fig. 59.

TIME-OF-FLIGHT MASS SPECTROMETER

In this type of mass spectrometer a pulse of ions of known energy is allowed to drift down a long evacuated tube. Since all the ions experience the same electrostatic field the lighter ions will be given a greater acceleration than the heavier ions. The dispersion therefore takes place as a function of time of arrival at the detector. The time interval between arrival of masses m_1 and m_2 at the collector is proportional to $\sqrt{m_1} - \sqrt{m_2}$. The ions are detected at the end of the tube by means of an electron multiplier. The spectrum is displayed upon a cathode-ray tube whose time-base is triggered by the original pulse. The same data can be presented through analogue detectors into standard strip-chart recorders.

As many as 10,000 individual analyses can be made per second. Successive spectra can be photographed with a standard Polaroid camera for most monitoring operations. This speed of analysis has led to the use of this type of mass spectrometer in tandem with gas chromatographic equipment [5]. Spectra may be photographed on each side of the chromatographic peak so that it can be easily seen whether this peak actually consists of two overlapping distribution peaks. The aim, of course, is to use the gas chromatographic equipment as a separating device followed by identification using the mass spectrometer.

The time-of-flight spectrometer is rather limited for structural analysis owing to the low resolution possible. This is at present unit mass up to mass 200 with the latest commercial equipment. It covers a mass range of 1 to 5000.

Applications

HYDROCARBONS

The determination of the structure of the parent hydrocarbon is often an important part of the structural determination of lipids and these are discussed here. Because of their importance in the petroleum industry the mass spectra of a large number of long-chain hydrocarbons have been studied. A large number of these spectra are included in the American

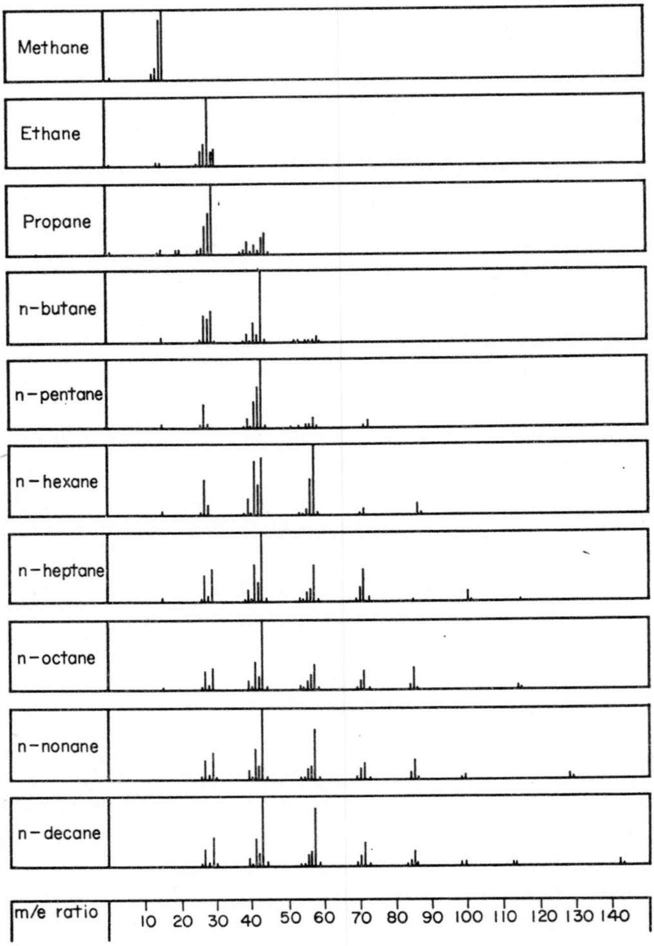

Fig. 60. Mass spectra of the straight-chain paraffins up to *n*-decane. (Beynon, J. H. *Mass Spectrometry and its Applications to Organic Chemistry*. Elsevier Publishing Company, Amsterdam, 1960.)

Petroleum Institute catalogue of mass spectral data. Many empirical rules concerning the breakdown of these molecules have been made.

The mass spectrum of a series of straight-chain paraffins are shown in Fig. 60.

A number of empirical rules have been obtained, based on the spectra of 18 isomeric octanes, and found to be applicable to describe the spectra of other paraffinic hydrocarbons.

(*a*) The relative height of the parent peak is greatest for the straight-chain compound and decreases as the degree of branching increases.

(*b*) Loss of a fragment containing a single carbon atom is unlikely unless the compound contains methyl side chains.

(*c*) Fragmentation is most likely at highly branched carbon atoms.

(*d*) Ions of odd mass tend to be more abundant than those of even mass, and secondary fragmentation involving loss of hydrogens or larger fragments also tend to give odd mass-ions, especially for straight-chain compounds. Most of the ions are formed by fragmentation of a single C—C bond in the parent ion.

(*e*) Prominent peaks at even mass numbers are indicative of fragmentation of two separate side chains and hence a high degree of branching.

(*f*) The peaks corresponding to C_3 and C_4 ions are always large in the spectra of paraffins.

The mass spectrum of a longer-chain hydrocarbon, *n*-eicosane, is shown in detail in Fig. 61. The most prominent series of ionized fragments are the singly charged alkyl-type ions of empirical formula $[C_nH_{2n+1}]^+$. These ions have odd mass numbers and contain an even number of electrons. The parent peak is clearly seen at mass 282 of good intensity. Associated with it, and indeed all the other peaks in the spectrum, are smaller peaks of higher m/e, the strongest being that of $m/e = M+1$. These peaks are caused by the presence of C^{13} and deuterium in the natural abundance. The base peak of the spectrum is caused by butyl ions $C_4H_9^+$. The peak heights of the alkyl-type ions decrease in a regular manner with increase in the number of carbon atoms in the ionizing fragment.

The peaks of formula $[C_nH_{2n+1}]^+$ have been shown to arise by simple cleavage of the chain and partly from $[(CH_2)_n + H]$ a process of double cleavage and capture of one hydrogen atom from one of the fragments lost. Other prominent peaks occur at C_nH_{2n-1}. This is an example of the presence of ions which might not be expected on the simple basis of bond strengths in the parent molecule.

The correlations between structure and spectra are less satisfactory for olefines and acetylenes. This is because re-arrangement peaks, which usually make identification more difficult, are more abundant and the spectra of many isomers are so similar that they are difficult to distinguish. It is suggested that the excited parent ions of such isomers must be very similar and rearrangement of the carbon skeleton occurs before fragmentation is possible.

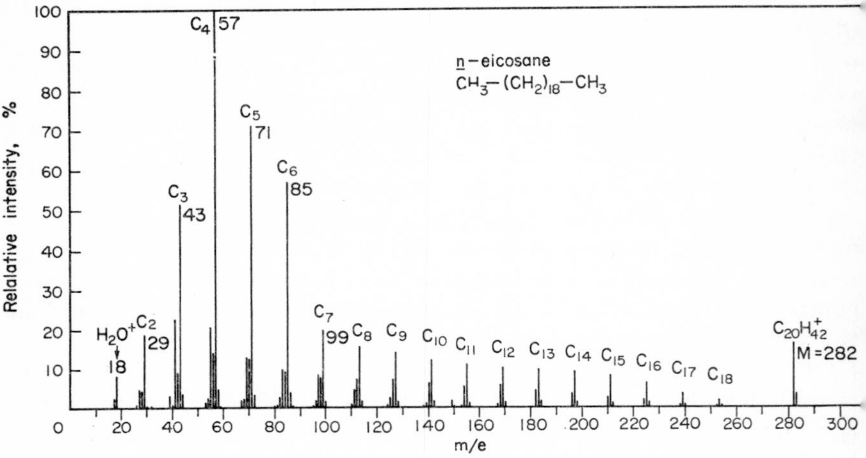

Fig. 61. Mass spectrum of *n*-eicosane. (Ryhage, R. and Stenhagen, E. *J. Lipid Res.*, **1**, 361, 1960.)

ALCOHOLS

The mass spectra of a number of alcohols have been studied including the primary, branched and unsaturated types [6–9]. The spectra of the primary straight-chain alcohols do not show quite the same regularities of pattern as the corresponding paraffins. The spectra of a series of straight-chain alcohols are shown in Fig. 62. The intensities of parent ions relative to the base peaks show a decreasing parent ion intensity with increasing molecular weight. A prominent peak in many spectra is attributable to loss of H_2O from the parent ion. There is a great similarity between the hydrocarbon part of the mass spectrum and that of the 1-olefin obtained by dehydration of the alcohol. An ion corresponding to $(CH_2OH)^+$ is prominent in many aliphatic alcohol spectra. This is formed by cleavage of the bond β to the oxygen atom. The ion of mass 31 is of intensity at least 50% of the base peak in all unbranched alcohols and also in most primary alcohols branched on the γ-carbon atom. It is also prominent in primary alcohols branched on the β-carbon atom but there is about 25% intensity of the base peak. This peak does occur, however, as a rearrangement peak in all other alcohol spectra and in the spectra of ethers and, to some extent, ketones. Often mass 45 is the base peak in secondary alcohols substituted with a methyl group on the α-carbon atom and 59 is the most prominent peak in the spectra of tertiary

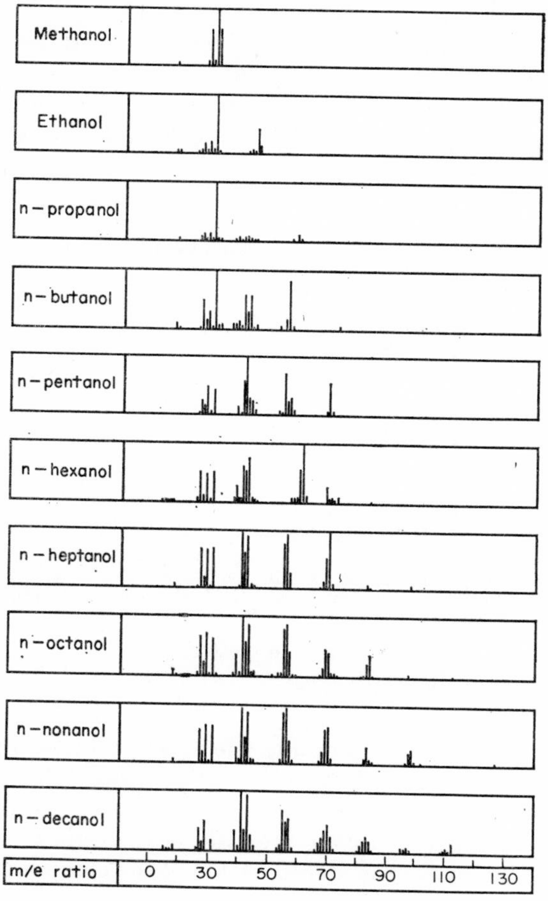

Fig. 62. Mass spectra of a series of straight-chain alcohols. (Beynon, J. H. *Mass Spectrometry and its Applications to Organic Chemistry.* Elsevier Publishing Company, Amsterdam, 1960.)

alcohols having two methyl groups on this position. There is a smaller number of strong peaks in the spectra of secondary and tertiary alcohols than in primary alcohols. The parent peaks are small and may be overlooked with the secondary and tertiary alcohols.

The spectra of branched primary alcohols are the most complicated and difficult to understand. The mass spectrum of isostearyl alcohol [3] is shown in Fig. 63 with assignments to the breakdown fragments.

Long-chain methyl ethers have also the base peak at *m/e* 45 due to ions $[\text{—CH}_2\text{—O—CH}_3]^+$. The ether is readily distinguished from the isomeric 2-alkanol by the absence of a peak at *m/e* = M-18.

The mass spectrum of batyl dimethyl ether derived from a sample of synthetic batyl alcohol [3] is shown in Fig. 64. The fragmentation pattern is a highly characteristic one. The molecular weight is obtained from the even-numbered molecule-ion peak at *m/e* 372. High peaks occur at

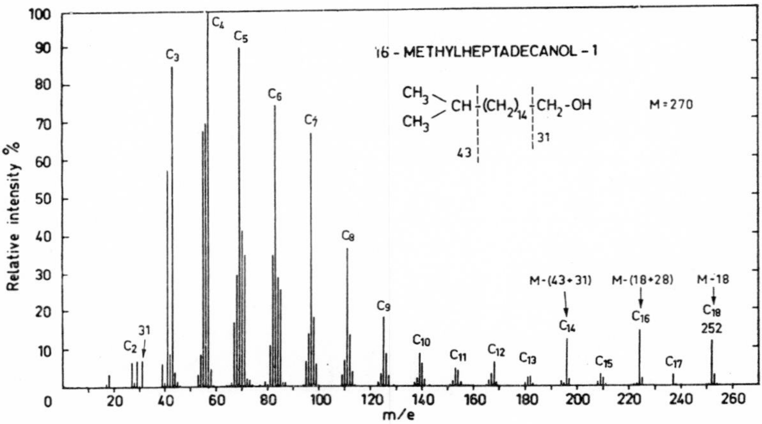

Fig. 63. Mass spectrum of 16-methylheptadecanol-1-(*iso*stearoyl alcohol). (Ryhage, R. and Stenhagen, E. *J. Lipid Res.*, **1**, 361, 1960.)

m/e 45 and 89 due to ions containing one and two methyl ether groups, respectively. The alkyl peak at *m/e* 253 indicates the presence of a saturated C_{18} chain. The high peaks at *m/e* 58 (base peak) and 59 are due to rearranged ions. Several characteristic peaks appear in addition to those mentioned, making the identification of the compound a relatively easy matter.

CARBOXYLIC ACIDS

It is easy to distinguish carboxylic acids from the hydrocarbons because the parent peaks are usually quite large and the presence of oxygen is easily deduced [10]. The molecular weights of a series of carboxylic acids are two greater than those of the corresponding hydrocarbons. Apart from the parent peak the main peaks are formed by fragmentation of the COOH group. Large peaks occur at masses 31, 45 and 59. The peak at

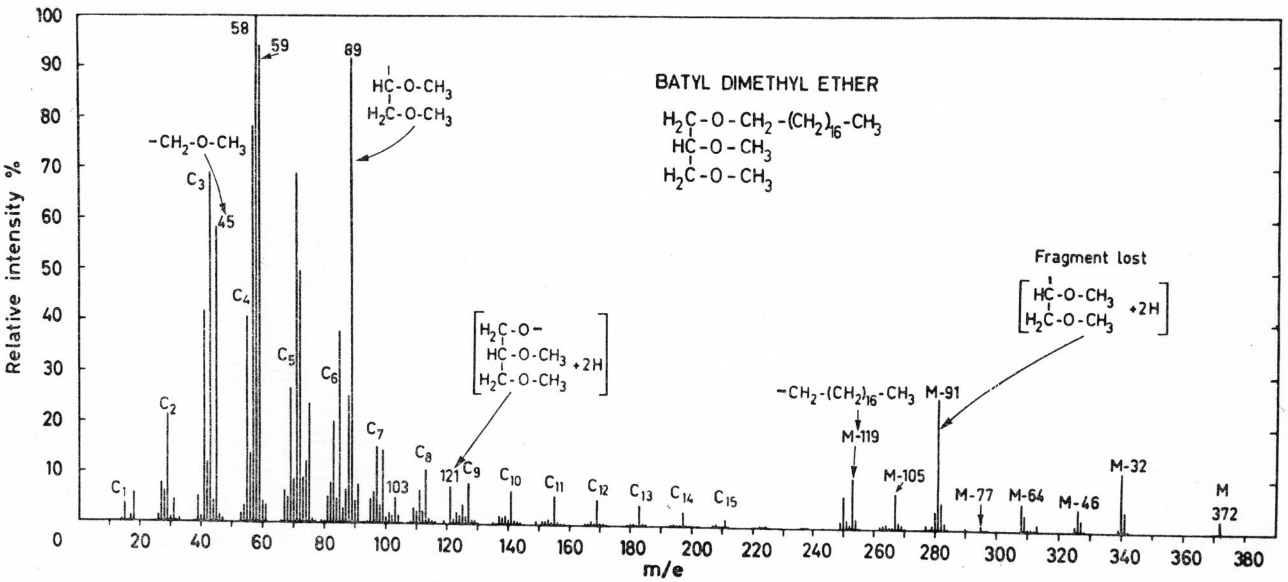

Fig. 64. Mass spectrum of batyl dimethyl ether. (Ryhage, R. and Stenhagen, E. *J. Lipid Res.*, **1**, 361, 1960.)

mass 45 due to the $(CO_2H)^+$ ion is usually stronger than the peaks at masses 31 and 59 and sometimes peaks also occur at masses 46 and 44. Peaks also occur at masses 17, 16 and 18. A very strong peak, and sometimes the base peak, occurs at mass 60. This arises from a rearrangement ion and corresponds to the molecular weight of acetic acid. It is the base peak in the spectrum of *n*-butyric and lauric acid and is about 80% of the

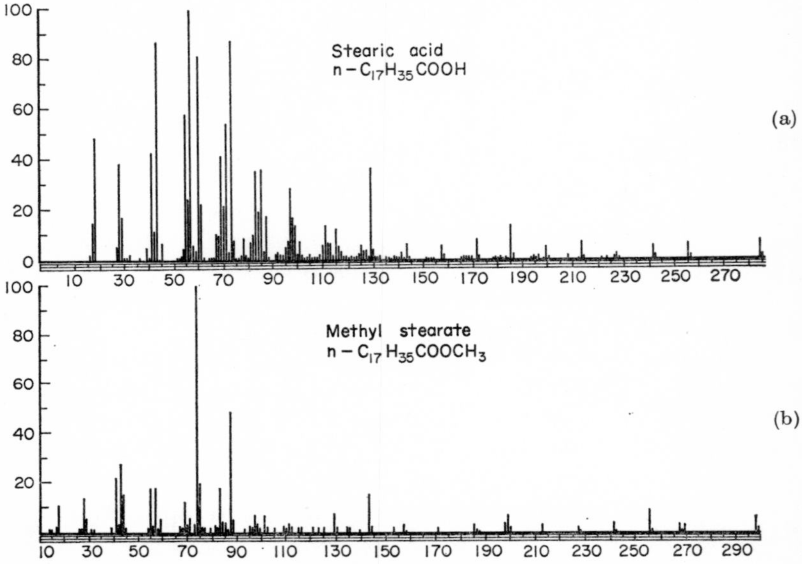

Fig. 65*a*. Mass spectra of stearic acid.

Fig. 65*b*. Mass spectra of methyl stearate. (Beynon, J. H. *Mass Spectrometry and its Applications to Organic Chemistry*. Elsevier Publishing Company, Amsterdam, 1960.)

base peak in the spectrum of stearic acid. The height of the parent peak relative to the base peak, increases from valeric to stearic acid and falls again for still longer chain acids. The parent peak for stearic acid is some 6·8% of the base peak (Fig. 65a).

METHYL ESTERS

The mass spectrum of a methyl ester is very similar to that of the corresponding carboxylic acid [11]. The methyl esters are more volatile than the free acids and therefore the easier to examine. In Fig. 65 the mass spectrum of stearic acid and methyl stearate are shown. The large parent peak associated with the carboxylic acid also occurs in the spectrum of the ester. The large peaks in the spectrum of the ester have the formula $[(CH_2)_nCOOCH_3]^+$ and are difficult to distinguish from the isobaric series of peaks of composition $[(CH_2)_{n+1}COOH]^+$. However, in the esters a rearrangement peak occurs at mass 74 analogous to the ions of mass 60 observed with the carboxylic acids. The peak arises from ions formed on 2,3 cleavage with simultaneous migration of one hydrogen atom from the fragments lost. (Some migration of two hydrogen atoms also occurs.)

The reaction thought to occur is shown

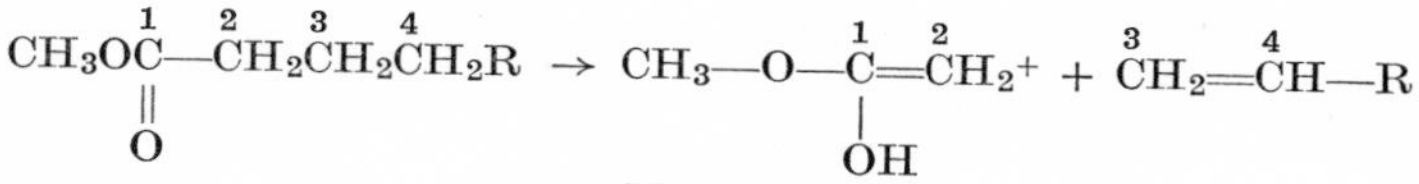

Mass 74

By using deuterated esters with one CD_2 group instead of CH_2 groups at positions 2 to 6 it has been shown [12] that the hydrogen atom is taken exclusively from carbon atom 4. Appearance potential measurements have been interpreted as showing that the ion has the hydroxyl rather than an alternative keto form.

The $[(CH_2)_nCOOCH_3]^+$ fragments have been shown to arise from two different mechanisms. The ions of lowest mass (87, 101, 115 and 129) are formed by simple cleavage of the chain. The ions of greater mass are partly formed by elimination of part of the chain. One hydrogen atom is lost in addition to a number of methylene groups giving rise to an odd-numbered even electron ion. The cleavage of the C—C bond β to the carbonyl group occurs readily.

If a branched-chain ester is examined cleavage still occurs readily at the bond β to the carbonyl group. If there is a methyl group in this 2-position the rearrangement peak has mass 88, the fragment now consisting of the ion

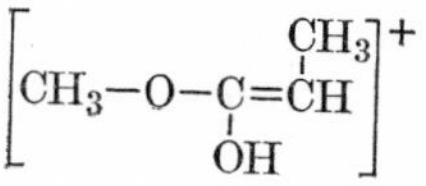

Peaks also occur due to ions formed with loss of

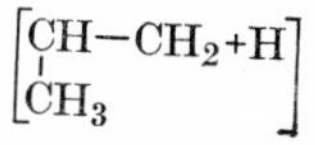

and

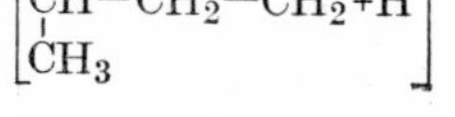

from the molecule-ion and the peak at M-29 is smaller than for normal chain esters.

When the side chain is an ethyl or longer alkyl group on the 2-position, two rearranged ions are observed

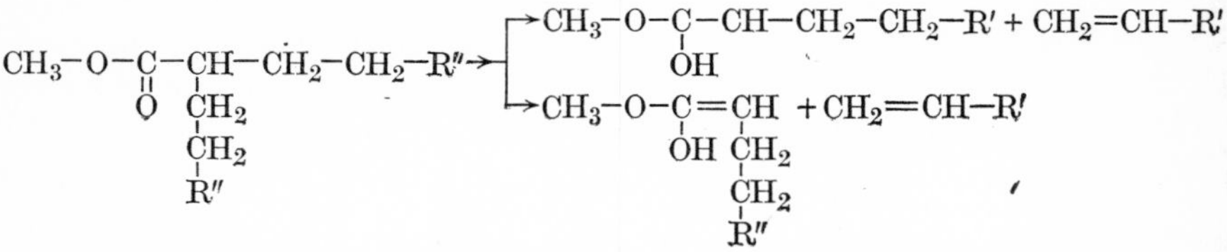

The mass spectrum of methyl tuberculostearate[∓]methyl-10-methyl-octadecanote has been obtained [13, 14] and it illustrates the way in which information about the position of the side chain can be obtained.

The position of the side branch is indicated by the very small peak at mass 185 as well as the fairly strong peaks at mass 171

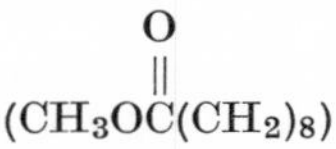

and 199

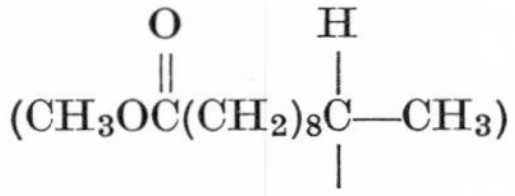

and mass 167 (199 − 32). The latter peak is considered to arise from a ketene-type ion

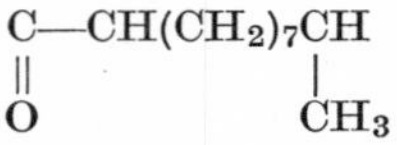

The parent ion peak is quite prominent.

The methyl esters of iso acids give mass spectra that are very similar to those given by normal esters and the iso structure is best recognized after reduction to the corresponding alcohol [15]. The spectrum of methyl isostearate is shown in Fig. 66.

Methyl esters of unsaturated acids

The molecule-ion peak is usually quite prominent with these esters and the molecular weight and the degree of unsaturation is readily obtained [16]. In a mixture of components of different carbon number and amount of unsaturation these peaks can be easily seen. The base peak of methyl oleate is at mass number M-32 corresponding to the loss of one molecule of methanol from the molecule ion. Other peaks occur at M-74 and M-116.

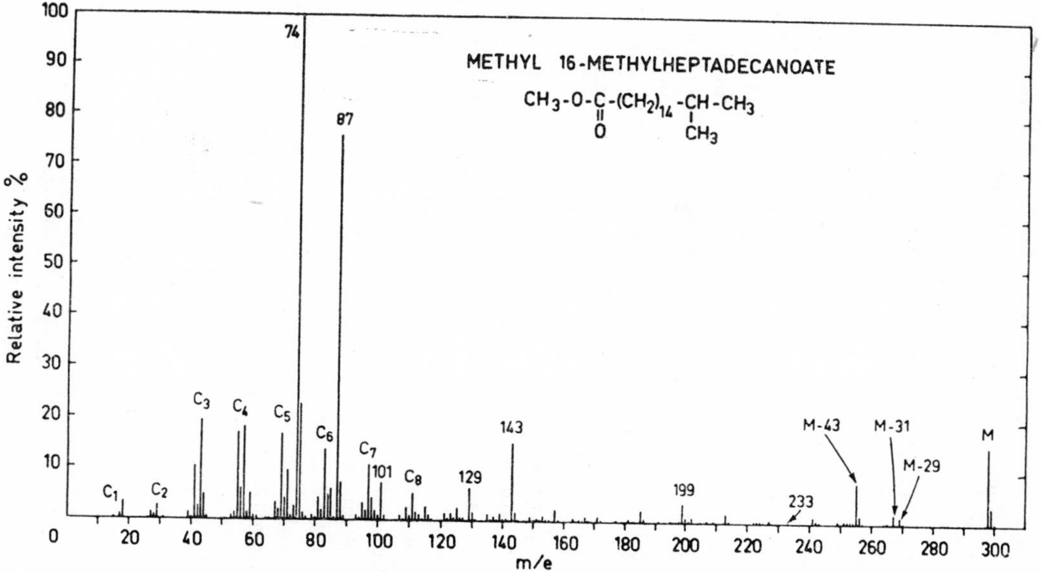

Fig. 66. Mass spectrum of 16-methylheptadecanoate (methyl *iso*-stearate). (Ryhage, R. and Stenhagen, E. *J. Lipid Res.*, **1**, 361, 1960.)

Unfortunately, the position of the double bond cannot be determined directly from the mass spectrum. This is because *cis*- and *trans*-isomers, as well as the positional isomers at present studied with the exception of the α,β-unsaturated esters, give nearly identical spectra. It is suggested that in its activated state before bond rupture and fragmentation that the unsaturated molecule assumes a generalized statistical structure independent of the initial position or configuration of the double bond. Dinh-Nguyen, Ryhage and Stenhagen [12] have, however, shown that by first saturating the double bonds with deuterium so that bond migration does not occur that it is then possible to determine the double bond position. This has been done with petroselenate, oleate and elaidate. Tetradeuterohydrazine deuterate is an excellent material for such deuteration. With methyl-6,7-dideuterostearate the fragment corresponding to 6 carbon atoms of the acid contains one deuterium atom and is at mass 130 rather than mass 129 when obtained from the stearate. The C_7 and higher fragments contain two deuterium atoms and are therefore two mass units higher than the corresponding fragments of the stearate. Further studies are in progress on this isotopic method and a number of esters with the double bond in different positions are being studied.

The mass spectra of esters such as methyl linoleate, methyl linolenate and methyl oleate differ quite considerably (Fig. 67). The parent peaks are at mass 294, 296 and 292. In all three spectra a peak occurs at mass 91. The height of this peak increases with the degree of unsaturation of the ester. The peak probably arises from the presence of tropylium ions due to rearrangement and cyclization [17].

The methyl esters keto, hydroxy, and methoxy acids have been examined. The presence and position of these groups can usually be determined from the mass spectrum [18]. Although the hydroxy esters do not show a molecular ion peak their molecular weight can be obtained from the peak at $m/e = \mathrm{M} - 50$ ($= -[32+18]$ (water in methanol). This peak is of significant height except with the 2-hydroxy esters. Two peaks at m/e 187 and 158 are formed by cleavage on either side of the hydroxyl group. The base peak at m/e 155 is believed to occur by loss of methanol from the 187 fragment. The methyl esters of 2-hydroxy acids give a large peak at $m/e = $ M-59 due to ions formed through the easy cleavage of the bond between carbon atoms 1 and 2. They also show a characteristic peak at m/e 90 corresponding to a rearranged ion

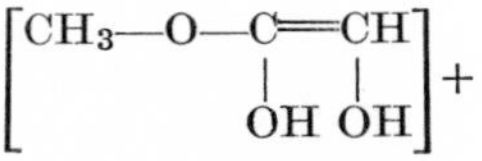

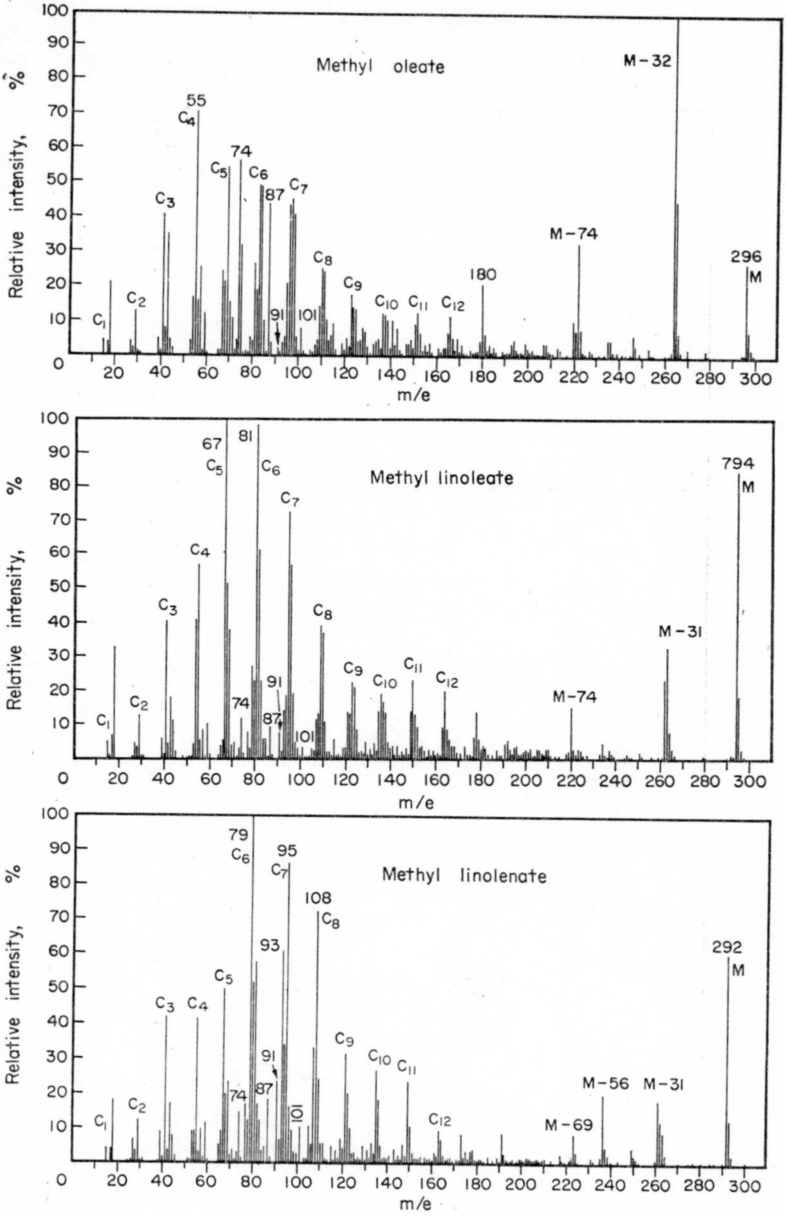

Fig. 67. Mass spectra of: (*top*) methyl oleate (methyl $\Delta^{9:10}$-octadecenoate) ($M = 296$); (*middle*) methyl linoleate (methyl $\Delta^{9:10,12:13}$-octadecdienoate) ($M = 294$); (*bottom*) methyl linolenate (methyl $\Delta^{9:10,12:13,15:16}$-octadec-trienoate) ($M = 292$). (Hallgren, B., Rvhage, R. and Stenhagen, E. *Acta Chem. Scand.*, **13**, 845, 1959.)

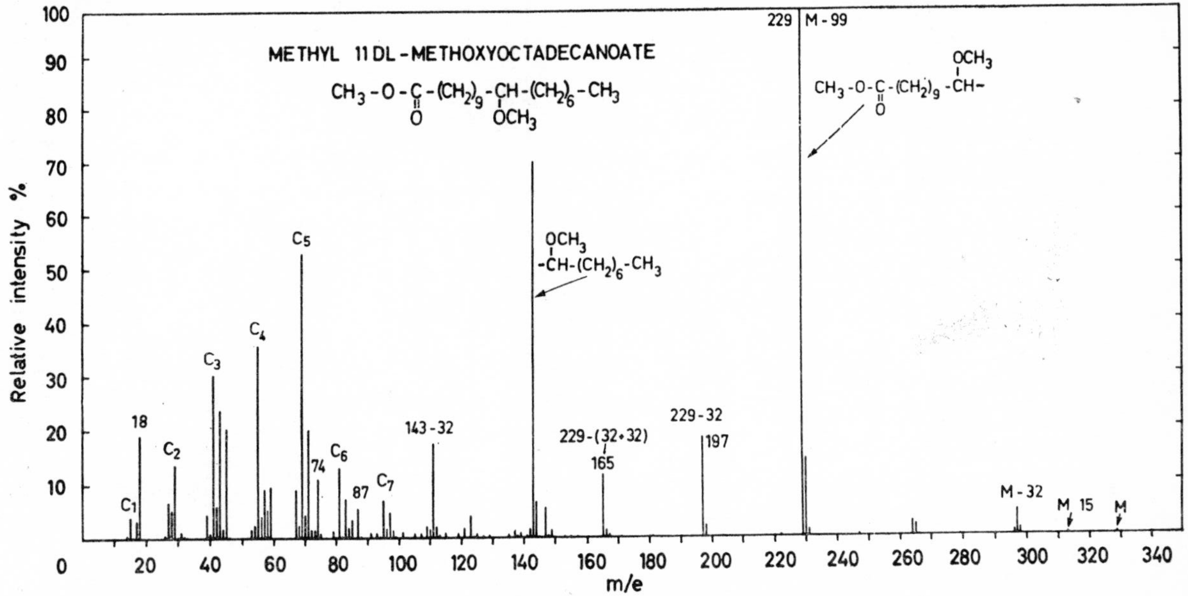

Fig. 68. Mass spectrum of methyl-11-DL-methoxyoctadecanoate. (Ryhage, R. and Stenhagen, E. *J. Lipid Res.*, **1**, 361, 1960.)

The methoxy esters usually give a fairly simple mass spectra. A parent peak is observed and, as with the 2-hydroxy esters, cleavage occurs between the carbon atoms 1 and 2. The spectrum of methyl-11-methoxy octadecanoate is shown in Fig. 68. The two strongest peaks are due to ions containing the methoxyl group formed through cleavage of the chain on either side of carbon atom 11. Methyl esters of keto acids usually cleave at positions α and β with respect to the keto group. The molecule ion gives a distinct peak in most cases; this, together with a peak at m/e = M-31 and peaks due to fragments from the cleavage with respect to the keto group, makes it easy to deduce the structure of the ester. The spectrum of methyl-8-keto-octadecanoate is shown in Fig. 69. The breakdown of methyl esters of keto acids is fairly complicated. As well as α cleavage on either side of the carbonyl group to give ions of the type RCO there is also a strong tendency for β cleavage followed by hydrogen rearrangement to occur, giving ions of the type R.C(OH)=CH_2. The position of the carbonyl group is usually easily deduced. The dimethyl esters of dibasic acids can readily be recognized from their mass spectra [19]. A small molecule ion peak, a strong peak at m/e = M-31 and fairly strong peaks at m/e = M-64, M-73, M-92 and M-105 are characteristic features in the high mass range. The presence of peaks at $m/e = 84 + n \times 14$ in the mass spectra of the methyl esters of the dibasic acids, but not present in the spectra of the methyl esters of the monobasic acids, enables a distinction between the two to be made. An epoxide ring in the middle of a chain gives rise to a very characteristic breakdown pattern.

The mass spectrum of a typical wax ester [20] is shown in Fig. 70. The base peak is due to ions formed with alkyl–oxygen cleavage of the alcohol used, followed by rearrangement of two hydrogen atoms. A molecule ion peak is present as well as a peak at m/e = M-85. The latter ion is formed by 1,2 cleavage of the acyl group. A hydrocarbon-type peak is observed corresponding in this case to those that would be obtained with *n*-docosanol-1. A characteristic feature of these esters is the occurrence of a small peak due to ions formed through 4,5 cleavage of the alcohol part with rearrangement of one hydrogen atom. In this case the peak is at 186.

GLYCERIDES

The mass spectra of glycerides would be of considerable interest but, because of their size and low volatility, it is difficult to introduce them into the mass spectrometer. It is also difficult to remove them from the ion source and persistent memory effects occur. Preliminary experiments have been reported and the mass spectrum of a triglyceride is shown in Fig. 71. The acyl ions at m/e 155 and 183 enable the identification of the

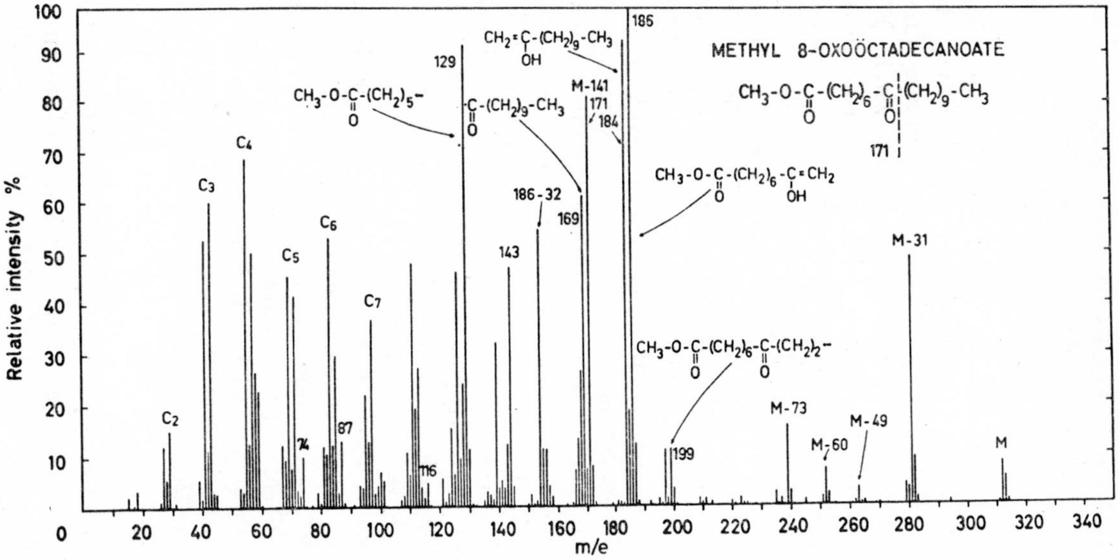

Fig. 69. Mass spectrum of methyl-8-ketooctadecanoate. (Ryhage, R. and Stenhagen, E. *J. Lipid Res.*, **1**, 361, 1960.)

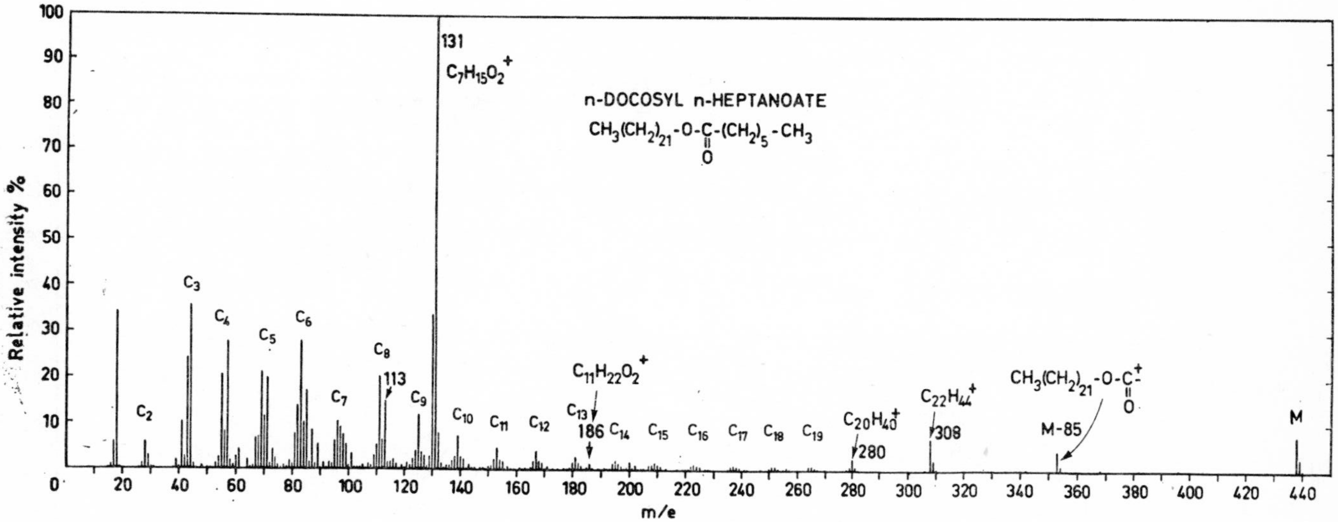

Fig. 70. Mass spectrum of *n*-docosyl. *n*-heptanoate. (Ryhage, and Stenhagen, E. *J. Lipid Res.*, **1**, 361, 1960.)

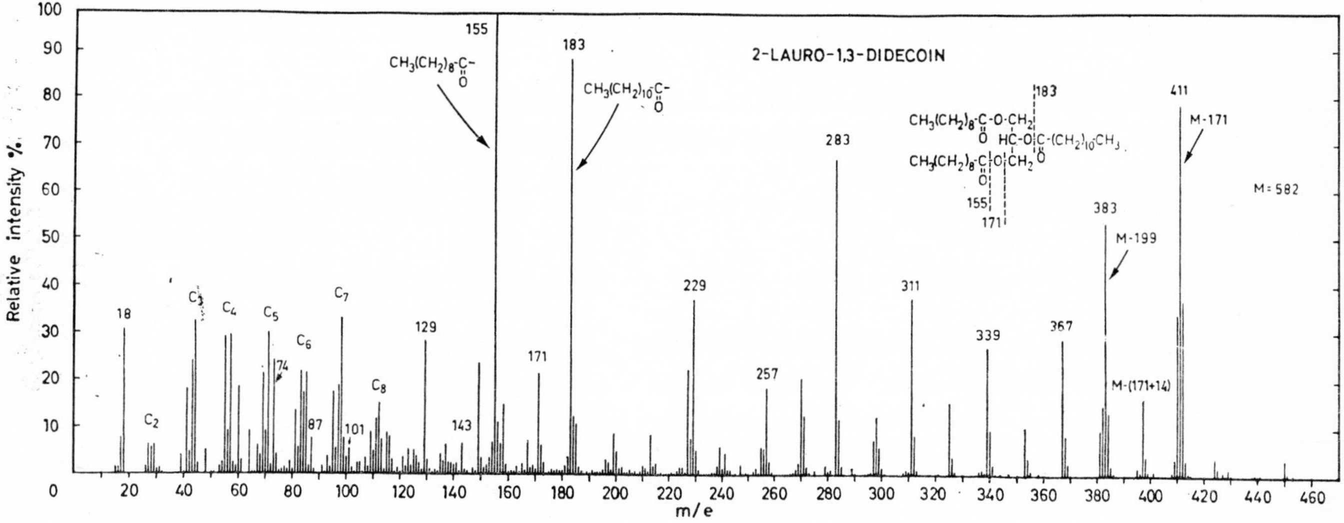

Fig. 71. Mass spectrum of 2-lauro-1,3-didecoin. (Ryhage, R. and Stenhagen, E. *J. Lipid Res.*, **1**, 361, 1960.)

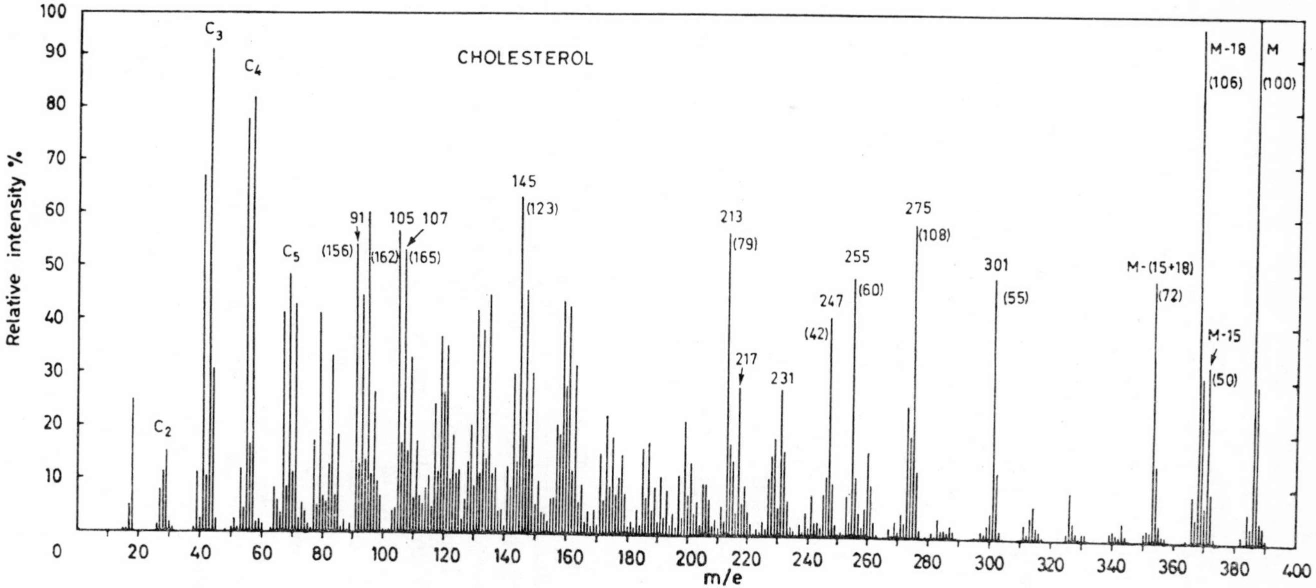

Fig. 72. Mass spectrum of cholesterol ($M = 386$). Temperature of inlet system, 200°. Temperature of ion chamber, 220°. Electron energy, 70 eV. The figures within parentheses are the relative intensities (with the intensity of the molecule-ion peak set at 100) recorded by Friedland, S. F., *et al Anal. Chem.*, **31**, 169 (1959)). (Ryhage, R. and Stenhagen, E. *J. Lipid Res.*, **1**, 361, 1960.)

acid groups present in the molecule. The existence of a peak at $m/e = M\text{-}(171 + 14)$ but no peak at $m/e = M\text{-}(199 + 14)$ shows that loss of acyloxymethylene occurs from positions 1 and 3 but not from position 2 of the glycerol moiety. It therefore seems possible to distinguish the acyl group attached at position 2 from those at positions 1 and 3.

Quite recently a number of triglycerides have been studied using [21] a direct sampling probe in a high-resolution A.E.I. M-S-9 mass spectrometer. The glycerides contained saturated and unsaturated fatty acids and ranged in weight from tripalmitin to tribehenin and also included tripentastearin, $C_{99}H_{190}O_{12}$ (M 1570). In all cases a parent molecular ion was observed. It is also possible with these glycerides to distinguish the acyl group attached at a position 2 from those at positions 1 and 3. The sample in the form of a solution or a suspension is coated on to a small ceramic tube containing a heated filament. Satisfactory spectra are obtained with 1 μg of material and hence the technique should be particularly useful for studies using thin layer chromatography.

If this work can be extended to other glyceride systems many useful applications will be possible. Some laboratories [22] report that with the mass spectrometers which they are using with inlet systems of temperatures of about 260° C, only the spectra of the constituent fatty acids are observed. As yet no investigation of the mass spectra of the phospholipids has been reported.

STEROIDS

Steroids give rise to complicated breakdown patterns [23, 24, 25], particularly with mass numbers below m/e 200. Characteristic peaks, however, occur in the high mass range that make the mass spectra useful for identification purposes [3]. The molecular weight can be determined and from the isotopic peaks associated with the parent ion the molecular formula can be deduced. The presence of hydroxyl groups can be deduced from the intensity of the m/e 18 peak, and the molecular formulae of side chains can be determined. Diastereoisomeric sterols usually give mass spectra that are significantly different from each other. The mass spectrum of cholesterol is shown in Fig. 72. The molecule ion gives the largest peak. Strong peaks at m/e 247, 275 and 201 are present in the spectrum of cholesterol but not in the spectrum of its dihydro derivatives. Care has to be taken to minimize thermal breakdown of these materials. Spectra of cholesterol taken immediately after volatilization and some time later have shown differences which have been attributed to thermal dehydration.

REFERENCES

1. BEYNON, J. H. (1960) *Mass Spectrometry and its Applications to Organic Chemistry*. Elsevier Publishing Company, Amsterdam.
2. BIEMANN, K. (1962) *Mass Spectrometry*. McGraw-Hill Co.
3. RYHAGE, R. and STENHAGEN, E. (1960) *J. Lipid Res.*, **1**, 361.
4. ELLIOTT, R. M., CRAIG, R. D. and ERROCK, G. A. (1960) *Proc. Int. Instrument & Measurement Conf.*, Stockholm, Sweden.
5. DUTTON, H. J. (1961) *J. Amer. Oil Chemists' Soc.*, **38**, 660.
6. BROWN, R. A., YOUNG, W. S. and NICOLAIDES, N. (1954) *Analyt. Chem.*, **26**, 1653.
7. BERGSTRÖM, H., RYHAGE, R. and STENHAGEN, E. (1956) *Svensk. Papperstidn*, **59**, 593.
8. MCLAFFERTY, F. W. (1955) *Technical Report Dow Chemical Company*.
9. FRIEDEL, R. A., SCHULTZ, J. L. and SHARKEY, A. G. (1956) *Analyt. Chem.*, **28**, 926.
10. HAPP, G. P. and STEWART, D. W. (1952) *J. Amer. Chem. Soc.*, **74**, 4404.
11. SHARKEY, A. G., SCHULTZ, J. L. and FRIEDEL, R. A. (1959) *Analyt. Chem.*, **31**, 87.
12. DINH-NGUYEN, NG., RYHAGE, R., STÄLLBERG-STENHAGEN, S. and STENHAGEN, E. (1960) ASTM E-14 Meeting on Mass Spectrometry, Atlantic City, June 1960.
13. PROUT, F. S., CASON, J. and INGERSOLL, A. W. (1948) *J. Amer. Chem. Soc.*, **70**, 98.
14. STÄLLBERG-STENHAGEN, S. (1948) *Arkiv. Kemi, Min., Geol.*, **26A**, (12).
15. RYHAGE, R. and STENHAGEN, E. (1960) *Arkiv. Kemi*, **15**, 333.
16. HALLGREN, B., RYHAGE, R. and STENHAGEN, E. (1959) *Acta Chem. Scand.*, **13**, 845.
17. RYLANDER, P. N., MEYEROON, S. and GRUBB, H. M. (1957) *J. Amer. Chem. Soc.*, **79**, 842.
18. RYHAGE, R. and STENHAGEN, E. (1960) *Arkiv. Kemi*, **15**, 545.
19. RYHAGE, R. and STENHAGEN, E. (1959) *Arkiv. Kemi*, **14**, 497.
20. RYHAGE, R. and STENHAGEN, E. (1959) *Arkiv. Kemi*, **14**, 483.
21. BARBER, M., MERREN, T. O. and KELLY, W. (1964) *Tetrahedron Letters*, **18**, 1063.
22. SHUTTLEWORTH, T. (private communication).
23. REED, R. I. (1958) *J. Chem. Soc.*, 3432.
24. FRIEDLAND, S. S., LANE, G. H., LONGMAN, R. T., TRAIN, K. E. and O'NEAL, M. J. (1959) *Analyt. Chem.*, **31**, 169.
25. BERGSTRÖM, S., RYHAGE, R. and STENHAGEN, E. (1958) *Acta Chem. Scand.*, **12**, 1349.

6. Nuclear magnetic resonance spectroscopy

The phenomenon of nuclear magnetic resonance spectroscopy was discovered simultaneously by Purcell and his associates at Harvard University and by Block and his associates at Stanford University, for which they were jointly awarded the Nobel prize in physics in 1952. In recent years considerable numbers of applications of the technique in chemistry have appeared [1, 2, 3]. Two main types of n.m.r. spectroscopy are carried out. There are the broad-line experiments concerned mainly with the spectra obtained from samples in the solid state, and high-resolution (or narrow line) experiments carried out with samples in the liquid, solution or gas phases. Both types of n.m.r. spectroscopy have been shown to be useful in the study of lipids and many future applications are to be expected.

Theoretical considerations

We are concerned here with the absorption of electromagnetic radiation in the region between 1 and 100 megacycles/sec. This arises from the resonant absorption of energy by atomic nuclei when they are placed in a strong magnetic field and subjected to a radio frequency field. Such resonance is confined to nuclei which have a magnetic moment and spin angular momentum. Over a hundred nuclei satisfy this condition but many important isotopes have zero spin angular momentum and zero magnetic moment. Included in the latter category are the important nuclei ^{12}C, ^{16}O, ^{25}Si and ^{32}S. Magnetic resonance spectra cannot be obtained from these nuclei nor for those nuclei that have an even mass number and an even charge (or atomic) number.

Nuclei may have an effective spin angular momentum expressed as $Ih/2\pi$ where h is Planck's constant, and this may have values $I = 0, \frac{1}{2}, 1, \frac{3}{2}, \ldots$ Due to the distribution in space of positive charge an effective flow of current along the axis of spin is produced for nuclei having values of I greater than zero. This causes the nuclei to possess a magnetic moment directed along the axis of spin of value $g\beta\{I(I+1)\}^{1/2}$ where β is the nuclear magneton and g is a nuclear factor determined by experiment.

If the nucleus is placed in a uniform magnetic field H_0 it will experience a torque so that it precesses about the applied field. (We can think of the nucleus as a small magnet which if placed in a magnetic field experiences a torque like a compass needle. Because of its spin it precesses at a characteristic frequency around the field just as a toy gyroscope precesses about the earth's gravitational field). The potential energy of this nuclear magnet under these conditions depends upon its orientation in the field.

Those nuclei with values of $I = \frac{1}{2}$ give spectra which can be most easily interpreted and these include ^{1}H, ^{19}F and ^{31}P. Nuclei with spin $I = 1$ include ^{2}H and ^{14}N.

If we consider a single proton in a magnetic field H_0, the proton may be in a configuration parallel to the field with potential energy $-\mu H_0$ where μ is the magnetic moment of the proton, or in a configuration anti-parallel to the field with energy μH_0. These two configurations correspond to the two possible values of the magnetic quantum number $m = \pm\frac{1}{2}$.

If the proton is also subjected to a radio frequency field of such a frequency that

$$h\nu = 2\mu H_0 \tag{6.1}$$

then it may absorb a quantum of radiation if it is in the lower level or emit radiation if in the upper state.

If we have a large assembly of protons they distribute themselves among the two energy levels at room temperature with more of them in the lower level than in the upper, the ratio of the populations of the two levels being given by the Boltzmann factor $e^{2\mu H_0/kT}$ where T is the temperature of the assembly and k is Boltzmann's constant. The excess

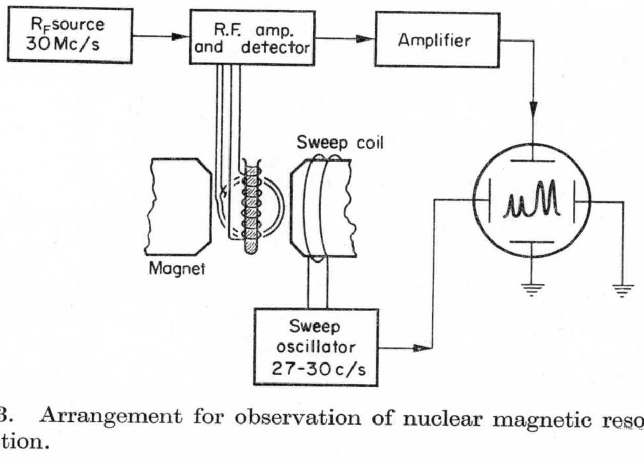

Fig. 73. Arrangement for observation of nuclear magnetic resonance absorption.

of population is usually extremely small, some three or four nuclei in a million. Since the transition probabilities for absorption and emission are equal there is a small nett absorption of energy by the nuclei from the electromagnetic radiation which can be detected by sensitive electronic circuitry.

The relative signal strengths obtained from different nuclei vary. The strongest signals are obtained from hydrogen ^{1}H and fluorine ^{19}F whilst phosphorus ^{31}P is considerably weaker in intensity and signals from ^{14}N are even weaker.

If we consider protons in a magnetic field of 10,000 gauss the frequency of the radiation for resonance is 42·6 Mc/sec. There is a linear relationship (eqn. (6.1)) between the resonance frequency ν and the magnetic field H_0. Spectra may be expressed as intensity of absorption plotted against frequency ν, or against magnetic field at fixed frequency. Generally the frequency of the electromagnetic radiation is fixed and the magnetic field is varied. The basic resonance circuit is shown in Fig. 73.

NUCLEAR RELAXATION

The magnetic nuclei can receive and transfer their energy to the surroundings. The thermal motions of other nuclei can produce random oscillatory magnetic fields which can have frequency components with frequencies equal to the precession frequencies of the relaxing nuclei thereby permitting the magnetic orientation energy to be converted to thermal energy. The rate of relaxation depends upon the concentration of magnetic nuclei, the temperature and the viscosity of the medium and is a first-order process. The thermal motions of substances with unpaired electrons are particularly effective in inducing thermal relaxation.

There are, in fact, two relaxation processes indicated by T_1 and T_2. The spin-lattice relaxation time T_1 is the time constant measuring the rate at which the energy can be exchanged between the spinning nuclei and the thermal degrees of freedom of the sample. The spin–spin relaxation time T_2 is the time constant measuring the rate at which the precessing nuclei get out of phase with one another and is determined by the spread of magnetic field within the sample. In many cases the inhomogeneity of the applied magnetic field is the most important factor determining T_2. Viscosity is also important since if it is high the nucleus of one atom may have a different neighbour than another nucleus. Since they will be subjected to differing magnetic fields they will have different precession frequencies and thus lose phase coherence. If the viscosity is low the fluctuations in the local magnetic fields are effectively averaged to zero and T_2 is increased. T_2 can be determined from the line width. The slope of the decay envelope of the relaxation wiggles is also a measure of T_2. When the sweep period equals T_2, beats occur because of interference between successive sweeps.

The values of T_1 and T_2 have been determined for liquid and supercooled glycerol of low water content in the temperature range 200 to 435°K. Certain difficulties were encountered in interpretations of the data but it was thought that the indications were that translational molecular motion was faster than rotational motion in the liquid glycerol and that dipole reorientation is faster than that of the whole molecule [4]. Different butyl alcohols have also been examined for T_1 values as a function of temperature using pulse methods to provide information about the molecular motions which occur with these molecules [5].

Broad line spectroscopy

With an isolated nucleus the absorption spectrum would be a single, very sharp line corresponding to absorption at the magnetic field H_0 at the resonance condition. However, in a crystal, interactions from other nuclei modify this so that the magnetic field at the nucleus is the sum of the applied magnetic field plus the field due to the neighbouring nuclei. Any particular nucleus may therefore be in a total magnetic field significantly lower or higher than the applied field. Thus the different nuclei in the assembly will undergo resonance at widely different values of the applied magnetic field. The resultant absorption line will be comparatively broad and be of the order of several gauss. In a liquid where all the molecules are in a state of violent thermal agitation the fields contributed by the nuclei at any given point are averaged out very rapidly compared with the period of precession and the absorption lines from liquids are very narrow. The line width is now determined principally by the inhomogeneity of the applied magnetic field.

This particular feature that the line width is affected by molecular motion was observed by Gutowsky and Pake [6]. The local field which each nucleus experiences is now no longer constant since its neighbours are moving. The criterion for narrowing to occur is that the rate of molecular reorientation shall exceed the spectral width when expressed as a frequency.[1]

Various types of molecular motion which may occur and affect the line width include rotation, quantum mechanical tunnelling and rotational oscillation. The fluctuating local magnetic field caused by molecular

[1] Van Vleck, J. H. (*Phys. Rev.*, 1948, **74**, 1168) has shown that, although a calculation of the line shape for general systems is not possible, it is possible to calculate the second moment of the line shape for a rigid lattice. The line narrowing observed with motional narrowing is reflected by a decrease in the magnitude of the second moment (gauss^2).

motion induces nuclear transitions and promotes spin–lattice relaxation. The efficiency of this mechanism depends upon the intensity of the Fourier spectrum of the fluctuating field at the Larmor frequency. (The correlation time is dependent upon the temperature.) This depends upon the correlation time τ_c of the random motion. The temperature variation of τ_c may be determined and may be of the type:

$$\tau_c = \tau_0 \exp(V/RT) \tag{6.2}$$

where V is the hindering barrier and τ_0 is a constant. From a plot of $\log \tau_c$ against $1/T$ the activation energy of the molecular reorientation process may be found.

With broad-line n.m.r. spectroscopy for good signal to noise characteristics the derivative of the absorption signal is recorded, in contrast to high resolution spectroscopy where the absorption curve itself is recorded.

Applications

HYDROCARBONS

As many lipids contain long hydrocarbon chains we will first indicate briefly the results of studies of the simple hydrocarbons. These studies are due to Andrew [7]. He examined *n*-octadecane, *n*-octacosane and dicetyl at different temperatures from 90°K up to their melting point. The second moment of *n*-octadecane was observed to decrease up to the melting point at which temperature the narrow line characteristic of liquids was obtained. The second moment of the other hydrocarbons decreases smoothly until a few degrees before the melting point where a discontinuity occurs in the second moment. Andrew showed that for the general hydrocarbon C_nH_{2n+2} assuming orthorhombic O$\perp$ packing, that the intramolecular contribution is $[18{\cdot}5+19{\cdot}1/n+1]$ gauss^2. Allowing for an intermolecular contribution of some 7·8 gauss^2, the total second moment is therefore $[26{\cdot}3+19{\cdot}1/n+1]$ gauss^2. By comparison of the calculated and the experimental values it was possible to decide whether the molecules are effectively stationary or not. It was deduced that *n*-octacosane and dicetyl are effectively stationary at temperatures below about 230°K but that in octadecane there is some motion. With increasing temperature an increasing number of molecules rotate about their length. It is concluded that above the transition temperature in the hexagonal form all the molecules rotate about their length. Andrew also calculated the reduction in second moment for different amounts of oscillation and concluded that oscillatory amplitudes of up to 45° are required to explain the second moment data below the melting point of octadecane and below the transition points for the other hydrocarbons.

A series of other long-chain hydrocarbons as well as polyethylene crystals have also been examined in a similar way [8].

ALCOHOLS

Andrew also examined dodecanol and concluded that the molecular motion with this alcohol is similar to that observed with octadecane up to the melting point. On cooling below the melting point a hexagonal form is obtained in which the motion is similar to that observed with octacosane and dicetyl.

The proton resonance spectrum of the long-chain alcohol from Carnauba wax has also been reported and gives similar results.

Measurements on some long-chain secondary alcohols [9] 8-eicosanol ($C_7H_{15}CHOHC_{12}H_{25}$) and 14-heptacosanol ($C_{13}H_{27}COOHC_{13}H_{27}$) have also been made. The inter-chain hydrogen bonding does not appear to affect the motion of the carbon chains significantly compared with the mobility observed with paraffin crystals of comparable length.

CARBOXYLIC ACIDS

Measurements of the n.m.r. absorption of some long-chain monocarboxylic acids, and particularly that of the *C*-form of stearic acid, have been reported [10].

With stearic acid the signal shows no fine structure from $-77°$ C to room temperature, but at about 24° C the derivative absorption line shows a narrow peak along with the broad peak of the type observed with solid paraffins. Above 24° C the narrow peak becomes more prominent until the broad peak disappears. From $-77°$ to 66° C the line width remains approximately constant with values ranging from 14·0 gauss to 14·6 gauss. At 69° C only a trace of this broad component remains.

It was suggested that two phases are present, in one of which the methyl end groups are free to rotate about their triad axes throughout the temperature range from $-78°$ C to the melting point, and in the other phase some form of pre-melting becomes important above 40° C. It was also concluded that the narrow component observed above 20° C does not correspond to a liquid condition. The observed line width at this temperature is about 0·1 to 0·001 gauss whereas for the liquid a line width of about 10^{-4} gauss would be expected. By estimating the area under the narrow peak as a function of temperature an estimate of the fraction of protons involved in rapid motion was made and is shown in Table 19.

The increase in the disordered phase below the melting point is suggested to account for the anomalous volume change which was previously observed to occur between 60 and 69° C. Other acids from capric to palmitic have also been examined with similar results; a line width transition occurs some 10° C below the melting point with all of them. Spin lattice-relaxation time measurements are being carried out on some of these acids.

Table 19. *Fraction of protons involved in rapid motion*

Temperature °C	Percentage area of narrow component
40°	0·9
45	1·1
54	2·5
58	5·9
66	27·4

An important aspect of this type of behaviour is that this so-called premelting phenomenon may be a direct result of the presence of tiny impurities present in the acids causing crystal lattice imperfections. It would be of interest to study line-width variation in the monocarboxylic acids as a function of added impurities.

GLYCERIDES

Nuclear resonance spectra of glycerides [11] in their variety of crystal forms have been obtained and studied and used to show that the degree of molecular motion varies with the different crystal forms. To do this, *a priori*, estimates of the second moment expected for the glycerides when undergoing various amounts of motion were calculated.

The second moments of the proton resonance were estimated in a similar way to that carried out with pure hydrocarbons. Thus the total second moment for an infinite chain of rigid CH_2 groups is about 27 gauss^2 whilst the contribution of terminal methyl groups is usually less than this because of rotational motion even at low temperatures. The CH group of the glycerol makes a rather small contribution. An estimate of the expected second moment for a glyceride of about 25 gauss^2 is predicted at low temperature. The line shape is expected to be structureless but the small second moment contribution of the methyl groups and of the CH group of the glycerol residue may cause the absorption curve to have a weak but narrow component. When hindered reorientational motion occurs the resulting second moment is reduced. For the hydrocarbon C_nH_{2n+2} the reduced intramolecular contribution to the second moment is $6{\cdot}8–11{\cdot}6/(n+1)$. If this is applied to a glyceride such as 1,2-distearin ($n = 18$) the intramolecular contribution is some 6·2 gauss^2.

When intermolecular broadening is included this gives a total of 8·8 gauss^2. If the observed reduction of second moments are less than that expected for rapid reorientation then some estimate of the amount of incomplete reorientation can be made as with the simple hydrocarbons, e.g. oscillation amplitude 60°, 45° or 30° reduces the second moment by 56, 43 or 25% respectively.

By various thermal treatments the glycerides were obtained in their different crystal forms and their n.m.r. spectra obtained. Some typical derivative spectra are shown in Fig. 74. At temperatures of about 90°K

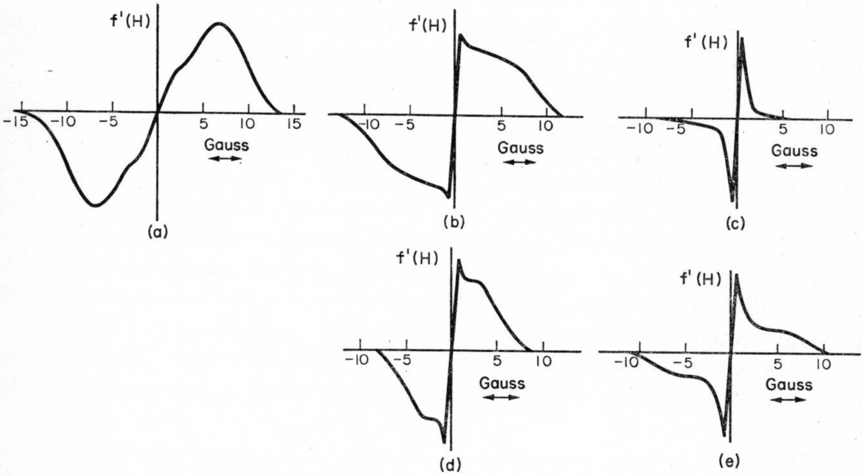

Fig. 74. Derivative of hydrogen resonance of (*a*) tristearin in β-form, (*b*) 1-stearodimyristin in β'-form, (*c*) 1-oleodistearin, mixture of α- and β'-forms, (*d* and *e*) 2-oleodistearin.

the second moments of all the glycerides examined were 24–25 gauss^2 and hence have 'rigid lattices' at these temperatures. At room temperature the β_L-, β'_L-, sub-α_L- and sub-β_L-forms have large second moments although some are smaller than the low temperature values. The α_L-forms, however, all have second moments at room temperature much smaller than the low-temperature values, showing that there is considerable molecular motion in this form even at room temperature. The nuclear resonance spectra support the conclusions obtained from infrared spectroscopy concerning the nature of the lowest melting form of the triglycerides in that the second moments observed for this form correspond to about 9 gauss^2 estimated for a crystal in which the hydrocarbon chains are freely reorienting about the chain axes.

The second moments at room temperature of the β_L-forms (the most stable crystalline forms) of tristearin and tripalmitin show that in this modification the chains are not reorienting at frequencies greater than 100 kc/sec. The values, however, are slightly lower (about 2 gauss^2) than the rigid value at low temperatures. This may be intepreted that reorientation of a few small segments of the chain occurs or as torsional oscillation of the whole chain about its axis. For tristearin this would be with an amplitude of about 17° whilst it would be somewhat greater for tripalmitin. The α_L-forms of these glycerides have second moments of 11·1 and 9·8 gauss^2 respectively. It is consistent with the hydrocarbon packing in this form being hexagonal. The glycerol residue in the glycerides may slightly hinder the free motion of the hydrocarbon chains. This could be the reason why the second moments of these forms are slightly greater than those estimated for straight-chain hydrocarbons. When the α_L-form is cooled to 90°K the observed second moments are of the order of 24–25 gauss^2. These conclusions are confirmed by independent studies [12].

The glycerides 1,2-distearin and 1,2-dipalmitin exist in two polymorphic forms designated α_L and β'_L. The second moments of the β'_L-form are nearly identical to those of the β_L-forms of tristearin and tripalmitin and similar conclusions are obtained with respect to the oscillations of the chains. The second moments of the lower melting α_L-forms are very close to the value of 9 gauss^2 expected for free reorientation of the chains confirming that this form has hexagonal packing of the hydrocarbon chains.

Interesting results were obtained with other glycerides including 1,3-diglycerides, 1-mono- and 2-monoglycerides and unsaturated glycerides. The observed line widths and second moment data are in Tables 20 and 21.

The unsaturated glycerides 1-oleodistearin and 1-oleodipalmitin showed some unusual characteristics. Thus the most stable crystalline β'_L-form shows a spectrum which appears to be made up of two superimposed parts, one of which has a much narrower line width than the other. The suggested interpretation for this is that the oleoyl chains have a double bond which disturbs the regularity of the chains so that they probably pack less tightly than the saturated chains and, as a result, have greater reorientational freedom. If y is the second moment of the oleoyl chain and the stearoyl chains have the same second moment as in tristearin the observed second moment $= 14{\cdot}9 = \frac{2}{3} \times 22{\cdot}2 + \frac{1}{3}y$ gauss^2 giving $y = 0{\cdot}3$ gauss^2. This would explain the very narrow line in the spectrum causing the unusual line shape.

At room temperature the α_L-forms of the unsaturated glycerides give remarkably narrow lines with second moments of less than 1 gauss^2. This

Table 20. *Line widths* (gauss)

Compound	β_L	β'_L	α_L	Sub-α_L	Sub-β_L	Temp. (°K)
Tristearin	12·9 ± 0·2		6·8 ± 0·1			293
	14·6 ± 0·3			14·8 ± 0·2		90
				14·3 ± 0·2		20
Tripalmitin	13·0 ± 0·4		6·8 ± 0·3			293
1,2-Distearin		13·5 ± 0·4	5·9 ± 0·1			293
		14·7 ± 0·4		14·8 ± 0·3		90
1,2-Dipalmitin		12·9 ± 0·6	5·2 ± 0·1			293
1,3-Distearin	12·1 ± 0·2	12·0 ± 0·1				293
1,3-Dipalmitin	11·1 ± 0·4	10·8 ± 0·5				293
1-Monostearin	12·7 ± 0·5			13·1 ± 0·2		293
			4·0 ± 0·1			323
1-Monomyristin	12·9 ± 0·4			12·6 ± 0·4		293
			4·3 ± 0·2			303
2-Monopalmitin	11·7 ± 0·6					293
1-Stearodimyristin	11·7 ± 0·2	0·9	6·5 ± 0·2			293
1-Oleodistearin		0·9	0·8			293
		13·4 ± 0·4		10·5 ± 0·3		195
		14·2 ± 0·2		14·0 ± 0·6		90
1-Oleodipalmitin		0·9	0·8			293
		14·2 ± 0·5		14·4 ± 0·2		90
2-Oleodistearin	11·6 ± 0·6		0·8/4·2 ± 0·2		10·4 ± 0·3	293
1-Mono-olein	8·0 ± 0·3	7·5 ± 0·6				293
			9·4 ± 0·8			273
Triolein	11·7 ± 0·2					273

Table 21. *Second moments* ($gauss^2$)

Compound	β_L	β'_L	α_L	Sub-α_L	Sub-β_L	Temp. (°K)
Tristearin	22·2 ± 0·7		11·1 ± 0·3			293
	24·7 ± 0·6			24·3 ± 0·2		90
				24·4 ± 1·1		20
Tripalmitin	20·4 ± 1·5		9·8 ± 0·4			293
1,2-Distearin		22·4 ± 0·9	8·1 ± 0·3			293
		25·2 ± 0·4		24·5 ± 0·5		90
1,2-Dipalmitin		20·6 ± 1·1	7·2 ± 0·2			293
1,3-Distearin	20·1 ± 0·7	19·0 ± 0·6				293
1,3-Dipalmitin	18·5 ± 1·3	17·6 ± 0·8				293
1-Monostearin	19·9 ± 1·7			20·0 ± 1·3		293
			4·5 ± 0·1			323
1-Monomyristin	19·7 ± 1·3			19·8 ± 1·4		293
			5·7 ± 1·0			303
2-Monopalmitin	18·2 ± 0·9					293
1-Stearodimyristin	19·1 ± 1·5	15·1 ± 0·4	9·3 ± 0·4			293
1-Oleodistearin		14·9 ± 1·0	0·5 (1) (< 1)			293
		20·4 ± 1·4		17·8 ± 1·4		195
		24·7 ± 0·6		24·9 ± 0·9		90
1-Oleodipalmitin		14·3 ± 0·5	0·6 (1) (< 1)			293
		24·3 ± 0·9		24·4 ± 0·5		90
2-Oleodistearin	20·3 ± 0·8		0·5/6·6 ± 0·6		16·1 ± 0·5	293
1-Mono-olein	13·1 ± 0·5	12·9 ± 1·4				293
			13·7 ± 1·2			273
Triolein	16·7 ± 0·3					273

line width is unusual in a solid and implies that other forms of motion apart from simple rotation are occurring, such as translational motion and flexing of the chains.

The molecular resonance method is in some ways complementary to infra-red spectroscopy for the study of the crystalline modifications of the glycerides in that the α_L-forms can be very readily distinguished from the β_L- and β'_L-forms. Where a double bond occurs in one of the chains or where there is a significant difference in chain length all three forms can be classified easily. A great deal of further work is possible with the glycerides, including more detailed measurements of the variation of the second moments with temperature, comparison made with the pre-melting observed with stearic acid, and measurements of relaxation times thereby leading to values of the activation energies of the molecular reorientation processes. The acetoglycerides would be rather interesting to study. These glycerides in their α_L-form can be stretched to 300–400 times their length; it would be of interest to see whether the second moment varies with the amount of stretching. The technique will also be useful for studying how the molecular motion is affected with mixtures of glycerides and on the formation of solid solutions. It will also be useful to correlate n.m.r. data with other physical characteristics of the glycerides.

The liquid crystalline transitions observed with some cholesterol esters have been studied [13] and spin-lattice (T_1) and spin–spin relaxation time (T_2) determined. Values of T_1 were about 0·06 to 0·15 sec and for T_2 0·02 to 0·03 sec. A pretransitional decrease of T_2 is observed as the temperature decreases towards the transition to the anisotropic phase.

LIQUID/SOLID CONTENT MEASUREMENTS

An interesting application of broad line n.m.r. spectroscopy has been for the measurement of the liquid/solid content of fats [14, 15]. We have seen that the width of the absorption line is related to the mobility of the protons in the sample or the mobility of the compound containing the hydrogen and to the field homogeneity. With a solid, due to the interactions between the nuclei, the line width is comparatively broad whilst in a liquid, in which the molecules are in a state of violent thermal agitation, the fields contributed by the hydrogen nuclei at any given point are averaged out rapidly. The absorption line is very narrow and is determined only by the homogeneity of the applied magnetic field. The inherent disparity in line width between solids and liquids (Fig. 75) has been used to provide a method for determining the liquid/solid content of fats. Other methods are available for this type of measurement including dilatation measurements and a dye dilution method, but the n.m.r. method appears to have the advantages of simplicity and speed.

The first attempts to use n.m.r. spectroscopy were based on the idea of measuring the area of the broad band of the solid and the narrow line of the liquid simultaneously: although this was not found to be favourable some interesting results were obtained. Thus the nuclear resonance spectra of margarine fat were obtained at different temperatures. At room temperature a derivative spectrum showed fine structure. The line width of the broader line was some 0·9 gauss, whilst the narrow line arises

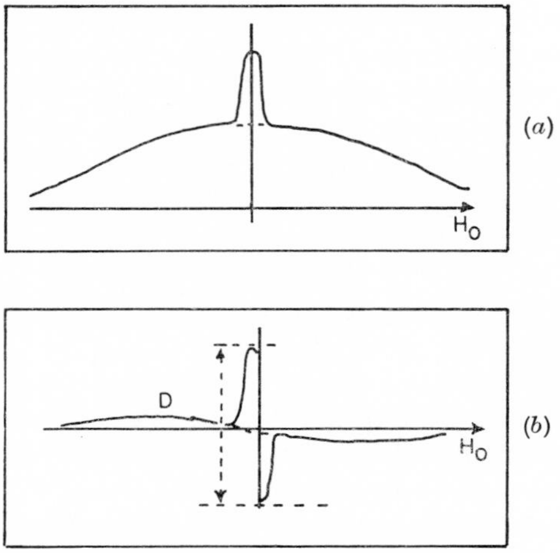

Fig. 75*a*. The absorption curve arising from liquid and solid materials.
Fig. 75*b*. The derivative curve.

from the liquid. (The width of the broad line is comparable with that of the unsaturated glyceride 1-oleodistearin in the α_L-polymorphic form, some 0·8 gauss.) Below $-24°$ C the line corresponding to the liquid disappears and at $-28°$ C a broad and a narrow line arising from the solid are observed. The line width of the broad line is some 7·6 gauss, and at $-35°$ C this has increased to 8·2 gauss and remains at this value down to $-78°$ C. The line width of the narrow line from the solid is 1·0 gauss at $-29°$ C and 1·5 gauss at $-57°$ C, and at $-64°$ C this line also disappears and only the broad line remains. At $-78°$ C the average line width was $8·2 \pm 0·3$ gauss and with a second moment of $17·6 \pm 1·1$ gauss^2. (This can be compared with the sub-α_L-form of 1-oleodistearin which has a line width of 10·5 gauss and a second moment of 17·8 gauss^2.) On further cooling to 90°K the average line width was $13{\cdot}9 \pm 0{\cdot}3$ gauss and second moment of $24{\cdot}7 \pm 0{\cdot}7$ gauss^2.

Further experiments were carried out with the magnetic field modulated at a sinusoidal frequency at about 40 c/s and with a magnitude of about 30 milligauss peak to peak and with the line width determined only by the magnetic field inhomogeneity. No signal due to the broad line of the solid is detectable and a measurement of the peak to peak height D (Fig. 75) is a direct measure of the amount of liquid present. Standard mixtures were examined of tristearin and triolein and good agreement obtained between determined and known values (Table 22).

Table 22. *N.M.R. values for liquid content* (*derivative*)

Known % liquid	Per cent. liquid found
75·1	74·0
50·2	51·2
25·1	25·4

As well as derivative curve measurements, absorption curve measurements have been made [16] and some typical results on tristearin/triolein are given in Table 23.

Table 23. *N.M.R. values for liquid content* (*absorption*)

Known % liquid	Per cent. liquid found
83·5	85 ± 2%
76·0	78
70·0	68
65·0	66
59·0	60
50·5	50
40·5	40
33·5	33
27·5	27

The method appears to have advantages in that fats may be examined in the state in which they are received, i.e. without altering the structure by melting and crystallization, it requires little preliminary work such as weighing, sample preparation, etc., and is rapid. Possible snags in the technique may arise from the narrowness of the lines which can occur with solid, unsaturated glycerides. If, due to considerable molecular motion, these lines are so narrow that they cannot be separated from the line from the liquid – due to, say, poor homogeneity of the magnet – then the method will fail. Given a magnet of good homogeneity the method appears to provide a useful means for measuring liquid/solid content. A considerable amount of information about the effects of solid solution would be obtained by further work on mixtures of pure glycerides. The important effect of impurities may also be studied as well as effects arising from pre-melting phenomenon. Relaxation time measurements may also show interesting results with mixtures of liquid and solid fat.

FUTURE APPLICATIONS

There are many future applications of broad line n.m.r. to the study of lipids. Some of the interesting applications are:

(*a*) The further study of the molecular motion which occurs in long chain monocarboxylic acids and esters using relaxation measurements to obtain information about the motion. The odd-membered carboxylic acids could be examined so as to contrast the degree of molecular freedom which occurs with their polymorphic phases, e.g. the C′-form, with that observed with the even-membered acids.

(*b*) Simple pure glycerides and the liquid crystalline form of the phospholipids require additional study. It may be useful to study lipid-water systems using D_2O as solvent, thereby eliminating the proton signal. Relaxation time measurements will also be useful. A correlation of physical characteristics with such measurements would be valuable.

(*c*) Further studies of the method of determining the liquid/solid content of fat mixtures are required. The results obtained at present differ from those obtained by other techniques. Since it may be possible to distinguish between actual liquid present and a pre-melting phenomenon involving molecular motion, it should be possible to be sure that the n.m.r. results are indeed valid. The technique will then provide a quick reference method for all liquid/solid content determinations. The comparison and correlation of such n.m.r. measurements with physical properties should be useful. Measurements of liquid/solid content may be significant for problems concerning atherosclerosis.

(*d*) There may be a number of interesting applications for studying the degree of hydrocarbon liquid-like character of lipids present in biological systems, for instance with natural membranes. The water content of nerves has been studied using this technique [17].

High resolution spectroscopy

The high resolution nuclear magnetic resonance spectra of molecules rotating rapidly in the liquid or vapour phase are determined by three main effects: (1) the chemical shift values, (2) the spin coupling interaction, (3) exchange effects.

CHEMICAL SHIFT

The field at a nucleus due to the field of the magnet is modified by the induced diamagnetic electronic currents. These set up a secondary magnetic field so that if H_0 is the field in the bulk of the specimen the field actually experienced by the nuclei is

$$H = H_0(1-\sigma') \tag{6.3}$$

where σ', the screening constant, is characteristic of the electronic environment of the nuclei. With nuclei in different chemical positions, the value of σ varies. The displacement of resonance produced by the additional field at the nucleus is proportional to the strength of the applied field and is called the chemical shift. (The chemical shift is a measure of the difference between values of σ' for different chemical positions.)

The screening constants are small in value, and are smaller for protons than for most other nuclei. The latter is due to the fact that the total number of electrons in the immediate vicinity of a proton is so much smaller than for any other nucleus. It is customary to use shielding constants such that

$$\sigma = \sigma' \times 10^6 = \frac{H-H_{\text{ref}}}{H_{\text{ref}}} \times 10^6 \tag{6.4}$$

where H is the field at which resonance occurs and H_{ref} the field at which the nucleus in the reference surroundings gives resonance at the same frequency.

The chemical shifts

$$\delta = \sigma_1 - \sigma_2 = \frac{H-H_{\text{ref}}}{H_{\text{ref}}} \times 10^6 \tag{6.5}$$

With protons a very convenient reference compound is tetramethyl silane and the quantity $\tau = 10-\delta$ has been introduced [18] so that

$$\tau(\text{p.p.m.}) = 10 - \frac{\Delta(\text{Me}_4\text{Si}) \times 10^6}{\text{oscillator frequency (c/s)}} \tag{6.6}$$

Δ is the displacement in frequency between the sample resonance and the Me_4Si resonance. On this scale τ is positive for all but very acidic protons. This is the scale now widely used for work with protons and is used in all our subsequent discussions.

Correlation with molecular structure

It is an important fact that not only do the different locations for nuclei within a given molecule give rise to different chemical shift values but also that the same chemical shift values are obtained for the nuclei in the same type of chemical location in different molecules. It is therefore possible to infer the particular types of chemical grouping present in the molecule from the experimental chemical shift values. This is rather analogous to the way in which different functional groupings are detected by means of their characteristic frequencies in their infra-red spectra (see Chapter 4).

Such correlations have been made from experimental data of Chamberlain and associates [19], G. Van Dyke Tiers [18] and other workers [3].

Some typical data are shown in Table 24, taken from the compilation of Jackman [3], which are pertinent to the spectra of lipids.

Table 24. *Alkyl groups adjacent to carboxyl groups*

X	CH_3—X	CH_2—X	$\rangle$CH—X
CHO	7·83	7·80	7·61
CO Alkyl	7·90	7·60	7·52
COPh	7·38	—	—
CO_2H	7·93	7·66	7·43
CO_2 Alkyl	8·00	7·90	—
$CONH_2$	7·98	—	—

Thus we can predict that a CH_3 adjacent to a CO alkyl group will show a resonance at 7·90 p.p.m. and examples of this are shown in Fig. 86.

For protons α to oxygen functions another list of useful correlations is available (Table 25).

Table 25. *Protons adjacent to oxygen*

X	CH_3X	—CH_2X	$\rangle$CHX
OH	6·62	6·44	6·15
O Alkyl	6·71	6·60	—
OPh	6·27	6·10	—
OCO Alkyl	6·35	5·90	4·99
OCOPh	6·10	5·77	4·88

Thus we can predict that CH_2 groups adjacent to an OH group will have a chemical shift value of 6·44 p.p.m. whilst a CH_2 group adjacent to an OCO alkyl group will have a value of 5·90 p.p.m.

For alkyl groups adjacent to nitrogen other correlations are available (Table 26), which may be useful for the spectra of phospholipids.

Table 26. *Alkyl groups adjacent to nitrogen*

X	CH_3X	$—CH_2X$	>CHX
N (acyclic)	7·85	7·5	7·13
N (cyclic secondary)	—	7·3	—
$NHCOCH_3$	7·15	6·8	—
Quaternary salts	6·67	6·60	—

With olefinic protons the proton shift value lies in the region 2·0–5·5. The non-conjugated hydrocarbons show resonance between 4·3 and 5·4 and the exact positions can provide some indication of the number and orientation of substituents (Table 27).

Table 27. *Olefinic protons*

Type	Unconjugated	Conjugated
Terminal methylene	5·35	5·10
Terminal allenic	5·6	—
Allenic	5·2	—
Acetylenic	7·65	7·30
Non-terminal acyclic	4·45–4·95	3·5–4·2

Aldehydic protons have a rather unique line position (0·0 to 0·7) which makes it convenient for study. Aliphatic aldehydes usually give a line near 0·35; α,β-unsaturation produces a small diamagnetic shift. By using the semicarbazones and 2,4-dinitrophenyl hydrazones, ketones and aldehydes may be distinguished.

The τ values of protons attached to oxygen are particularly sensitive to intermolecular environments and hence less valuable than those which we have already discussed. This is because hydrogen bonding and chemical exchange may occur. Hydrogen bonding gives rise to large paramagnetic shifts. The origin of this has been the subject of considerable discussion. The hydroxyl frequencies of alcohols can vary over a wide range, depending upon the nature of the solvent, concentration of solute and temperature. With carboxylic acids, the chemical shift value of the carboxylic proton is relatively invariant with concentration in non-polar solvents due to the existence of the acid in stable dimers.

It is often impossible on the basis of line position to identify the signals in the spectrum of a complex molecule, as they may sometimes overlap lines arising from other structural features. Temperature, or concentration variation is useful in identifying such lines. Jackman and co-workers [20] have studied the contribution that *cis*- and *trans*-β-substituents make upon the shielding of olefinic protons in simple ethylene derivatives such as 1,1-disubstituted ethylenes.

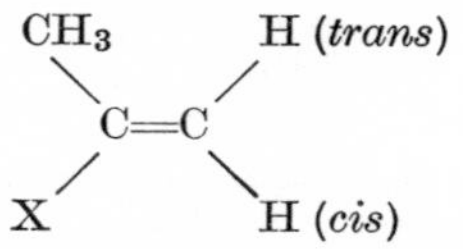

The separation of the olefinic protons as a consequence of some different substituents are given in Table 28.

Table 28. *Differential shielding of* cis *and* trans *olefinic protons by β-substituents*

Substituent X	Separation of olefinic proton lines (p.p.m.)
CH_3	0·00
$CH_2C(CH_3)_3$	0·175
CN	*ca.* 0·05
CO_2Me	0·50
COMe	0·20
CHO	0·275
Ph	0·26
OAc	0·05
$CONH_2$	0·40

In this case, since the shielding by X has to be averaged over all three conformations of the methyl group, the effects are expected to be small. The shielding of methyl groups attached to double bonds have also been studied in systems such as

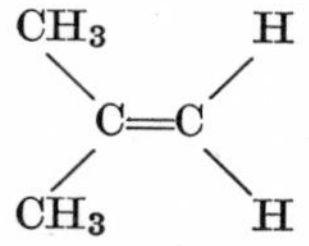

The data [20] for some pairs of *cis*- and *trans*-α,β-unsaturated esters are given in Table 29. Such measurements show that the careful analysis of chemical shift data can provide valuable information in lipid chemistry about the configurations of ethylenic isomers.

Table 29. *Shift of β-olefinic and β-methyl proton frequencies in* cis–trans *α-β-unsaturated acids*

Compounds	$\tau_A - \tau_B$ p.p.m.	
	β-methyl proton	β-olefinic proton
Dimethyl maleate (A) Dimethyl fumarate (B)	—	0·53
Methyl angelate (A) Methyl tiglate (B)	−0·25	0·75
Methyl citraconate (A) Methyl mesoconate (B)	0·20	0·80

SPIN–SPIN COUPLING

The second important feature of high-resolution n.m.r. spectroscopy is due to the effect of spin–spin coupling between nuclei. This arises as a result of the interaction of one nuclei with another via electron structure. One contribution is the action of electronic currents induced by one nuclear magnetic moment on the other whilst another contribution arises because the nuclear moments cause a slight spatial redistribution of electron spins throughout the molecule.

The usual example of this effect is shown by the n.m.r. spectrum of ethyl alcohol. Under lowish resolution three lines are observed corresponding to the chemical shift values of the different protons in the molecule, OH, CH_2 and CH_3, with line intensities in the ratio 1:2:3 respectively. With greater resolution, however, considerable multiplicity is observed and there are four lines corresponding to the CH_2 group and three lines corresponding to the CH_3 group. (With greater resolution further lines are observed as a result of second-order spin–spin couplings.) This fine structure is not a chemical shift phenomenon, since on observing the spectrum at different field strengths the principal lines of the methylene, methyl and hydroxyl groups shift closer together or further apart, whilst the spacings of the three-line and four-line multiplets remain unaltered. (The second-order splitting is, however, field dependent.) The spacings in the CH_2 multiplet and in the CH_3 multiplet are the same and are indicated by J, the spin coupling constant.

We can see how the multiplicity arises for an ethyl group by means of the following simple considerations (see Fig. 76). The two methylene protons can have any one of four possible combinations of their magnetic quantum numbers, one way to give $+1$, two ways to give zero and one to give -1. Thus the methyl protons will 'feel' one of three effective fields depending upon the instantaneous spin arrangement of the methylene group. Hence the methyl resonance will be split into a triplet of intensity 1:2:1. Similarly the methylene protons will 'feel' the effective fields of the four possible instantaneous spin arrangements of the methyl group and its signal will consist of four lines of intensity 1:3:3:1. The lack of multiplicity of the hydroxyl proton signal and any

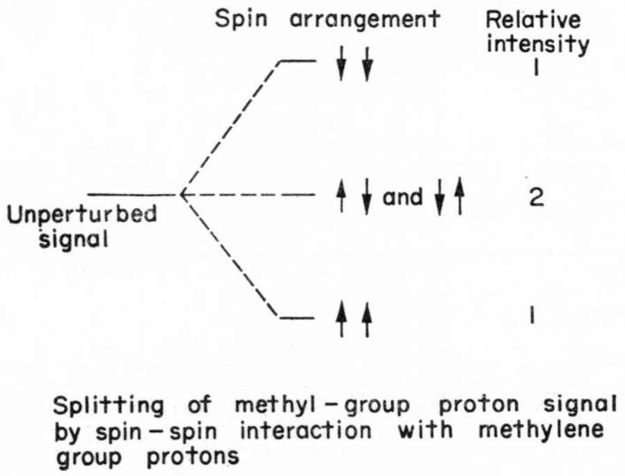

Fig. 76. Splitting of methyl-group proton signal by spin–spin interaction with methylene group protons.

further splitting of the methylene group signal in the spectrum of ethyl alcohol is due to rapid exchange of the hydroxylic protons. The hydroxylic proton will, in a given interval of time, be attached to a number of different ethanol molecules and will therefore experience all possible spin arrangements of the methylene group. If the chemical exchange occurs with a frequency greater than the frequency separation of the components of the multiplet from the hydroxylic proton, the magnetic effects are averaged and a single sharp absorption line is observed.

If we consider the more general case of a proton or other magnetic nucleus of spin $\frac{1}{2}$ with n-equivalent neighbours then its resonance will be split into $(n+1)$ fine structure lines with relative intensities given by the coefficients of the various terms of a binomial expansion of the type $(x+y)^n$, e.g. for $n = 2$; this is 1, 2, 1.

In general, the effect of one proton on the resonance of another proton or group of equivalent protons depends upon the number and kind of intervening chemical bonds and upon the stereo-chemical relations of the interacting groups. The splitting for non-equivalent protons in saturated systems is about 15 c/s when on the same carbon, about 5 to 8 c/s when on contiguous carbon atoms and zero when separated by more than two carbons. The splitting for phosphorus can extend over as much as two bonds. Chemically equivalent hydrogen nuclei do not cause mutual multiplicity. The effect of restricted rotation can cause apparently equivalent protons to become, in fact, non-equivalent.

The simple relationship described for the multiplicity only occurs when the spin coupling constant is small compared to the chemical shift difference (as in AX cases, see later) between the two resonance signals. If these two are comparable, complex patterns are obtained which have to be analysed by appropriate calculations of the energy levels and spectroscopic transitions [21, 22].

An example of the application of this to an AB system gives the determinant

$$\begin{array}{llll} H_{11}-E & 0 & 0 & 0 \\ 0 & H_{22}-E & H_{23} & 0 \\ 0 & H_{23} & H_{33}-E & 0 \\ 0 & & & H_{44}-E \end{array}$$

In this case E_1 and E_4 are obtained immediately, whilst E_2 and E_3 are obtained as the roots of a quadratic equation.

The general selection rules for transitions are:

1. In any allowed transition the change of total spin
$$\Delta F = \pm 1$$
2. All allowed transitions must be between two states of the same symmetry.
3. The intensity of the transition between two states p and q is proportional to the square of the transition moments
$$(\phi_p|M_x|\phi_q)$$

where ϕ_p and ϕ_q are stationary state wave functions and M_x is the x component of the magnetic moment operator

$$M_x = \sum_i \eta_i I_x(i)$$

CLASSIFICATION OF NUCLEAR GROUPS

A nuclear resonance notation has been introduced for typical groups of nuclei which occur in molecules. Thus symbols A, B ... are used for non-equivalent nuclei of the same species whose relative chemical shifts are of the same order of magnitude as the spin coupling between them. Equivalent nuclei are described by the same symbol, e.g. A_2, B_4, etc. The symbols X, Y are used for another set whose signals are widely separated from those of the set A, B ... and the nuclei may or may not be of the same species. Examples of the nomenclature are:

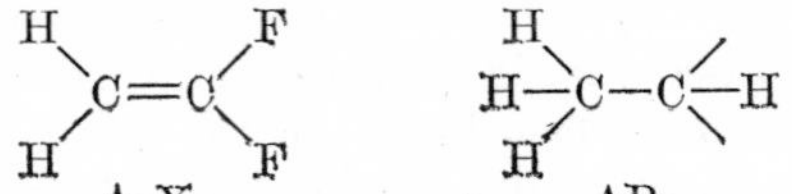

A_2X_2 AB_3

The AB system

This is the simplest system of two non-equivalent nuclei in which the effects of chemical shift and spin coupling intermingle. At one extreme we have the AX system and this gives rise to a pair of doublets of equal intensity, whilst at the other extreme we have the A_2 system giving rise

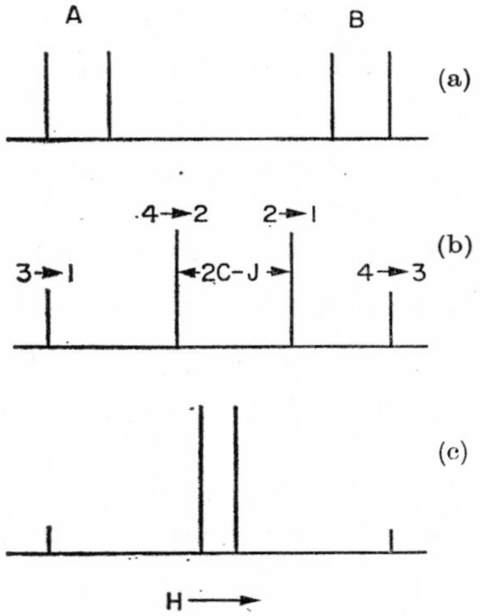

Fig. 77. AB spectra for differing values of R $(=J/\delta)$. (a) $J \ll \delta$; (b) $J \approx \delta$; (c) $J \gg \delta$.

to a single line. The intermediate situation, in which the chemical shift δ_{AB} between the nuclei is similar to the spin coupling constant J_{AB}, also consists of a pair of doublets but the intensities of the four lines are no longer equal. This requires theoretical analysis.

The general appearance of the spectrum depends only upon the ratio $|J/\nu_0\delta|$ and is independent of the signs of J and $\sigma_B - \sigma_A$. The spectrum for some values of this ratio are shown in Fig. 77. With the lines labelled as shown the following relations hold:

$$(3-4) = (1-2) = J_{AB} \text{ in cycles} \tag{6.7}$$

$$(1-3) = (2-4) = \sqrt{\{(\delta_A - \delta_B)^2 + J_{AB}^2\}} \tag{6.8}$$

From these $\delta_B - \delta_A$ can be determined and hence δ_A and δ_B.

AB_2 systems

The energy level system for AB_2 has been calculated by a number of workers [22, 23]. There are eight energy levels and nine allowed transitions. The appearance of the spectrum depends only on the ratio of J_{AB}/δ_{AB} and is independent of J'_{BB}. At large chemical shift differences the spectrum is an AX_2 type. Here the A lines 2 and 3 coalesce and the A resonance becomes a symmetrical triplet of relative intensities 1:2:1 and spacing J_{AB}. The B lines 5, 6, 7 and 8 also coalesce to a doublet of spacing J_{AB}.

AB_3 systems

The AB_3 grouping often occurs in the form of the grouping

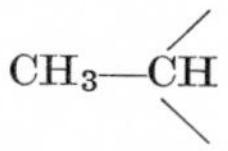

and we will consider it briefly. The methyl group is usually rotating rapidly about its three-fold axis of symmetry and the three AB coupling constants have the same average value. Such a system has sixteen allowed transitions of the B nucleus. When the coupling value is small (5–7 c/s) only a broad envelope is observed and the individual lines are not resolved. At large chemical shift in an AX_3 system the X_3 band consists of a doublet of equal intensity. At low values of J_{AB}/δ_{AB} the low frequency line increases in relative intensity compared with the other component. At high values the high frequency line only appears as an inflexion on the side of this component. The A lines and B lines also overlap at this stage.

AB_4 system

The protons in the glyceryl residue of triglycerides, the CH_2CHCH_2 grouping has been regarded as an approximate or pseudo AB_4 system [24]. Whilst this is a gross approximation it is instructive to compare the experimental spectra with the theoretical calculations (see later). The method used for its calculation is that of the composite particle technique. Each group of identical nuclei is considered as a composite particle with fixed total spin. The single proton forms a particle of spin $\frac{1}{2}$ whilst the four equivalent protons form a particle with possible states of spin 0, 1 and 2. The spectrum depends only upon R, the ratio of the spin coupling constant J to the chemical shift difference J_{AB}/δ_{AB}. When $R \rightarrow 0$ the AX_4 condition holds and the A group is observed as a quintet with a doublet for the X-group. As R approaches 1 the lines 24, 21, 8, 17

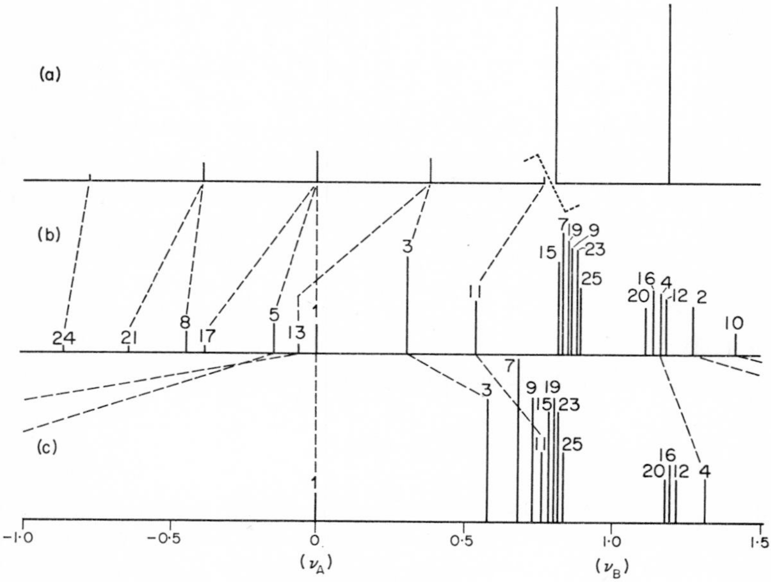

Dots indicate break in spectrum (a)
Intensity scale of (b) and (c), $2\frac{1}{2}$ times that of (a)
Greatest intensity of any line off scale in (c) is only $\frac{1}{10}$th of that of line 1
The horizontal scale is in units of δ_{AB}

Fig. 78. AB_4 spectra for differing values of R $(=J/\delta)$. (*a*) $R \rightarrow 0$ $(\delta \rightarrow \infty)$; (*b*) $R \sim 0{\cdot}4$ (J as for (*a*)); (*c*) $R \sim 2{\cdot}0$ (δ as for (*b*)).

5 and 13 move away from the other lines and begin to decrease in intensity. This also occurs with lines 2 and 10 of the B group. As R approaches, a collapse into a single line takes place (Fig. 78).

Data are being collected so as to be able to correlate spin coupling constants with structure. Thus the constant for two non-equivalent protons in a saturated methylene group (CH_AH_B) is of the order of 12–15 c/s. For protons attached as in H_A—C—C—H_B the value is 0–12 c/s and coupling is usually almost negligible (< 1 c/s) when the protons are separated by more than two other saturated atoms. Fluorine and phosphorus coupling can, however, extend over more bonds.

The spin coupling is observed to vary with olefinic protons, the *trans* pair have J value of 17·8 c/s, whilst for the *cis* pair J is 11·3 c/s and the order $J_{trans} > J_{cis} > J_{gem}$ apparently holds. The J value is also considered to be a sensitive function of the H—C—H bond angle. The value is 20 c/s for a bond angle of 105° and falling to zero when the angle is widened to 125°. Greater angles are suggested to lead to small negative J values. The hydrogens of the grouping $C{=}CH_2$ are predicted to be weakly coupled with $J \sim 1$ c/s once the H—C—H angle is large.

INTERNAL ROTATION

In ethyl alcohol the methyl group can freely rotate about the C—C bond and the protons within the group are equivalent. We can see that this is so by considering the molecule CH_3CH_2R. The molecule has three rotational isomers of equal energy and population. The staggered configurations are assumed to be more stable than the eclipsed form. One of the *trans* forms is:

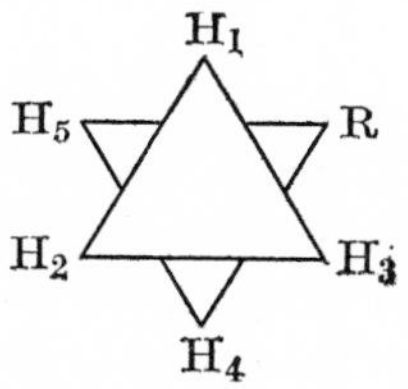

At slow rotation of the methyl group the spectrum is typical of one structure. Proton H_2 will have a different screening constant than H_1 and H_3. Protons H_4 and H_5 will have the same screening constant. If the chemical shifts are large enough the spectrum would show three types of protons and be of the type AB_2X_2. At rapid rotation the screening constants become equal and the spin coupling constants between any hydrogen on the CH_3 group and the protons of the CH_2 group become equivalent. Thus for rapid rotation the spectrum becomes of the type A_2B_3 with all AB coupling constants equal.

Information about the rate of rotation can be provided from the spectra.

The possibility of internal rotation occurring and also the hindering of rotation must always be considered in the interpretation of the spectra. The non-equivalence of what superficially may be equivalent nuclei must always be considered. In glycerol itself there is the possibility of rotation about two positions in the molecule simultaneously and the number of formal isomers is quite large.

Exchange effects

If protons are moving between two environments A and B they have an average residence time τ_A and τ_B at each site. These are given by

$$\tau_A = 1/K_A \quad \text{and} \quad \tau_B = 1/K_B \qquad (6.9)$$

where K_A and K_B are the first-order rate constants for exchange. Even when a chemical shift difference occurs between the two protons if the residence times are short, only a single absorption line is observed corresponding to a weighted average of the resonant frequencies (corresponding to the 'resident' proton chemical shift).

When the values $\tau_A = \tau_B = \tau$, the populations at both sites are equal. With larger chemicals shift or longer residence times, separate resonance lines will be observed where δ_e, the observed chemical shift, is given by

$$\delta_e = \delta_\nu[1 - 2/(\tau\delta_\nu)^2]^{1/2} \qquad (7.0)$$

where δ_ν is the chemical shift between the protons in the two environments. The activation energy for the process can be determined by measuring δ_e, and therefore τ, as a function of temperature.

EXPERIMENTAL TECHNIQUES

A number of commercial instruments are now available for high-resolution studies, having some variations in their basic design. Two types of detection of the resonance signal have been used. These are the single coil (bridge method) and the double coil (induction method). The single-coil method has been described in the section on broad line studies. In this method nuclear resonance is detected by changes in the impedance of a tuned circuit, whilst with the induction method two coils at right angles are used. The receiver coil is wound around the sample with its axis perpendicular to both the axis of a transmitter coil and to the direction of the field. The signal is detected and isolated from the background signal by the arrangement of the two coils. The transmitter and receiver coils are almost at right angles to each other. There is still residual coupling between the transmitter and receiver coils, called leakage. By varying the phase of the leakage either the absorption or dispersion mode may be obtained. This is commonly accomplished by means of a paddle control. Permanent and electromagnets are used in commercial equipment and have their own particular advantage: thus good temperature control is required with the permanent magnet. It is limited in field strength and variability of field but it is extremely stable. The electromagnet has many obvious advantages, but stability and uniformity of field can be quite difficult to obtain and hold. Pre-cycling is required.

High-resolution spectrometers are available from Varian Associates, Palo Alto, California. They are of the cross-coil type and use electromagnets with stabilized power supplies. There are two main types of instrument. The A-60 instrument is a specially designed analytical instrument which operates at a magnetic field strength of 14,092 gauss and at 60 Mc/s operating frequency. The resolution is 1 in 10^8. It features a control system which 'locks' the magnetic field strength and the effective transmitter frequency. This enables the system to be very stable. It is locked in this way by means of a nuclear side-band oscillator which applies a modulation frequency of approximately 5 kc to the modulating coils in the sample probe. This produces two side bands at 60 Mc/s $\pm$ 5 kc. At the control receiver the 60 Mc carrier is demodulated and only the 5 kc sideband signals remain. The upper side-band signal is applied to the input of the field modulator. This amplifies the audio voltage, and again applies it to the modulating coils, thus completing the loop. The circuit therefore attempts to remain in oscillation and shifts the side-band frequency to maintain just the right combination of field strength and effective transmitter frequency. This system enables preprinted charts to be used and spectra obtained on a routine basis. An integrator is attached and the integral can be recorded on the spectrum for direct correspondence. This instrument is only suitable for protons. The Varian HR-60 and DP-60 dual-purpose spectrometers are also manufactured and nuclei such as ^{19}F, ^{31}P, ^{11}B, ^{13}C and ^{17}O can be studied, as well as hydrogen nuclei. The DP-60 instrument also enables broad line studies to be made. A recent instrument is the HR-100, operating at 100 Mc/s. The advantage for a particular nucleus of working at higher field strength and also higher radio frequency is the resultant improvement in sensitivity. This means that smaller samples are required. This, and the greater separation of lines of different chemical shift, helps to increase the available resolution.

The Perkin–Elmer n.m.r. spectrometer is a permanent-magnet type instrument having a field strength of about 14,092 gauss corresponding to 60 Mc/s for protons of 1 in 10^8 with a field drift of less than 2 c/s. The spectrum is recorded on pre-printed charts calibrated in c/s. Using an internal standard tetramethyl silane, chemical shift values can be determined directly to 0·1 c/s. Interchangeable frequency sources for hydrogen, fluorine, phosphorus, boron and nitrogen can be obtained. Maximum resolving power is assisted by means of Golay coils fitted at the pole faces. An optional extra is a printing integrator.

The sample, in either the liquid state or in solution, is placed in a thin-walled cylindrical tube of about 4 mm diameter and made to spin by means of an air jet. The sample volume is about 0·01 to 0·5 c.c. Ideal solvents for work with protons are CCl_4, CS_2, C_2Cl_4, chloroform water, benzene and cyclohexane. (At times the deuterated compounds D_2O and $CDCl_3$ are convenient to use.) The concentration of the solutions used varies from 5 to 30% by weight. (The spectra of large molecules are relatively weaker than small ones, as the solubility in gram molecules per litre is less.) With proton spectra the usual reference compound, tetramethyl silane, is added to the solution or placed in a closed capillary in the sample tube. The position of this peak is taken as being 10 p.p.m. With some instruments the spectrum is recorded on a pre-printed chart calibrated in cycles per second, whilst some older instruments do not have printed scales on the chart and side bands are used to provide a scale for measuring chemical shift.

The area under the absorption band is directly proportional to the number of atoms of the observed isotope in the effective sample volume. The proportionality constant varies with the instrumental factors but does not vary with the chemical or physical environment of the isotope. Quantitative measurements require calibration with only a single standard for each isotope, hence there is no need to determine absorption lines for individual compounds.

The advantages of n.m.r. measurements are, that they are non-destructive, which is important when limited amounts of sample are available, it is relatively fast, of the order of 10 to 30 min per sample, and good quantitative precision and accuracy are available. The total hydrogen content of a sample can be measured with a standard deviation of 0·2% of the sample level of 10%.

Limitations on precision and accuracy of the n.m.r. measurements are caused by those environmental factors which broaden the resonance and reduce the signal to noise ratio.

RESONANCE OF OTHER NUCLEI

Phosphorus

The stable isotope of phosphorus is ^{31}P which has a spin of $\frac{1}{2}$. The resonance frequency is less than that for the proton, about 17·2 Mc/sec in a magnetic field of 10,000 gauss. Unfortunately the signal strength of the phosphorus resonance, because of its smaller magnetic moment, is only some 7% of that of the ^{1}H or ^{19}F nuclei at the same field strength. However, the chemical shifts cover a range of 500 p.p.m. compared with about 10 p.p.m. for H' resonance and therefore overlapping of peaks is less important with phosphorus and a lower signal to noise ratio is acceptable. Lower resolution can be tolerated and sample tubes of larger diameter may be used and non-spinning conditions apply. The samples commonly examined nevertheless had to have been of high concentration, at least 1 M in phosphorus. This limits its usefulness to solid samples. Recently a technique has been described for measuring the chemical shifts of weak spectra containing broad resonance peaks. In this way adenosine di- and tri-phosphate in 0·09 M solutions were examined [25] and it was suggested that the method might be capable of use with solutions as dilute as 0·01 M. As yet no application to the study of phospholipids has been made and it may be that such applications will be rather limited to short-chain derivatives.

The reference material frequently used is 85% aqueous phosphoric acid which is used as an external standard.

The spin coupling constant for compounds with a hydrogen or fluorine atom directly attached is very large (some 500–700 c/s for hydrogen atoms); for compounds with one or two other atoms separating the phosphorus and the proton the splitting is much smaller. However, with $P(OMe)_3$ eight of the ten expected lines can be resolved [26].

Nitrogen (^{14}N)

The nitrogen nucleus possesses a quadrupole moment and therefore signals are broad. Chemical shifts have, however, been observed for the ^{14}N nucleus in various molecular environments. When a proton is bonded to a nitrogen atom the proton signals are often broad and sometimes the signal is hardly detectable. This occurs because the quadrupole moment of the nitrogen nucleus gives rise to a strong relaxation mechanism. A proton attached to a nitrogen atom gives rise to three lines due to the spin–spin splitting of the ^{14}N ($I = 1$). Broadening of the signal can be sometimes reduced by double-irradiation experiments.

Carbon (^{13}C)

The exciting possibility of obtaining high-resolution spectra corresponding to the ^{13}C nuclei is being studied. This means that direct information on carbon atoms which are not attached to hydrogen atoms such as carbonyl groups is possible. Although the natural abundance of ^{13}C is only 1·1%, Lauterbur [27, 28] has developed a technique, using dispersion signals recorded with sweep rates of the order of 1000 cycles per minute to enable the detection of signals from compounds with molecular weights up to 400. This work was carried out with a Varian 4300-B high-resolution n.m.r. spectrometer operating at a frequency of 8·5 Mc/s. The resonant field at this frequency is about 7940 gauss. For accurate calibration a sample of methyl iodide enriched to 60% ^{13}C was used and the absorption mode employed. The arbitrary zero of reference for most of the ^{13}C shifts obtained was the resonance of the carboxyl carbon in acetic acid. The ^{13}C isotope has a spin of $\frac{1}{2}$.

A typical spectrum of acetic acid is shown in Fig. 79. The larger peak arises from the carbon in the carboxyl group, whilst the four smaller peaks arise from the methyl carbon resonance. The spin–spin interaction with the three methyl protons splits the methyl carbon resonance into four components. There is no observable coupling of either the methyl

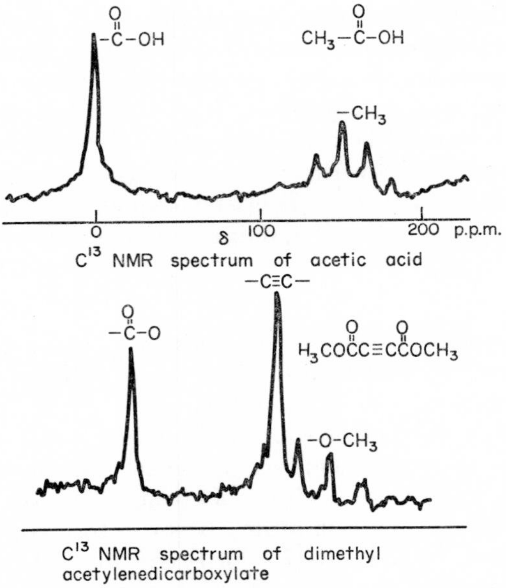

Fig. 79. C^{13} N.M.R. spectrum of acetic acid and dimethyl acetylene-dicarboxylate. (Lauterbur, P. C. *Ann. N. Y. Acad. Sci.*, **70**, 841, 1958.)

or the hydroxyl protons with the carboxyl carbon. The spectrum of the dimethyl ester of acetylene dicarboxylic acid is also shown. The three types of carbon present are clearly resolved, the C=O and C=C groups being particularly outstanding.

It is clear that ^{13}C spectra will be very useful in the future study of lipid molecules and it seems only a question of time before the study on almost a routine basis of ^{13}C spectra becomes available.

Applications

ALCOHOLS

The high-resolution n.m.r. spectra of the simple aliphatic alcohols are useful as a means of characterizing them as far as chain length and branching is concerned by observing the τ-values, spin–spin coupling and intensities. Thus, the spectra of *n*-propyl and isopropyl alcohols can be clearly distinguished.

MONOCARBOXYLIC ACIDS

Saturated

In the n.m.r. spectrum of saturated monocarboxylic acids [29, 30] lines occur corresponding to the CH_3 (9·1 p.p.m.), CH_2 chain (8·7 p.p.m.), the $CH_2\alpha$ to the carboxyl proton is at 7·7 p.p.m. The signal corresponding to the carboxyl proton is strongly affected by concentration and its position is quite variable.

The spectra of branched-chain acids show differences in the 9·2 p.p.m. region corresponding to the additional methyl groups present. The extra line may be close to or superimposed upon the usual line of the terminal methyl group. The isopalmitic acid (14-methyl pentadecanoic acid) has the larger part of the terminal CH_3 peak at 9·13 p.p.m. and the smaller at 9·22 p.p.m. The ante-iso C_{18} acid (15-methyl heptadecanoic acid) shows the peaks overlapping to give a quite different pattern. The 9-methyl stearic acid has a branch in the middle of the chain and the spectrum shows only a slight variation from that of the normal acids. The intensity of the terminal CH_3 line is, however, double that for an unbranched acid. The spectrum of 2-methyl octadecanoic acid shows a new line at 8·87 p.p.m. which is considered to be part of a well-separated doublet, the other component lying within the broad band of the CH_2 chain. The area of the line at 7·6 p.p.m. is only half its usual area, corresponding to the single proton on the carbon atom adjacent to the carboxyl group. The spectra of two dextro-rotatory optical isomers of 3,4-dimethyl docosanoic acid have been obtained and show differences in the terminal CH_3 and the α-CH_2 regions. It may be possible to determine which isomer has the *cis* conformation by comparison with model compounds.

Hydroxy acids

The spectra of hydroxy acids are also informative since, although the chemical shift of the hydroxyl proton is concentration dependent, the OH proton to which the hydroxyl group is attached gives a definite line. The 12,13-dihydroxy acid gives a signal at 6·4 p.p.m. corresponding to the **CH**—OH line (Fig. 80). Ricinoleic acid gives rise to a similar spectrum, whilst a shoulder at 8·2 p.p.m. on the main CH_2 peak is assigned to the CH_2 groups adjacent to the CHOH groups.

In the spectrum of 17-hydroxy stearic acid the terminal methyl line is shifted because of its nearness to the CHOH group, causing some of it to appear at 8·9 instead of 9·1 p.p.m. The line corresponding to the C**H**OH proton is at 6·2 p.p.m., slightly lower than usual. The spectrum of 18-hydroxy stearic acid does not show a line corresponding to a terminal methyl group; however the C**H**—OH proton is in its usual place

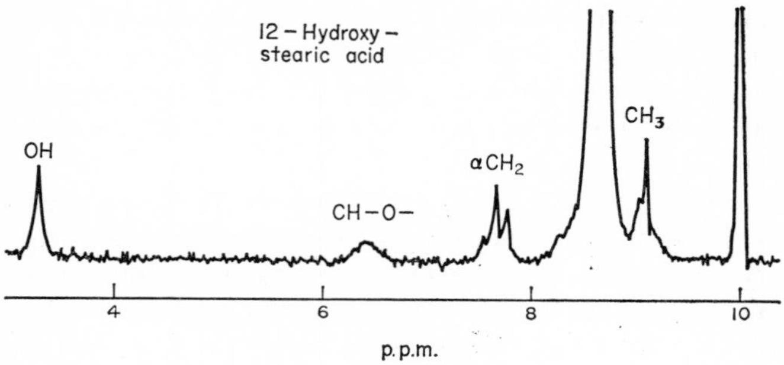

Fig. 80. Spectrum of an hydroxy acid, showing two peaks produced by the two different hydrogens of the CHOH group. Line at 10 p.p.m. is Me_4Si. (Hopkins, C. Y. *J. Amer. Oil Chemists' Soc.*, **38**, 664, 1961.)

at 6·3 to 6·4 p.p.m. In this way it is possible to ascertain rapidly whether the OH group of an hydroxy fatty acid is on the end or next-to-end carbon atom.

Unsaturated

The unsaturated acids give lines at low fields. Thus oleic acid shows lines corresponding to the protons of the HC=CH grouping at 4·7 p.p.m. The lines for the conjugated double bonds are at lower field than with the non-conjugated double bonds. The complex line for the unsaturated group extends below 4·7 p.p.m.

The spectrum of linoleic acid is also characteristic (Fig. 81). The triplet at 7·2 p.p.m. is associated with the CH_2 group between the double bonds =CH—CH_2—OH= grouping. The lines correspond to the olefinic protons, CH_3 groups adjacent to only one double bond, aliphatic CH_2 groups and the end methyl group. Small differences in the fine structure of the lines near 4·7 p.p.m. distinguish the *cis*- and *trans*-isomers, e.g. methyl oleate and methyl elaidate.

Unsaturation at the end of the chain gives a different spectrum in that the methyl line is absent. The lines at 4·4 and 5 p.p.m. correspond to the CH and CH_2 protons about the double bond and multiplet structure occurs.

Acids with cyclic groups

A particular acid of this type is the naturally occurring sterculic acid

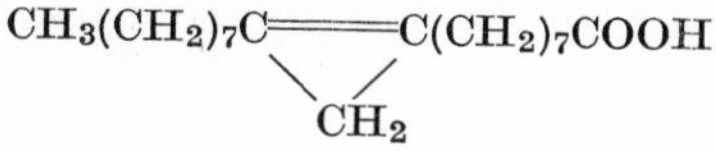

This acid comprises more than 70% of the total fatty acids of the seed fat *Sterculia foetida*.

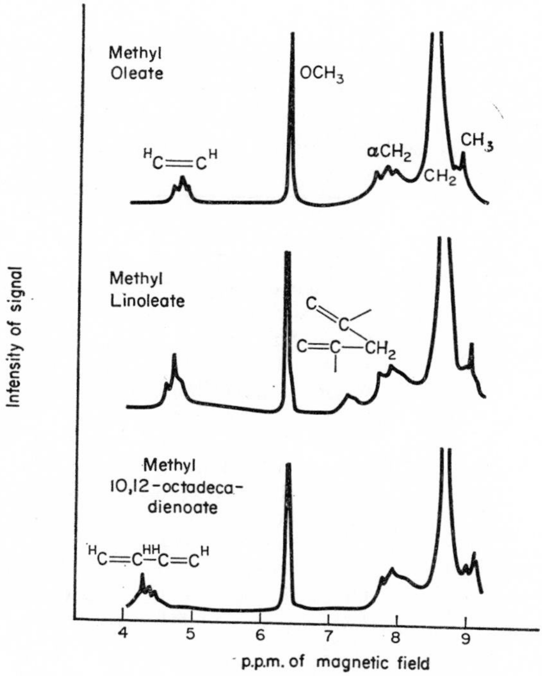

Fig. 81. N.M.R. spectra of some unsaturated methyl esters. (Hopkins, C. Y. *J. Amer. Oil Chemists' Soc.*, **38**, 664, 1961.)

Various arguments have been proposed for its precise structure. One structure, according to Nunn [31], was with a cyclopropene ring ω-(2-*n*-octacycloprop-1-enyl) octanoic acid based mainly on inference from infra-red data on the hydrogenated product. Another alternative structure, due to Verma [32], was ω-(2-*n*-hexycyclopropyl)-9-10-decanoic acid, also based on infra-red data. Dijkstra and Duin [33] supported the first structure.

An n.m.r. study of the acid [29] shows no peak near 4·7 p.p.m. characteristic of the olefinic=CH group and none for the cyclopropane ring at 10·3 p.p.m. This confirms the original structure of Nunn. It is suggested that the reason for the disagreement has been the fact that the substance examined by Varma and co-workers was a spontaneously polymerized sterculic acid.

In chaulmoogric acid the cyclopentene ring gives rise to a line at 4·3 p.p.m. assigned to the CH=CH proton. A complex pattern in the 7·8–8·3 p.p.m. region is associated with the remaining ring protons. The line at 4·2 p.p.m. is a singlet.

Table 30. *Approximate peak positions of groups in fatty acids and esters* [30] *expressed as parts per million relative to tetramethylsilane* = 10·00

2–4	α,β-unsaturation
2·75	(chloroform)
4·2	conjugated double bonds in carbon chain
4·7	ethylenic double bond
4·8	CHO of glyceride
5	vinyl CH_2=
5·8	CH_2O of glyceride
6·3	CH_3 of methyl ester
6·4	CH of CHOH in chain (or **CH**OCOCH$_3$)
7	CH—CH in epoxy-ring
7·2	CH_2 of 1,4-diene (=CHCH$_2$CH=)
7·5	CH≡, acetylenic
7·7	CH_2 adjacent to carboxyl
7·9	CH_3 of acetyl group
8	CH_2 adjacent to —CH= in chain
8·2	CH_3 attached to ethylenic C
8·7	CH_2 of carbon chain
9·1	terminal CH_3
9·2	CH_2 of cyclopropene ring
9·4, 10·3	cyclopropane ring

A useful collection of data for acids and esters is shown in Table 30.

ESTERS

The spectra of some methyl esters are shown in Fig. 81. The line corresponding to the CH_3 of the methyl ester group is clearly shown.

GLYCERIDES

The n.m.r. spectra of glycerol and a number of pure glycerides have been studied [24]. The spectra can be interpreted mainly in an empirical manner using chemical shift data, but an attempt has been made to discuss them in more detail.

Interpretation of the nuclear resonance spectrum of the glyceryl residue, the CH_2CHCH_2 group, is rather difficult. It involves five

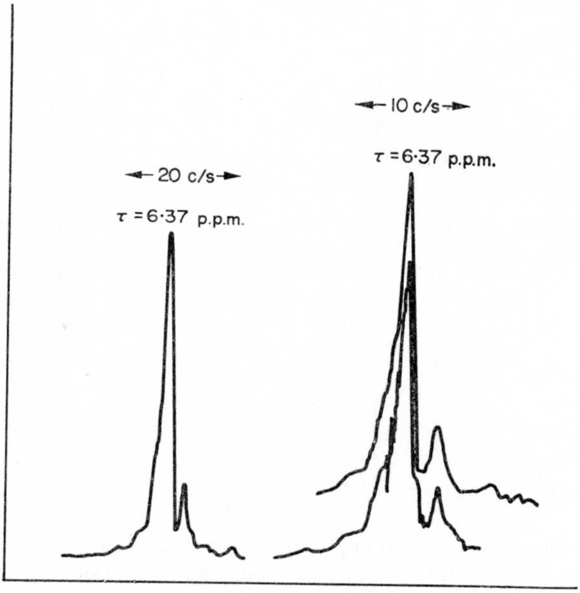

Fig. 82. N.M.R. spectrum of glycerol in D_2O.

chemical shift values and ten coupling constants. In addition to this, hindered rotation can occur about two positions within the molecule and nine isomers are possible. Whilst some of the isomers are expected to be unstable the system is nevertheless of great complexity. Even when the substituents are all the same the theoretical system is just as complex and of the A B B′ C C′ type. If an attempt to approximate is made and the system regarded as an AB_2C_2 type this still requires considerable computation. A crude approximation is to an AB_4 system where we regard the chemical shift of each proton as equivalent and only one coupling constant is required. This system can be readily calculated and a comparison of this theoretical system is useful.

With glycerol in water or deuterium oxide the chemical shift difference between the CH and CH_2 protons is small and only a strong line at 6·37 p.p.m. with a weaker line 10 c/s to high field is observed (Fig. 82). The spectrum of 1,2,3-trichloropropane, examined as a model related compound interestingly shows a greater difference in the chemical shift values of the two groups some 10–15 c/s. With triacetin the chemical shift difference is even greater, some 40 c/s. These differences may be related to greater steric hindrance of the larger substituent groups, thereby providing magnetic interactions which are not averaged out.

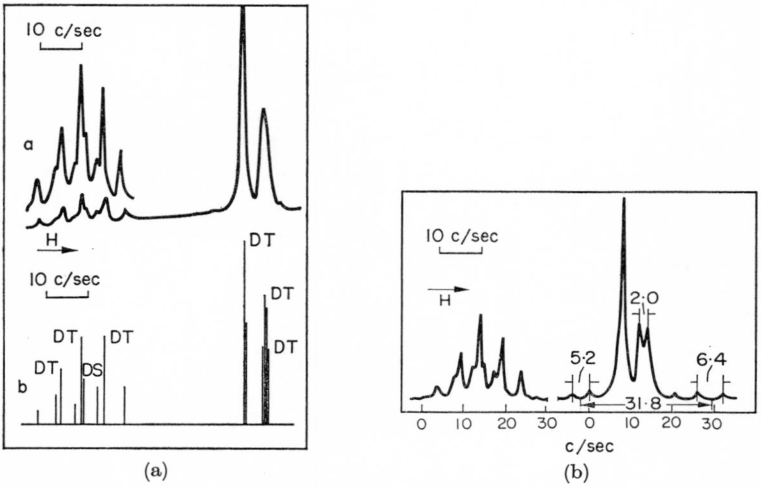

Fig. 83. Spectra of triacetin in different solvents, (*a*) in acetonitrile with calculated spectrum, $R = 0{\cdot}13$, (*b*) in chloroform solution.

When the 1,2,3-trichloropropane and triacetin are in solution in acetonitrile the n.m.r. spectrum can be fitted by an AB_4 approximation. With other solvents such as chloroform the approximation no longer holds.

The three groups of lines in triacetin at 4·7, 5·75 and 7·92 p.p.m. are readily assigned to the protons in the groupings H—C—O, H_2CO and H_3C—C=O respectively (Fig. 83). The line corresponding to the methyl protons is single, showing that these nuclei are equivalent. The spectra of the higher chain length triglycerides can also be interpreted approximately on the basis of first-order coupling (Fig. 84, Table 31).

The practical application of n.m.r. spectra to saturated triglycerides is facilitated by the built-in intensity reference system of the $2CH_2$ and one CH group of the glyceryl residue. Integrating devices for counting the number of groups are available and should be particularly useful (see page 203). The aceto group is particularly easy to pick out of the spectrum and n.m.r. spectroscopy should be particularly useful for the study of lipids containing this grouping.

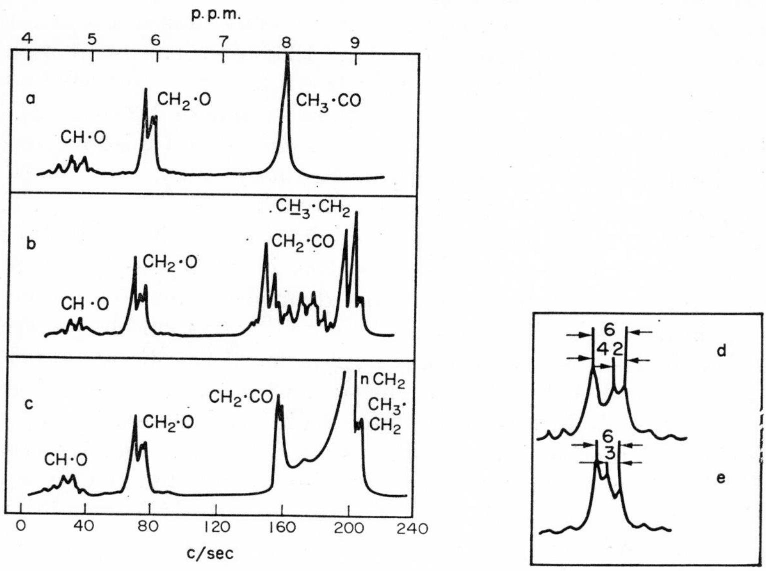

Fig. 84. Experimental spectra of (*a*) triacetin, (*b*) tributyrin, (*c*) tricaprin, (*d*) 1,2-dibutyro-3-palmitin, and (*e*) 1,3-dibutyro-2-palmitin (in chloroform).

Table 31. *Chemical shift and multiplicity for glycerides (tributyrin)*

Group	Chemical shift	Theoretical multiplicity (First-order)
$CH_2\mathbf{CH_3}$	9·05	Triplet
$CH_2\mathbf{CH_2}CH_3$	8·45	Quartet × Triplet
O—C—CH_2	7·75	Triplet
H_2C—O—C	5·77	Doublet
HC—O—C	4·75	Quintet

Diglycerides

With the diglycerides greater complexity of behaviour can arise compared with the triglycerides. This arises for the following reasons: (*a*) the introduction of the hydroxyl group means that unless exchange of this proton takes place so rapidly that its presence on the system can be ignored, coupling to it can take place from the protons in the glyceryl residue and a six-proton system is involved; (*b*) the effect of hydrogen bonding can vary the chemical shift value of the hydroxyl proton so that its position in the spectrum is uncertain; (*c*) acyl migration can occur with the diglycerides so that some of the 1,2-isomer is present with the 1,3-isomer. (Migration is particularly fast with the short chains and hence it is very difficult to prepare a pure sample of 1,3-diacetin. The particular sample examined certainly had some of the 1,2-isomer present making interpretation of the n.m.r. spectrum difficult).

The spectrum of 1,3-diacetin in chloroform is shown in Fig. 85a. There are only two groups of lines in the spectrum, a single line at 7·95 p.p.m. corresponding to the presence of the protons in the $H_3C—C$ group and a group of lines near 6·0 p.p.m. with the strongest line at 5·9 p.p.m. (At higher gain lines are observed near 5·0 p.p.m. corresponding to protons present in the H—C—O group of the 1,2-isomer.) Empirical data shows that the chemical shift value for the protons in the H—C—OH group will be rather close to that of the protons in the $H_2C—OC$ group, and hence that interaction between the protons will be large. We can see that the lines due to the protons of the H—C group and H_2C group are superimposed on top of each other. We also note that the chemical shift value for the H—C group is slightly greater than that for the CH_2 protons in contrast to the situation with triacetin. Attempts to fit the experimental spectrum with calculated AB_4 systems of ratio $R = 1·0$ and 2·0 were not successful although similar qualitative spectra were obtained. The experimental spectra of solutions in acetonitrile showed that shifts occurred but did not clarify the situation. It is, of course, not certain whether a crude AB_4 approximation would hold at these rather small chemical shift differences. An XB_2C_2 treatment is also not adequate because of the greater interactions of the five protons in the system and it appears that a much fuller theoretical treatment is required.

The spectra of a number of 1,3-diglycerides are also shown in Fig. 85a for chloroform solutions. In all cases the line due to the $H_2C—O—C$ groups is single and lacks the doublet structure present in the spectra of the triglycerides and we can appreciate that this is due to the small chemical shift difference of the protons on the glyceryl residue. A line near 7·0 p.p.m. is assigned to the proton of the hydroxyl group. This line can shift with concentration and with solvent and is not present in the spectrum given for the chloroform solution of diacetin.

The isomer 1,2-distearin has also been examined. The relative proportion of protons in the glyceryl residue compared with those in the long-chain (combined with limits on the concentration) hinder good resolution of the lines due to the glyceryl protons. With the 1,2-isomer the glyceryl residue contains protons in groupings H_2C—O—C, H_2C—OH and H—C—OC, and lines are observed to occur at 5·88, 6·27 and 4·95 p.p.m.

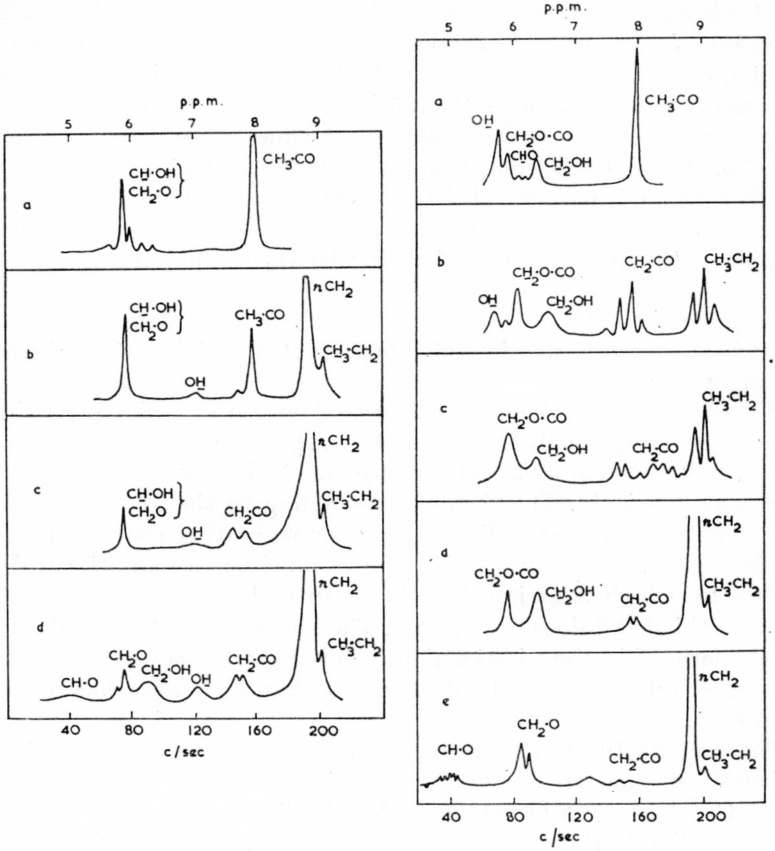

(a) (b)

Fig. 85*a*. Experimental spectra of (*a*) 1,3-diacetin, (*b*) 1-aceto-3-palmitin, (*c*) 1,3-distearin, and (*d*) 1,2-distearin (in chloroform).
Fig. 85*b*. Experimental spectra of (*a*) 1-monoacetin, (*b*) 1-monopropionin, (*c*) 1-monobutyrin, (*d*) 1-monostearin, and (*e*) 2-monostearin (in chloroform.)

Some sort of doublet structure is observed in the first of these lines, poorly resolved structure on the second and considerable multiplicity on the third line. The line at 4·95 p.p.m. is absent in the 1,3-isomers and may help to distinguish the two isomers. However, the high multiplicity makes this signal difficult to detect and may limit its usefulness. It probably consists of a sextet due to two overlapping triplets, but the resolution available is inadequate to be sure of this. The line near 6·4 p.p.m. is probably the best for distinguishing the 1,2- from the 1,3-isomers and for analysing the two in mixtures, with the lines near 4·95 p.p.m. providing additional confirmation. The diglyceride isolated from Vernonia seed oil has been readily identified by means of its n.m.r. spectrum as being the 1,3-isomer from the absence of a line at 6·3 p.p.m. The ratio of the intensities of the lines at 5·8–5·9 p.p.m. to that at 4·7 p.p.m. of 4·9:4, compared with the theoretical (5:4), shows that the diglyceride is mainly this isomer. (The line at 4·7 p.p.m. represents the four protons of the ethylenic groups, whilst the line at 5·9 p.p.m. represents the five protons of the CH_2CHCH_2 grouping.)

Monoglycerides

Many of the factors affecting the n.m.r. spectra of diglycerides also affect the monoglycerides.

With 1-monoglycerides three types of proton grouping occur in the glyceryl residue, namely the H_2C—O—C, H—C—O and H_2C—O groups. Lines are found near 5·95 and 6·39 p.p.m. which are assigned to the CH_2 groups respectively. The lines corresponding to the H—C—O proton appear between these two lines at 6·25 p.p.m. and are partly submerged by these lines. 1-Mono-acetin in chloroform shows an additional line at 5·8 p.p.m. which is assigned to the hydroxyl protons. In acetonitrile solution this band does not appear. The longer chain 1-monoglycerides are similar to this; the additional lines in the spectra can be satisfactorily accounted for on the basis of chemical shift and first-order coupling (Fig. 85b).

The 2-monoglycerides are distinguished from the 1-isomers by the presence of the H—C—O—C grouping and the absence of the H_2C—O—C group. Consistent with this, lines occur near 5·0 p.p.m. corresponding to the single proton and there are no lines at 5·95 p.p.m. The chemical shift difference between the H_2—C—O protons near 6·27 p.p.m. and the single proton at 5·0 p.p.m. is quite large, some 50 to 60 v/s, and hence the glyceryl residue gives lines corresponding to an AX_4 type of spectrum, i.e. a doublet occurs for the $2CH_2$ protons separated by some 5·1 c/s whilst the quintet splitting for the single protons has similar splitting. With 2-monostearin the concentration of the compound in solution in chloroform is such that it is difficult to measure anything other than the first three lines of the quintet. The type of spectrum obtained for the glyceryl residue can be compared with that observed with 2-acetoxy-1,3-dichloropropane. The absence of a line at

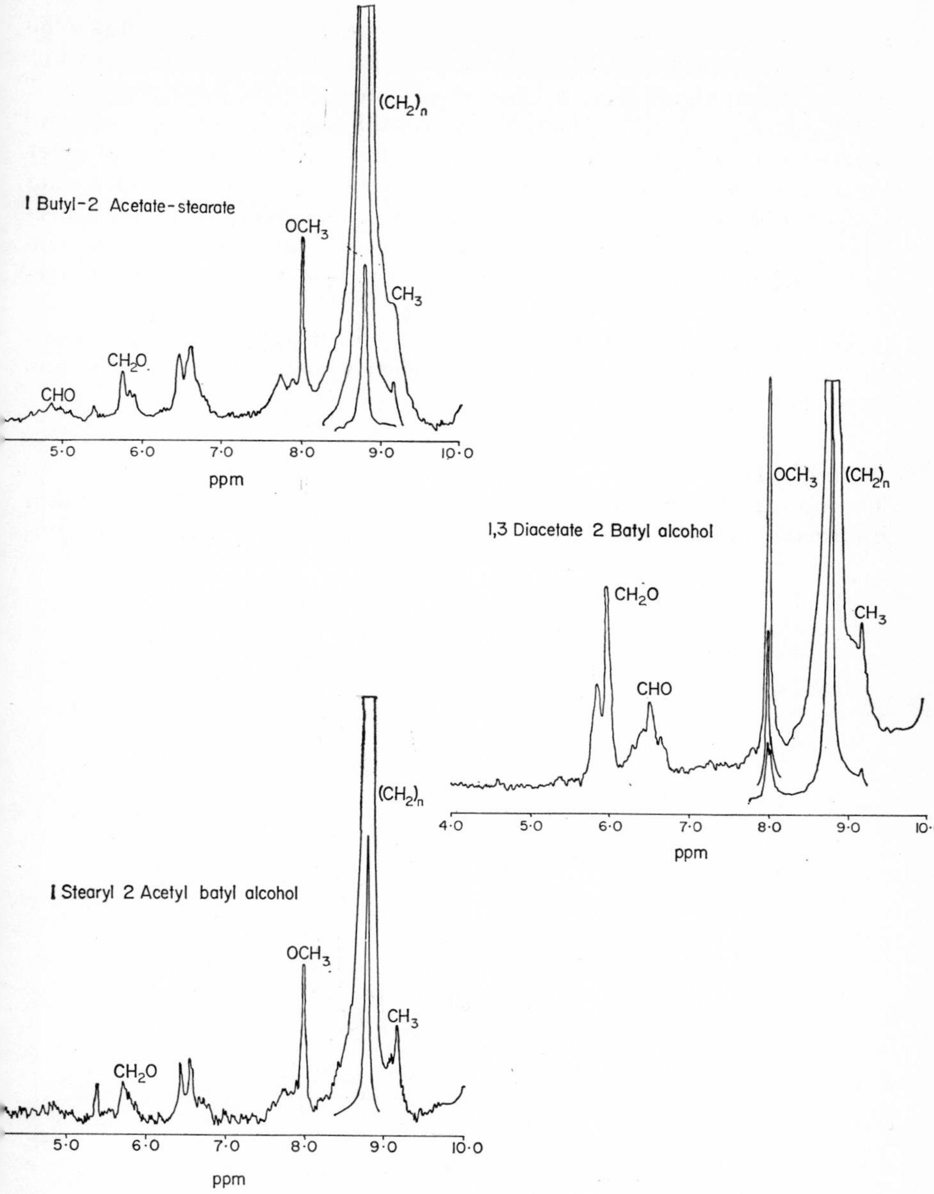

Fig. 86. N.M.R. spectra of some short-chain mixed-triglycerides.

5·95 p.p.m., along with the presence of lines near 5·0 p.p.m., appears to be the best method for distinguishing these isomers. The presence of unsaturated groupings may also give rise to lines near the latter region.

The identity of a new ethanolamine-containing lipid from egg yolk was arrived at by using n.m.r. data. The spectrum of the degradation product diacetate was compared with a number of model compounds, including 2-stearyl-diacetate, 1′-stearyl-1-2-diacetate, 1-octadecyl-glycerol-ether-diacetate and 2-octadecyl-glycerol-ether-diacetate and showed the degradation product to be identical with the 1-octadecyl-glycerol-ether-diacetate.

The n.m.r. spectra of some short-chain mixed triglycerides are shown in Fig. 86. The acetate groupings are clearly distinguished by the line from the OCH_3 group.

Natural oils

The n.m.r. spectra are useful for the study of natural oils to obtain information on the presence of free carboxyl, hydroxyl, 1,4-diene, con-

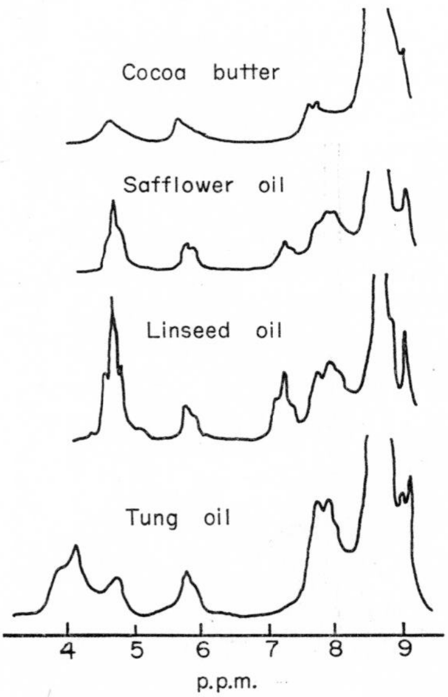

Fig. 87. N.M.R. spectra of glyceride oils.

jugated and isolated double bonds. Signals from the isolated double bonds overlap those of the glyceryl residue, but the latter can be removed by converting to the methyl esters. The presence of hydroxyl groups can be confirmed by acetylating the oil. A new signal is produced corresponding to the presence of an acetoxy group.

The spectrum of cocoa butter is shown in Fig. 87 and certain deductions can be made about the ratios of the amounts of saturated : monoene : diene fatty acids present. Thus the absence of a signal at 7·7 p.p.m. shows that there is little 1,4-diene present. It is assumed, therefore, that only saturated and monoenoic acids are present. The ratio of the area of lines at 4.7 p.p.m. to those at 5·8 p.p.m. would be 7 : 4 if the acids were entirely monoenoic (i.e. three molecules of monoenoic acid to one of glycerol). The contribution to the intensity of the lines at 4·7 p.p.m. is one-quarter of that of the intensity of the lines at 5·8 p.p.m. (one proton compared with four). By subtracting this intensity from the total intensity at 4·7 p.p.m. the contribution of the protons from the HC=CH group can be estimated. For entirely monoenoic acids the ratio of this to that at A would be 6 : 4. Measurements show the ratio to be 2·4 : 4. The ratio of mono-unsaturated acids to total acids is calculated to be $(2{\cdot}4/6) : 1 = 0{\cdot}4 : 1$ in the particular sample examined.

By including the signal at 7·2 p.p.m. due to the diene content, the ratios of saturated : monoene : diene in cottonseed and similar oils can, in principle, be calculated. Tung oil has also been examined and the proportion of conjugated acid present deduced by similar argument.

Using the areas of the signals produced by the glycerol moiety as an internal standard, careful intensity measurements of the n.m.r. spectrum, using an electronic integrator and a d.c. digital voltmeter, have been shown to be valuable for determining the number of olefinic protons and the total number of hydrogen atoms in natural oils [34]. From these determinations the average molecular weight can be calculated. This enables an iodine value to be calculated for the oil. The agreement

Table 32. *Comparison of iodine values*

Oil	n.m.r. values	Wijs iodine value
Coconut	10·5 ± 1·3	8·0–8·7
Olive	80·8 ± 0.9	83·0–85·3
Soybean	127·1 ± 1·6	125·0–136·1
Peanut	94·5 ± 0·6	95·0–97·2
Sunflower	135·0 ± 0·9	136·0–137·7
Whale	150·2 ± 1·0	149·0–151·6
Safflower seed	141·2 ± 1·0	140·0–143·5
Linseed	176·2 ± 1·2	179·0–181·0
Tung	225·2 ± 1·2	146·0–163·5

obtained between the n.m.r. and saponification values are shown to be quite good, whilst agreement with iodine values calculated by the Wijs method and the n.m.r. method are good except for tung oil, where it was thought that conjugated bonds introduce errors into the Wijs method. A comparison of the iodine values obtained by the two methods is shown in Table 32.

The time spent in obtaining the n.m.r. data is about 20 min for each sample, and the time for calculating the results can be made quite short.

PHOSPHOLIPIDS AND CHOLESTEROL ESTERS

As yet, no detailed study of the n.m.r. spectra of phospholipids has appeared, although use of the technique is occasionally mentioned. We

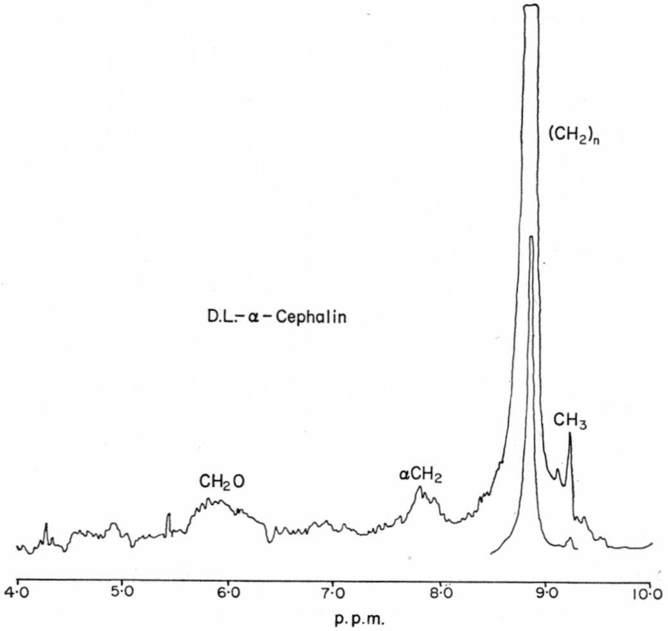

Fig. 88*a*. N.M.R. spectrum of a DL-α-cephalin.

might expect that with these molecules the spectra will be rather similar to those obtained with the glycerides, and usually they will be dominated by the signals from the fatty acids groups that are present. The spectra of a typical phosphatidyl ethanolamine and a lecithin are shown in Fig. 88 with tentative assignments. Studies of phospholipid molecules in water may be useful for providing information about the state of the long chains and the ionic groupings and for studying proton transfer reactions with the water.

The n.m.r. spectra of cholesterol and of one of its long-chain esters are shown in Fig. 89. The spectrum of the former shows a line at 6·8 p.p.m. due to the hydroxyl proton and at 9 p.p.m. due to the CH_1, CH_2 and CH_3 groups in the molecular skeleton. In the spectrum of the ester, the line due to the CH_2 groups of the chain rather dominates the spectrum.

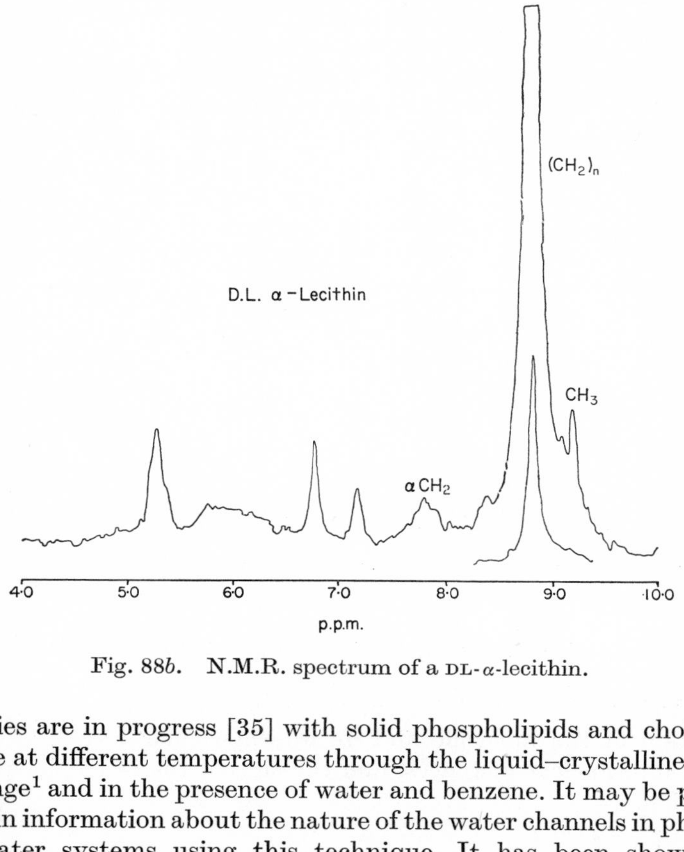

Fig. 88*b*. N.M.R. spectrum of a DL-α-lecithin.

Studies are in progress [35] with solid phospholipids and cholesterol stearate at different temperatures through the liquid–crystalline transition range[1] and in the presence of water and benzene. It may be possible to obtain information about the nature of the water channels in phospholipid–water systems using this technique. It has been shown that benzene in liquid–crystalline systems such as *p*-butoxybenzoic acid shows considerable structure in the n.m.r. spectrum [36]. This arises

[1] We expect that phospholipids will give, above the transition temperature to the liquid–crystalline phase, a line narrow enough to be observed by high resolution techniques. The extent of motion of the chains in this phase is pertinent to the degree of order of the hydrocarbon chains in biological membranes.

from the orienting effect produced by the magnetic field of the rod-like molecules of the liquid crystal and the resulting partial orientation of the benzene molecule. A splitting of lines extending over some 2000 c/s

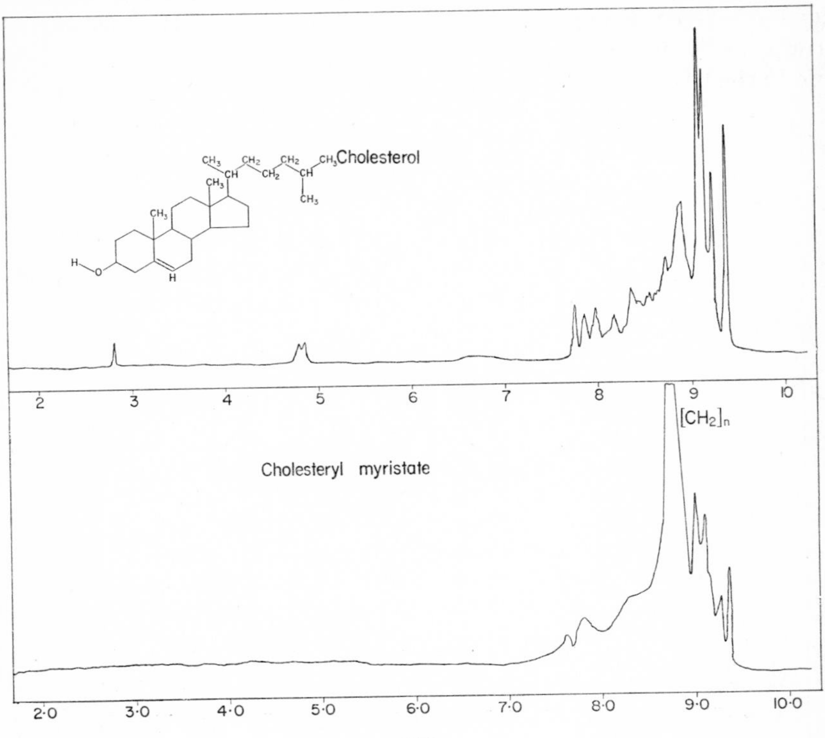

Fig. 89. N.M.R. spectra of cholesterol and cholesterol myristate.

occurs. Using this method, information can be obtained on the average orientation of the molecule and on intermolecular forces, as well as relative internuclear distances, and the sign of the isotropic spin–spin interaction.

REFERENCES

1. POPLE, J. A., SCHNEIDER, W. G. and BERNSTEIN, H. J. (1959) *High-resolution Nuclear Magnetic Resonance*. McGraw-Hill.
2. ANDREW, E. R. (1955) *Nuclear Magnetic Resonance*. Cambridge University Press.
3. JACKMAN, L. M. (1959) *Nuclear Magnetic Resonance*. Pergamon Press.

4. LUSZCZYNSKI, K., KAIL, J. A. E. and POWLES, J. G. (1960) *Proc. Phys. Soc.*, **75**, 243.
5a. POWLES, J. G. and NEALE, D. J. (1961) *Proc. Phys. Soc.*, **78**, 377.
5b. POWLES, J. G. and HARTLAND, A. (1960) *Proc. Phys. Soc.*, **75**, 617.
6. GUTOWSKY, H. S. and PAKE, G. E. (1950) *J. Chem. Phys.*, **18**, 162.
7. ANDREW, E. R. (1950) *J. Chem. Phys.*, **18**, 607.
8. ODAJIMA, A., SAUER, J. A. and WOODWARD, A. E. (1962) *J. Phys. Chem.*, **66**, 718.
9. POWLES, J. G. and KAIL, J. A. E. (1960) *Trans. Faraday Soc.*, **56**, 1.
10. GRANT, R. F. and DUNELL, B. A. (1960) *Canad. J. Chem.*, 359.
11. CHAPMAN, D., RICHARDS, R. E. and YORKE, R. W. (1960) *J. Chem. Soc.*, 436.
12. NAKAJIMA, H. (1961) *J. Phys. Soc. Japan*, **16**, 1778.
13. RUNYAN, W. R. and NOLLE, A. W. (1957) *J. Chem. Phys.*, **27**, 1081.
14. CHAPMAN, D., RICHARDS, R. E. and YORKE, R. W. (1959) *Nature*, **183**, 44.
15. CHAPMAN, D., RICHARDS, R. E. and YORKE, R. W. (1960) *J. Amer. Oil Chemists' Soc.*, **5**, 243.
16. CLIFFORD, J. (private communication).
17. DENIS, P., CSAKI, A., DELCO, M., SPRENGER, J., FERNANDEZ-MORAN, H. and RAWGLER, W. (1957) *Arch. Sci.*, **10**, 223.
18. TIERS, G. V. D. (1958) *J. Phys. Chem.*, **62**, 1151.
19. CHAMBERLAIN, N. F. (1959) *Analyt. Chem.*, **31**, 56.
20a. JACKMAN, L. M. and WILEY, R. H. (1960) *J. Chem. Soc.*, 2881.
20b. JACKMAN, L. M. and WILEY, R. H. (1960) *J. Chem. Soc.*, 2886.
21. MCCONNELL, H. M., MCLEAN, A. D. and REILLY, C. A. (1955) *J. Chem. Phys.*, **23**, 1152.
22. BERNSTEIN, H. J., POPLE, J. A. and SCHNEIDER, W. G. (1957) *Canad. J. Chem.*, **35**, 65.
23. RICHARDS, R. E. and SCHNEIDER, T. (1958) *Mol. Phys.*, **1**, 331.
24. CHAPMAN, D. (1963) *J. Chem. Soc.*, 131.
25. COHN, M. (1963) *Biochem. J.*, **2**, 623.
26. CALLIS, C. F., VAN WAZER, J. R., SHOOLERY, J. N. and ANDERSON, W. A. (1957) *J. Amer. Chem. Soc.*, **79**, 2719.
27. LAUTERBUR, P. C. (1958) *Ann. N.Y. Acad. Sci.*, **70**, 841.
28. LAUTERBUR, P. C. (1963) *J. Chem. Phys.*, **38**, 1406.
29. HOPKINS, C. Y. and BERNSTEIN, H. J. (1959) *Canad. J. Chem.*, **37**, 775.
30. HOPKINS, C. Y. (1961) *J. Amer. Oil Chemists' Soc.*, **38**, 664.
31. NUNN, J. R. (1952) *J. Chem. Soc.*, 313.
32. VERMA, J. P., NATH, B. and AGGARWAL, J. S. (1955) *Nature*, **175**, 84.
33. DIJKSTRA, G. and DUIN, H. J. (1955) *Nature*, **176**, 71.
34. JOHNSON, L. F. and SHOOLERY, J. N. (1962) *Analyt. Chem.*, **34**, 1136.
35. CHAPMAN, D. and SALSBURY, N. J. (1964) (in progress).
36. SAUPE, A. and ENGLERT, G. (1963) *Phys. Rev. Lett.*, **11**, 462.

7. Electron-spin resonance spectroscopy

Little application of electron-spin resonance spectroscopy has been made to the field of large lipids. However, as more instruments become available it is expected that a considerable variety of applications will emerge, e.g. studies of X-ray and γ-irradiation of lipids, and their autoxidation and pyrolysis.

Theoretical considerations

The basic principles of electron-spin resonance [1] are similar to those of nuclear-magnetic resonance spectroscopy. However, resonance is only observed with substances which contain unpaired electrons. The technique is therefore applicable to lipid systems where radicals occur. If the material containing the unpaired electron is placed in a magnetic field the unpaired electrons can orient themselves to the direction of the field. This is because the electron has an intrinsic angular momentum called its spin, which has a value of one-half quantum unit. The spin can have two values, $+\frac{1}{2}$ and $-\frac{1}{2}$, representing the fact that the spin can be in either of two opposite senses. The spins are referred to as an α spin and a β spin. Because of its spin the electron has a magnetic dipole moment. When there is no external magnetic field the free electron has no preference for an α or β spin as they are of equal energy. However, when a magnetic field is applied the electron has lower energy if its spin magnetic moment is aligned so as to be parallel to the applied field, rather than anti-parallel. Thus two energy levels are available, their separation being proportional to the product of a constant β (the Bohr magneton) and the strength of the field H. The proportionality constant is referred to as the g-value. When the electron is irradiated with electromagnetic radiation possessing energy with a quantum value $h\nu$ equal to the separation between the two energy levels, the electron will absorb energy. This absorption of energy enables the electron to flip over to a state in which its spin magnetic moment is aligned anti-parallel to the magnetic field. The resonance conditions is represented by the equation $h\nu = g\beta H$. The change in the spin is governed by the selection rule that it must be increased or decreased by unity. ($\Delta M_s = \pm 1$.) As with nuclear resonance, electron resonance can be produced by varying either the magnetic field or the frequency. In practice it is convenient to fix the frequency and to change the field. Absorption spectra represent absorption plotted against magnetic field and are usually presented as derivative spectra.

The free electron has the g value 2·0023. This is the value usually found with organic free radicals. The hydrogen atom, the simplest free radical, introduces a further possibility. The proton nucleus itself possesses a spin of $\frac{1}{2}$, with a resulting magnetic moment, and it prefers to align this magnetic moment parallel, rather than anti-parallel, to the electron-spin magnetic moment. Since there are two ways of aligning the electron-

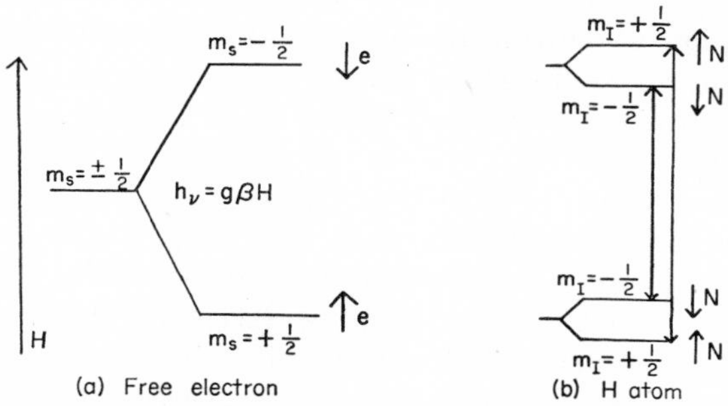

Fig. 90. Energy levels in the magnetic field (*a*) free electron, (*b*) in hydrogen atom.

spin magnetic moment in an external magnetic field, there are four possible arrangements (Fig. 90).

The nuclear spin, M_I, can have a value of $\pm\frac{1}{2}$; two of the four possible transitions involve no change of M_I, and two of them involve a change of unity. In fact, the selection rule is that there shall be no change in M_I, so that only two absorption lines are observed. The resonance spectrum of the hydrogen atom has been observed by several different workers, and the splitting between the lines, the so-called 'nuclear hyperfine splitting', corresponds to a field change of 500 gauss.

In general, in a system where the unpaired electron can interact with n-equivalent protons, there are $n+1$ hyperfine lines with a binomial distribution of relative intensities. We shall see examples of this later. It has been shown that this hyperfine splitting a_H due to a ring proton is directionally proportional to ρ at the neighbouring carbon atom, i.e. $a_H = Q\rho$ where Q is a constant about 25 gauss (ρ-electron density).

In solution the anisotropy of the hyperfine structure and of the g-value usually disappears because of the rapid movement of the molecule. This is not the case with free radicals in the solid state.

Experimental techniques

A typical magnetic field used in the electron-spin resonance spectrometers is about 3000 gauss and the frequency of about 9000 Mc/s in the microwave region is used to induce electron resonance. The radiation is supplied by a Klystron and is led through a wave guide to a resonance cavity which contains the specimen. When energy is absorbed it is detected by a crystal, amplified, and displayed on an oscilloscope or a pen recorder. The cavities are constructed so as to permit temperature variation and at the same time irradiation by light. A number of commercial ESR spectrometers are now available.

Electron-spin resonance can readily be studied with radicals either in solution or in the solid material. Flow techniques have now been developed to obtain the spectra of short-lived radicals.

Applications

FREE RADICALS IN SOLIDS

Aliphatic radicals are usually too reactive to be studied in solution and until recently have therefore been investigated mainly in the solid phase [2, 3, 4]. A common way of producing these radicals is by irradiation of the parent compound at low temperatures with ultraviolet rays, X-rays, gamma rays or high-voltage electrons. Fragments of molecules are formed and prevented from further reaction so that relatively large concentrations of radicals can be obtained. The γ-irradiation of frozen paraffins and olefins have given rise to electron-spin resonance spectra and a number of alkyl radicals.

Free radicals have also been formed in the gaseous phase and trapped on a sapphire rod, cooled in liquid helium. When enough radicals have been trapped in the inert matrix material the rod is removed and placed in the cavity of an electron-spin resonance spectrometer [5]. In another method for producing radicals, layers of alkyl radicals are formed on top of one another by subliming alternately alkyl halide and sodium metal on to a suitably cooled surface [6]. Free radicals have also been produced with alcohols by hydrogen extraction [7]. The mixture of alcohol and a little hydrogen peroxide is frozen, transferred to the cavity of an electron-spin resonance spectrometer and irradiated with ultraviolet radiation. Hydroxyl radicals are initially produced and they diffuse and react, producing secondary radicals. Isopropanol, with this technique gives a spectrum containing seven lines associated with six equivalent hydrogen atoms of the radical $\cdot C(CH_3)_2OH$.

When the radicals are randomly oriented it is difficult to interpret the ESR spectra because of the anisotropy of the proton hyperfine structure. Studies of this type have, however, been made on simple alcohols and carboxylic acids [8, 9]. Irradiated acetic acid gives a spectrum consisting of a doublet of 25 gauss separation and lines of fairly broad width. It is

Table 32. *α Hydrogens*

(i.e. hydrogen attached to free radical carbon; sometimes called σ hydrogens)

Radical	Isotropic Mc/s	Anisotropic Mc/s
$\dot{C}H_3$	−65·07	
	−64·64	
	−64·39	
	−68	
$CH_3\dot{C}H_2$	−63	
$\dot{C}H_2OH$	−53	
$\dot{C}H_2COOH$	−59	+29+3−32
	−63	+26+4−29
$\dot{C}H(COOH)_2$	−60	+31−1−31
$(COOH)\dot{C}HCH_2CH_2COOH$	−56	+30+3−32
	−51	+28−1−28
$(COOH)\dot{C}HCH_2CH_2CH_2COOH$	−57	+29+7−37
$(HO)\dot{C}HCOOH$	−57	+27+2−29
$(HO)\dot{C}HCO_2^-$	−51	+28+1−29
	−50	+27+3−29
	−54	+27+3−31
$CH_3\dot{C}HCOOH$	−55	+30+5−34
$—CH_2—\dot{C}H—CH_2—$	*c.* −70	

suggested that the doublet arises from a direct dipole–dipole interaction between an electron localized on the hydroxyl oxygen and the hydroxyl proton. Various spectral changes occur on heating which are interpreted in terms of a radical CH_3CO_2 and later formation of $(CH_2CO)^+$. Similar effects are observed with irradiated formic acid [9]. Irradiated polyenes

[10] have been studied and some triglycerides [11]. Tristearin appears to form different radicals, depending on the temperature of irradiation. Oxygen was found to affect the free radical decay rates.

The study of single crystals are much more informative and there are now a number of examples of this. A typical example is the γ-irradiation of a single crystal of succinic acid. This removes a hydrogen atom and forms the radical $(CO_2H)CH_2\dot{C}H(CO_2H)$. The ESR spectrum shows hyperfine lines from the CH and CH_2 protons. The separation between the lines varies with the orientation of the magnetic field with respect to the crystal. In Table 32 are presented data on some aliphatic radicals taken from a recent compilation of Whiffen [12] of hyperfine coupling constants. Some g anisotropic values are given in Table 33.

Table 33. *g-factors*

(only where three principal values are known)

Radical	Principal values		
$H\dot{C}(COOH)_2$	2·0035	2·0033	2·0026
$(COOH)CH_2\dot{C}HCOOH$	2·0045	2·0026	2·0019
$HO\dot{C}HCOOH$	2·0053	2·0038	2·0017
$HO\dot{C}HCO_2^-$	2·0054	2·0039	2·0021
	2·0051	2·0039	2·0021
	2·0043	2·0041	2·0021
$(CH_3)_2\dot{C}COOH$	2·0034	2·0030	2·0022

The hyperfine coupling constants and g values are second rank tensors and can be characterized by their three principal components. The isotropic coupling is the arithmetic mean of the principal components and the anisotropic contributions are the deviations of the principal components from the mean, hence their algebraic sum should be zero.

The hyperfine coupling tensors of α-hydrogen atoms have a large and fairly constant anisotropic contribution and the average isotropic coupling is about -60 Mc/s. The isotropic coupling for β-hydrogen atoms varies from about 10 to 120 Mc/s. The anisotropy is of the order of 2–10 Mc/s so α- and β-hydrogens can be distinguished by examining the single crystal spectra.

As yet no studies have been reported for radicals obtained with phospholipids. Information about such radicals and their behaviour and stability as the temperature is varied may be useful for providing information about the effect of γ-irradiation on cell membranes.

FREE RADICALS IN SOLUTION

The main disadvantage of the solid-state studies is that the radicals formed are aligned at random so that anisotropic coupling broadens the lines and makes interpretation difficult. Solution studies or the study of single crystals enable one to overcome these difficulties. Aliphatic radicals have been observed in solution such as the ketyl radicals [13] and the ethyl radical formed by irradiation of liquid ethane with electrons [14]. In general, however, irradiation of solutions does not provide a practicable method for studying the radicals because they are generated comparatively slowly and are usually too short-lived to reach a large steady concentration. Recently a method has been described which generates radicals by a fast reaction using a flow system in which the radicals can be observed less than 0·022 sec after mixing the reactants [15]. The flow system consists of two concentric tubes carrying the reactant solutions. The inner one has four small holes at its end, through which the inner solution is forced into the outer one perpendicular to the direction of flow. The maximum flow rate is 5 ml/sec. The reacting mixture enters the flattened section of an aqueous solution cell in the spectrometer within 0·02 sec. A method found to be particularly useful has been one which uses the reaction of titanous ions with hydrogen peroxide in acidic solution. By itself the titanous ion does not give a detectable signal, but on reaction gives a sharp line. It is considered that the radicals are hydroxyl and perhydroxyl, produced by the reactions:

$$\begin{aligned} Ti^{3+} + H_2O_2 &\rightarrow Ti^{4+} + \cdot OH + OH^- \\ \cdot OH + H_2O_2 &\rightarrow H_2O + \cdot O_2H \end{aligned} \tag{7.1}$$

The main contribution to the signal is suggested to arise from the hydroxyl radical. The titanous ion and *t*-butyl hydroperoxide gives a quartet (1:3:3:1) coupling constant 22 gauss characteristic of the methyl radical, consistent with the formation of the *t*-butoxyl radical which is known to break down to methyl. When aliphatic materials are added to the reactants a new spectrum is obtained arising from the organic radicals. Thus methanol gives rise to a triplet each of whose lines is apparently an incompletely resolved doublet. This is suggested to arise from the $\cdot CH_2OH$ radical in which there is coupling with the two protons on the carbon and possibly very weak coupling with the proton on the oxygen. Ethanol gives two quartets corresponding to $CH_3CH(OH)\cdot$ in which the stronger coupling occurs with the three

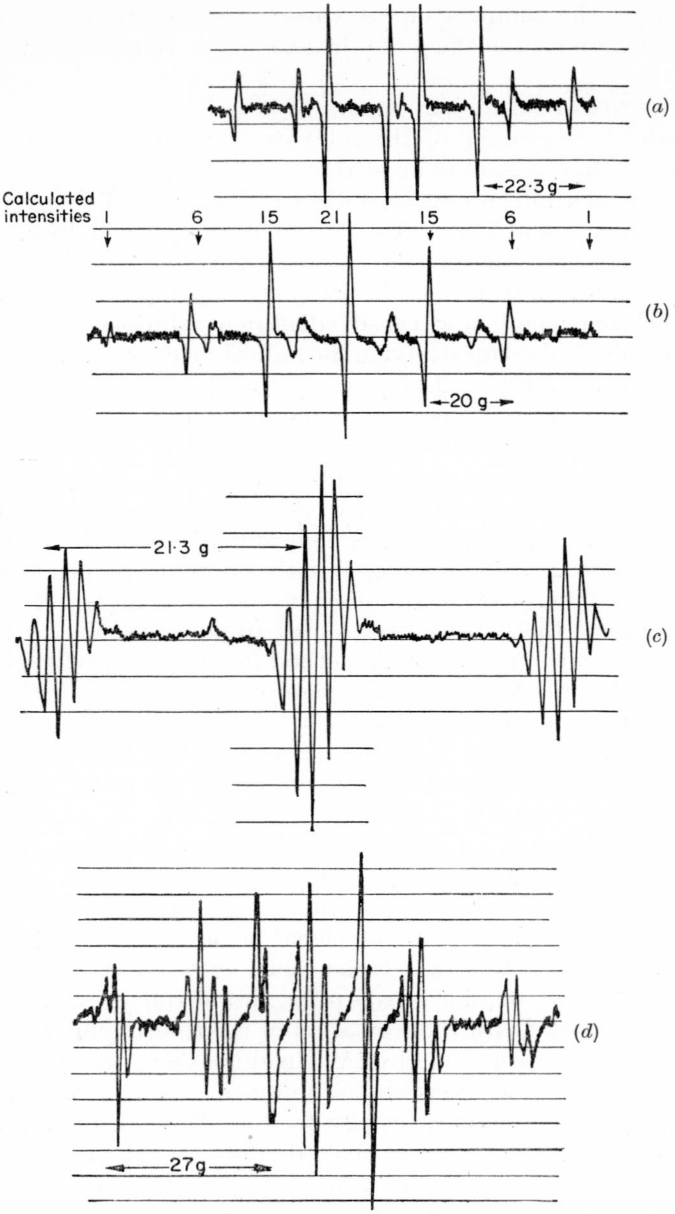

Fig. 91. (*a*) Spectrum from ethanol. (*b*) Spectrum from isopropanol. (*c*) Spectrum from t-butanol. (*d*) Spectrum from glycerol. (Dixon, W. T. and Norman, R. O. C. *J. Chem. Soc.*, 3119, 1963.)

equivalent protons (Fig. 91a). Isopropanol gives seven lines corresponding to the radical $(CH_3CH_3)C(OH\cdot)$ (Fig. 91b). This is formed by extraction of the α-hydrogen. A weak quartet which is also present is associated with a radical formed by abstraction of a β-hydrogen. Glycol and propane 1:2 diol gave ill-defined lines suggested to arise from the super-position of several spectra. In both cases the main spectrum appears to be a triplet 1:2:1 with coupling constants in the region of 18 gauss. This may arise from the $\cdot CH_2OH$ radical. Pentaerythrytol gives a simple spectrum, just a doublet, whilst pinacol gives a triplet. Propargyl alcohol gives four lines of equal intensity, each of which is itself a doublet. This is associated with the radical $CH{\equiv}C\cdot CH(OH)\cdot \leftrightarrow \cdot CH{=}C{=}CH\cdot OH$ in which the principal coupling occurs with the two protons on carbon and the smallest coupling arises from the proton on oxygen. Glycerol gives a complex spectrum which has not yet been analysed (Fig. 91).

In general the hydroxyl radical abstracts a hydrogen atom from the aliphatic alcohols, α-CH being rather more reactive than β-CH. Unsaturated alcohols, on the other hand, can undergo either addition or abstraction, dependent on their structure. Coupling of the unpaired electron in the radical is strong with respect to the protons on the carbon atoms next to the one which bears the unpaired electron. The extent of the coupling is dependent on the nature of the adjacent groups. Coupling with protons on oxygen are usually rather weak and coupling with protons on carbon atoms two away from the one on which the electron resides is also usually small.

Similar studies have been carried out with carboxylic acids [16]. Acetic acid gives rise to a triplet associated with a $\cdot CH_2COOH$ radical (Fig. 92). The splitting constant is 20·5 gauss. A quartet, attributed to the methyl radical, is also present. Formic acid gives rise to a single line which is associated with the $\cdot COOH$ radical. The $HCOO\cdot$ radical is also a possibility. Propionic acid gives a mixture of signals but nine lines have been assigned to the $\cdot CH_2CH_2COOH$ radical (Fig. 93). Succinic acid gives a spectrum which has not yet been analysed and is associated with a mixture of radicals. Glycolic acid gives a pair of doublets associated with the $\cdot CHOHCOOH$ radical. Lactic acid gives a quartet of doublets associated with the $CH_3\dot{C}OHCOOH$ radical. Other acids which have been examined include oleic, fumaric, crotonic, acrylic and halogenated acids.

Aldehydes such as formaldehyde have also been examined. Formaldehyde gives a mixture of radicals, in particular a triplet of doublets associated with the $\cdot CH_2OH$ radical. Acetaldehyde gives a spectrum containing a double quartet associated with the CH_3COOH radical. Radicals have also been observed with meso-inositol. This gives a well-defined spectrum with a mixture of a triplet and two doublets. The two spectra are thought to arise from hydrogen abstraction from two different sides of the ring. Table 34 shows some of the coupling constants observed in this work.

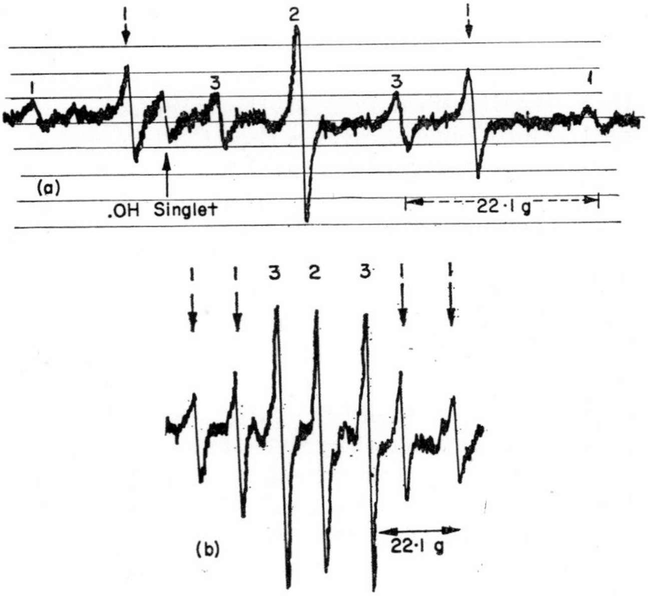

Fig. 92. E.S.R. spectrum obtained with acetic acid. (*a*) $Ti^{3+} + H_2O_2 +$ acetic acid. (*b*) Ti^{3+} + peracetic + acetic acids. (Dixon, W. T. D.Phil. Thesis, Oxford, 1963.)

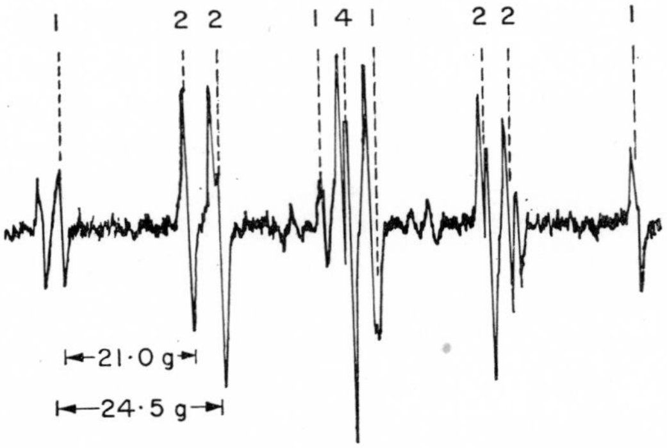

Fig. 93. E.S.R. spectrum from propionic acid. (Dixon, W. T. D.Phil. Thesis, Oxford, 1963.)

Table 34. *Coupling constants of various radicals*

Radical type	Splitting constants (gauss)	Source	Radical type and splitting constants (gauss)	Source
$\cdot CH_3$	23·1	(Ti^3 + peracetic)	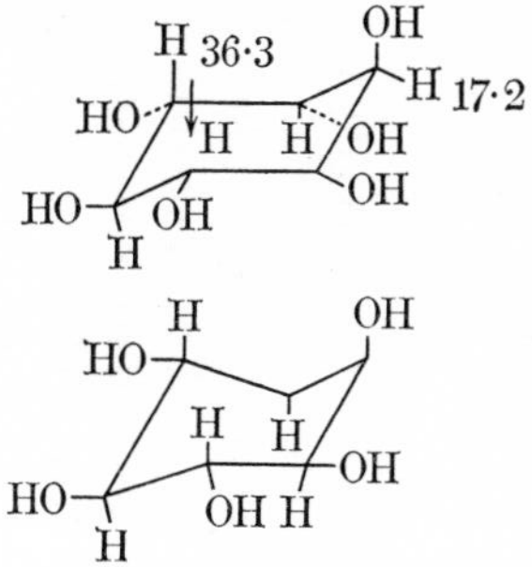	Meso-inositol
$\cdot CH_2OH$	17·2	Methanol		
$\cdot CH_2COOH$	21·8	Acetic/malonic acid		
$\cdot CH_2COCH_3$	20·3	Acetone		
$CH_3\dot{C}HOH$	22·0, 15·0	Ethanol		
$(CH_3)_2\dot{C}OH$	20·0	*i*-Propanol		
$CH_3\dot{C}HOC_3H_5$	13·8, 21·9	Ether		
$\cdot CH_2C(CH_3)_2OH$	21·3, 1·3	*t*-Butanol		
$COOH—CHOH—\dot{C}OH—COOH$	3·9, 1·6	Tartaric acid	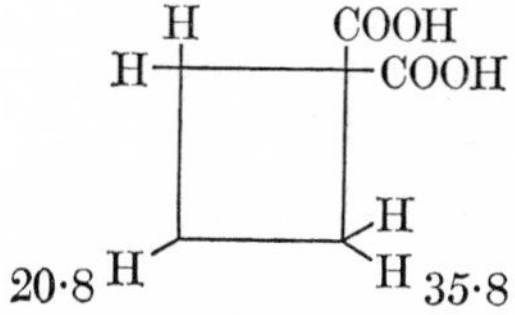	Cyclobutane-1,1-dicarboxylic acid
$CH_3\dot{C}(OH)COOH$	17·1, 2·0	Lactic acid		
$\cdot CH(OH)COOH$	17·8, 2·6	Glycollic acid		
$HO_2CCH_2\dot{C}(OH)COOH$	10·0, 2·0	Malic acid		
$HO_2\dot{C}CHCH(OH)COOH$	21·1, 12·7	Maleic/fumaric acids	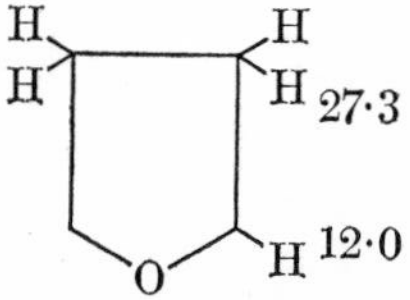	Tetrahydrofuran
$\cdot CHClCOOH$	20·9, 3·8	Chloroacetic acid		
$CH_3\dot{C}ClCOOH$	20·9	α-Chloropropionic		
$\cdot CH_2CH_2CH_2NH_2$	22·5, 26·9	*n*-Propylamine		

AUTOXIDATION STUDIES

Experiments have been reported on the irradiation of alkyl hydroperoxides [17] which are of interest for autoxidation studies with lipids. The basic instrument was a Varian V-4500 EPR Spectrometer with associated 6-in electromagnet. The spectrometer was provided with 100 kc field modulation (instead of the lower audio frequencies), allowing a factor of 16 improvement in sensitivity. In the case of the steady-state intermediates for the *n*-butyl hydroperoxide, at least, observation and identification would have been impossible without this enhancement in basic sensitivity.

A specially designed 'multi-purpose' sample cavity was also provided, with a screen of open gridwork at the end to permit *in situ* ultraviolet irradiation. A single all-quartz 11-mm OD Dewar insert was fitted through sample ports in the cavity, and connected in turn to a simple heat-exchanger system capable of temperature variation over the range, liquid nitrogen to over +300° C. Dry nitrogen gas passes through a copper heat-exchanger coil immersed in a flask of liquid nitrogen, through a Vycor transfer tube with built-in heater to the quartz Dewar insert in the cavity.

The photochemical decomposition of primary, secondary and tertiary butyl hydroperoxide was studied by photolysing the pure liquids at a variety of temperatures and the rate of formation and rate of decay of the free radical intermediates examined. A simple G.E. medium-pressure mercury lamp was used as the ultraviolet source, and the ultraviolet radiation focused on the cavity slots by means of an aluminized parabolic mirror. Rapid decay rates were measured with a graphic recorder.

The EPR spectra of the steady-state free radicals produced in the photolysis of *n*-butyl, *sec*-butyl and *t*-butyl hydroperoxide are shown in Fig. 94. These spectra are interpreted from the hyperfine pattern observed together with a consideration of the possible free radicals that could be formed in the dissociation.

From simple bond-energy considerations it was expected that the photo-induced dissociation would take place at the O—O bond, yielding the alkoxy and hydroxy radicals. Formation of alkyl R• and HO_2• radicals by rupture at the C—O bond is also a possibility whilst the production of peroxy ROO• and hydrogen radicals is also possible.

The experiments showed that the steady-state radicals are alkoxy radicals RO•. A triplet is observed with a hyperfine coupling of 3·5 gauss for the *n*-butyl case, a doublet of 2·8 gauss for the *sec*-butyl, and a single line for the tertiary. The unpaired electron density at the α- and β-carbon atoms are attenuated by the oxygen and are therefore reduced at the α-carbon atom and negligible at the β-carbon atom. A resonance for the hydroxy radical, which would have been produced simultaneously with the alkoxy is not observed. The lifetime of the hydroxy radical is probably far too short for any signal to be detected at the temperatures at which these experiments were conducted.

In order to decrease the decay rate of the *n*-butoxy radicals sufficiently to create an observable steady-state concentration, temperatures of

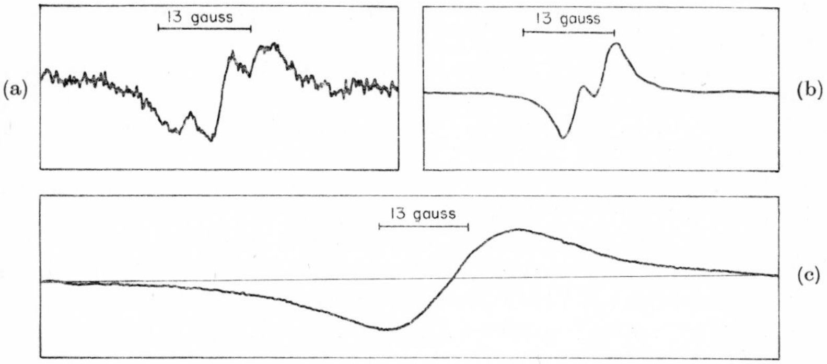

Fig. 94. E.S.R. spectra of *n*-butyl-, sec-butyl-, tertiary-butyl-hydroperoxide respectively after photolysis. (Piette, L. H. and Landgraf, W. C. Varian report.)

about 175°K were used. The *sec*-butoxy radicals require temperatures below 230°K; *t*-butoxy radicals require a temperature under 273°K. These steady-state temperatures reflect the decreased order of reactivity of these particular radicals towards recombination – i.e.

$$n\text{-butoxy} \gg sec\text{-butoxy} \gg t\text{-butoxy}.$$

By measuring the time rate of decay of the signals when the ultraviolet lamp is switched off, rate studies of the decay process can be made on the three free radicals. The decay curves were found to fit a second-order dependence. Rate constants of approximately 10^5 l/m sec were obtained for the recombination of two alkoxy radicals.

In addition to obtaining rate data on the free radical decay process, activation energies can also be obtained by measuring the rate constants at various temperatures. The activation energies of these free radical recombinations are approximately 4 kcal.

STUDIES OF PYROLYSIS

Large concentrations of radicals are trapped in organic materials when they are charred, and have been studied by ESR spectroscopy [18]. With carbon samples no resolved hyperfine structure is observed and the g-values are close to 2·00. Interesting studies of the effects of pyrolysis should be possible with many lipid systems.

REFERENCES

1. INGRAM, D. J. E. (1958) *Free Radicals*. Butterworth, London.
2. AYSCOUGH, P. B. and THOMPSON, C. (1962) *Trans. Faraday Soc.*, **58**, 1477.
3. HORSFIELD, A. and MORTON, J. R. (1962) *Trans. Faraday Soc.*, **58**, 470.
4. INGRAM, D. J. E., HODGSON, W. G., PARKES, C. A. and REES, W. T. (1955) *Nature*, **176**, 1227.
5. JEN, C. K., FOUER, S. N., COCHRAN, E. L. and BOWERS, V. A. (1958) *Phys. Rev.*, **112**, 1169.
6. BENNETT, J. E. and THOMAS, A. (1962) *Nature*, **195**, 995.
7. GIBSON, J. F., INGRAM, D. J. E., SYMONS, M. C. R. and TOWNSEND, M. G. (1957) *Trans. Faraday Soc.*, **53**, 914.
8. GORDY, W., ARD, W. B. and SHIELDS, H. (1955) *Proc. Nat. Acad. Sci. U.S.A.*, **41**, 983.
9. GORDY, W., ARD, W. B. and SHIELDS, H. (1955) *Proc. Nat. Acad. Sci. U.S.A.*, **41**, 966.
10. HELLER, C. and MCCONNELL, H. M. (1960) *J. Chem. Phys.*, **32**, 1535.
11. TRUBY, F. K. (1955) U.S. South West Research Institute.
12. WHIFFEN, D. H. (1961) National Physical Laboratory Report, March.
13. HIROTA, N. and WEISSMAN, S. I. (1960) *J. Amer. Chem. Soc.*, **82**, 4424.
14. MERZ, J. H. and WATERS, W. A. (1949) *J. Chem. Soc.*, 2427.
15. DIXON, W. T. and NORMAN, R. O. C. (1963) *J. Chem. Soc.*, 3119.
16. DIXON, W. T. (1963) D.Phil. Thesis, Oxford.
17. PIETTE, L. H. and LANDGRAF, W. C. Varian Report.
18. INGRAM, D. J. E. and BENNETT, J. E. (1954) *Phil. Mag.*, **45**, 545.

8. X-ray diffraction studies

The crystallographic behaviour of lipids is particularly interesting in its variety and complexity. The use of X-ray techniques have been most valuable in elucidating their structure and behaviour. The manner of arrangement of the molecules, their multiple melting phenomena, phase behaviour and the characterization and identification of individual molecules have all been furthered by X-ray powder and single-crystal studies. Whilst most of the work on lipids has been carried out using the powder technique, the speed of modern computing techniques has helped to increase the number of more informative single-crystal studies. As well as providing valuable information about the chain packing of individual lipids the technique has also been of value in the study of lipid–water systems and of natural lipoprotein systems, such as myelin.

Theoretical considerations

The application of X-ray electromagnetic radiation to solids arises from the fact that most solids are crystalline and the ordered arrangement of the atoms or molecules in the crystal causes them to behave as a three-dimensional diffraction grating [1]. The wavelengths of the electromagnetic radiation required for these diffraction effects are of the same order as the interatomic distance from 1 to 4 Å.

The particular feature of a crystal is that the atoms or molecules are arranged in such a way as to repeat a pattern in three dimensions. The distance at which the repetition occurs is termed the identity period. In a three-dimensional structure three non-coplanar directions together with the identity periods describe the periodicity of the structure. The *lattice* is the mathematical term expressing the mode of repetition producing the structure and a set of identity periods along three non-coplanar directions is sufficient to define a lattice. A space lattice, defined by the choice of three co-ordinate axes, is divided into a set of identical parallelepipeds. The repetitive action of the lattice translational elements on one of these parallelepipeds generates the whole lattice. Such a parallelepiped is called the *unit cell* of the lattice. By varying the choice of axes to describe the lattice, there is an infinite choice of unit cells.

In a three-dimensional infinite lattice it can be shown that a plane passing through three non-colinear lattice points passes through an infinite number of lattice points. These planes are termed rational. The action of lattice translations on a rational plane is to generate a family of parallel planes. The perpendicular distance d between successive planes is a particularly convenient single parameter. It is these interplanar spacings which are determined directly by X-ray powder photography. To describe these planes numerically and to express its angular relation to the axes of a unit cell of the lattice, Miller indices are used; (h, k, l). A plane having these particular values makes intercepts on the axes proportional to a/h, b/k, c/l.

If we allow monochromatic X-rays to pass through a crystal, each atom scatters a very small fraction of the incident wave and each becomes an emitter of secondary wavelets similar to the elements of the wave front in the Huygens construction for the propagation of light waves. The scattered wavelets reinforce in a given direction only if they are in phase.

Thus, if parallel radiation incident at a glancing angle θ is reflected at the same angle from successive planes $P_1 P_2$ which are distance d apart, the retardation between the two beams is $2d\sin\theta$. If $2d\sin\theta = n\lambda$ where n is an integer there will be reinforcement for wavelength λ in the direction θ whilst in all other directions there will be destructive interference. This equation is known as Bragg's law. For a specific wavelength, the directions in which diffraction is possible are determined by the interplanar spacings d of the rational planes. These are a property of the lattice and not of the distribution of the diffracting material within the unit cell.

The diffracted waves from different points within a unit cell differ in phase by an amount which is a function of their relative co-ordinates and the direction of diffraction. The amplitude of the total diffracted beams, therefore, depend upon the arrangement of the atoms within the unit cell. When the amplitudes are added, one obtains the structure factor F_{hkl} which is related to the total number of atoms within the unit cell, the relative phase of the radiation scattered by each atom and the scattering power of each atom f.

$$F_{hkl} = \sum_{n=1}^{N} f_n \exp\{2\pi i(hx_n + ky_n + lz_n)\} \tag{8.1}$$

A useful method for enabling a complete description of the X-ray diffraction properties of the crystal lattice is to use the reciprocal lattice. This is constructed by marking points distance $K(1/d)$ from the origin along the normal to the rational planes in real space (d is the spacing of the plane). If K is made equal to the wavelength of the radiation, the distance of a point from the origin is equal to $2\sin\theta$ and the direction of the reflected beam is obtained by simple geometrical construction. The set of reciprocal points form a true lattice in which each point corresponds to a reflecting plane.

SYMMETRY OF CRYSTALS

The majority of crystals have some elements of symmetry. By elements of symmetry are meant those operations which when acting upon a body turn it into an orientation indistinguishable from the first. Thus a body may have an n-fold axis such that rotation of $2\pi/n$ about the axis produces a congruent orientation. Only one, two-, three-, four- and six-fold axes are found in crystals. Another symmetry operation is represented by a plane of symmetry (m); if this is present one-half of the body is a reflection of the other half in the plane. The body may have a centre of symmetry or centre of inversion ($\bar{1}$) such that when a line is drawn from any point on the figure through this centre and produced an equal distance on the other side of the centre it meets an identical point.

All the symmetry which a body may have can be represented by means of these operations or by combinations of them. These symmetry elements for a given body form a set and the collection of operations form a group in the mathematical sense.

It can be shown that there are only thirty-two possible ways of combining the various crystallographic angular symmetry elements. These thirty-two combinations constitute crystal classes or *point groups*.

Crystals can be grouped into seven systems, each having a certain minimum symmetry requirement. The lattice of a crystal displays the same basic symmetry and it is therefore possible to choose a co-ordinate system and hence a unit cell, so that the symmetry of the lattice is given in metrical terms. The relation in terms of length and angle are given in Table 35

When the primitive unit cell does not display the full symmetry of the lattice it is necessary to choose a non-primitive unit cell. Three sorts are used: these are, the body centred cell, with a lattice point at the intersection of the body diagonals of the cell, the face-centred cell with lattice points at the intersection of the diagonals of one pair of all the faces, and the end-centred cell with lattice points at the intersections of the diagonals of one pair of opposite faces. It can be shown that fourteen different types of lattice symmetry can be distinguished by applying this criterion [2]. These are termed the *Bravais lattices*.

By applying to the fourteen Bravais lattices the thirty-two points group symmetries with translational and non-translational symmetry elements, all the crystallographically possible three-dimensional symmetry arrangements, the *space groups* can be derived. There are 230 in all. A typical space group is: *Pbca.* This crystal class is in the orthorhombic system and the lattice is primitive. There are three glide planes, one perpendicular to a with glide component $b/2$, one perpendicular to b with component $c/2$ and one perpendicular to c with component $a/2$.

Table 35. *Crystal systems and their characteristic symmetry*

System	Lattice constants	Characteristic symmetry
Triclinic	$a \neq b \neq c$ $\alpha \neq \beta \neq \gamma$	One-fold rotation or rotation inversion axis
Monoclinic	$a \neq b \neq c$ $\alpha = \gamma = 90° \neq \beta$	One two-fold rotation or rotation inversion axis
Orthorhombic	$a \neq b \neq c$ $\alpha = \beta = \gamma = 90°$	Three mutually perpendicular two-fold axes, which can be rotation or rotation inversion
Tetragonal	$a = b \neq c$ $\alpha = \beta = \gamma = 90°$	Only one 4 or $\bar{4}$ axis
Trigonal or rhombohedral	$a = b = c$ $\alpha = \beta = \gamma \neq 90°$	Only one 3 or $\bar{3}$ axis
Hexagonal	$a = b \neq c$ $\alpha = \beta = 90° \neq \gamma = 120°$	Only one 6 or $\bar{6}$ axis
Cubic	$a = b = c$ $\alpha = \beta = \gamma = 90°$	Four three-fold axes inclined at 54° 44′ to each axis

Experimental techniques

X-ray radiation is produced by the interaction of moving electrons with matter. Electrons are produced at a cathode and after acceleration hit a target. This causes (*a*) emission of radiation, and (*b*) ejection of one or more photoelectrons from the atom. The radiation generated by the first process has a continuous range of frequencies with a sharp upper-limit corresponding to the maximum energy of the incident electrons. This radiation is called white radiation and it can be a nuisance in powder-diffraction work. The second process also gives rise to electromagnetic radiation since if the incident electron has sufficient energy to remove an electron from one of the inner orbits of the target material, say the K-orbit, then an electron from an outer orbit will fall into this orbit and a photon of radiation will be emitted. This gives rise to a line spectrum superposed on the background continuous radiation. In practice, instead of a single line a group of lines is observed. The K_α is a doublet (there is also a K_β line) and there is also softer radiation consisting of longer wavelength radiation, the L-rays consisting of three complex lines L_α, L_β and L_γ. By isolating a narrow band of radiation in the vicinity of the K_α line essentially monochromatic radiation is observed. The ratio of intensity of the K_α line to the adjacent background is generally about 100 to 1. The target material is usually copper, molybdenum, nickel silver, cobalt, iron or chromium.

There are two classes of X-ray tube, the cold cathode and the hot cathode type. The latter is the type commonly in routine use. Here the source of electrons is an electrically heated filament, usually a bare tungsten wire. The tubes are kept at working pressures of less than 0·1 μ. The anode consists of a water-cooled metal target either made or faced with the metal whose characteristic radiation is required. The target material must have either a good thermal conductivity or a high melting point, and copper satisfies these conditions best of all. The anode may be arranged to rotate so that the X-rays are produced from a source fixed in relation to the cathode but the area of target surface bombarded and cooled in a given time is much longer. The tungsten filament of the cathode is usually placed inside a metal focusing cup maintained at the same potential as the filament. A line-focus is usually employed in diffraction work and for this the filament is usually in the form of a narrow helix. Microfocus tubes are now available enabling a finely focused beam about 40 μ in diameter to be obtained. A fine focus of this type enables greater loadings to be made and therefore enables much shorter exposure times to be used. The tubes can be either sealed or continuously pumped, and each has its own particular advantages.

There are three main methods for separating radiation of the desired wavelength from the background. These are (*a*) filters for K_β radiation, (*b*) crystal monochromators, and (*c*) proportional or scintillation counters used with electronic discriminating circuits.

There are two main types of experimental method, those dealing with polycrystalline material, i.e. the powder method, and those dealing with single crystals.

THE POWDER METHOD

In this method monochromatic radiation is used and the specimen may be in the form of a crystalline powder contained in a small tube or in the form of a thread or ribbon. Reflections occur only at values of $\sin\theta$ equal to $n\lambda/2d$ and hence the powder reflections form cones about the incident X-ray beam. On a plane photographic plate placed normal to the incident beam there will be one circle for each order of reflection from each set of crystal planes having a given spacing. If a film strip is used, the photograph consists of a series of slightly curved lines. From the position of the lines, relative to the position of the central beam, information about the spacing d or d/n can be made (Fig. 95)

There are a variety of cameras used for this method and various arrangements made for the film position. A common arrangement in Britain is the Bradley camera. The sample is placed at the centre of the camera, which is in the form of a cylinder around the inside of which

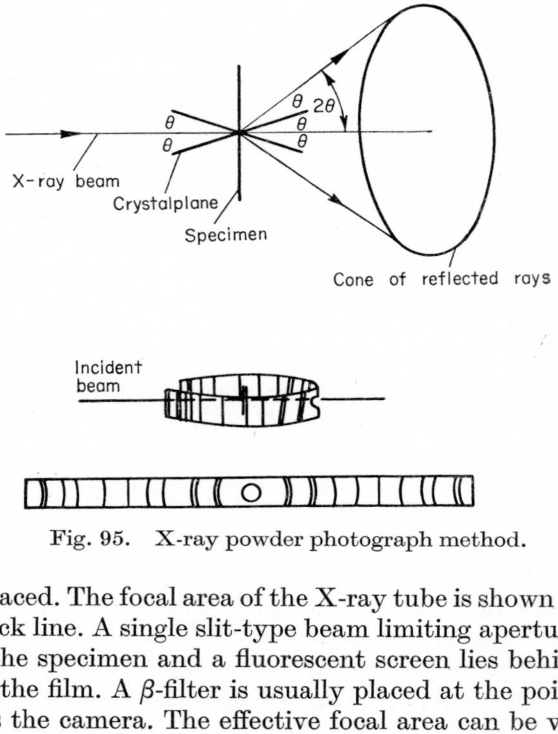

Fig. 95. X-ray powder photograph method.

the film is placed. The focal area of the X-ray tube is shown on the target face as a thick line. A single slit-type beam limiting aperture is situated in front of the specimen and a fluorescent screen lies behind the beam exit hole in the film. A β-filter is usually placed at the point where the beam enters the camera. The effective focal area can be varied on one dimension over a wide range. The size of the focal spot plays an important part in determining the definition of the lines on a powder photograph, and the definition can often be considerably improved by using the X-ray tube so that the focal line is vertical instead of horizontal. Collimated beam-type cameras are also used.

Disadvantages with these Debye–Scherrer type cameras arise because of the absorption of X-rays by the specimen. This causes lines to be displaced from their true positions in a direction of increasing Bragg angle. The effect is largest at the low-angle end of the pattern. Whilst corrections are sometimes possible, the focusing camera precludes absorption errors. A typical example of a focusing camera often used is the Guinier type [3].

Interpretation of X-ray powder photographs

By measuring the X-ray diffraction pattern, the Bragg angle and interplanar spacings can be determined. There is no direct analytical technique for deducing unit-cell parameters from Bragg angles, but there are certain semi-systematic approaches to the problem. It is easy to index the diffraction patterns of substances with cubic symmetry, almost impossible with materials of triclinic symmetry and occasionally possible with tetragonal, hexagonal, orthorhombic and monoclinic symmetry.

SINGLE-CRYSTAL METHODS

The Laue method

In this method the crystal is stationary and hence the value of the glancing angles between the incident X-ray beam collimated to a parallel beam and the various crystal planes are also fixed. The incident X-radiation is 'white' containing a continuous range of values of the wavelength λ. As long as $2d/n \sin\theta$ comes within the range, the conditions $n\lambda = 2d \sin\theta$ can be satisfied. Thus on a plane photographic film or plate placed perpendicular to the incident beam with the crystal a distance D away we observe a number of reflection spots at various distances R from the primary beam origin where $R = D \tan 2\theta$. Each spot is due to all the orders of reflection $n = 1, 2, 3$, etc., superimposed from a single plane given by the various wavelengths λ, $\lambda/2$, $\lambda/3$, etc.

The Laue method provides information about the orientations of planes that are not external faces. It does not give the size of the unit cell.

Rotating crystal method

In this method a monochromatic beam is used. The crystal is mounted with a principal crystallographic axis perpendicular or vertical to the reflection planes and is then rotated or made to oscillate. The rotation enables the Bragg law to be satisfied for a considerable number of planes when the angle made by each plane with the incident beam is

$$\theta = \sin^{-1}(n\lambda/2d). \tag{8.2}$$

The reflections are found to be drawn out upon layer lines and row lines. On a cylindrical film whose axis is the rotation axis of the crystal the layer lines are straight parallel lines, whilst if the rotation photograph is taken on a plane film parallel to the rotation axis the layer lines are hyperbolic.

In order to determine unequivocally the indices of reflecting planes and the angles between them rather than rotation, a small oscillation is used. The number of planes which can reflect during an exposure are thereby restricted, and the whole range is covered by a series of photographs at a succession of overlapping oscillations.

In the Weissenberg method, the crystal rotates completely, or almost completely, but the cylindrical film is translated parallel to the axis of rotation at the same time. The backward and forward movement of the film is synchronized with the crystal rotation. By means of screens successive layer lines may be recorded one at a time. Photographs are obtained from which both spacings and angles between planes are directly obtainable, each plane giving an individual reflection. The crystal symmetry can be obtained. From the absence of certain sets of reflections the Bravais lattice, screw axes or glide planes, and hence the space group, can be obtained.

Structure determination

From the observed positions of the diffracted beams it is possible to determine the nature of the lattice and the size of the unit cell and in many cases to determine the space group to which the crystal belongs. Chemical analysis and density specify the number and kind of atoms in the unit cell, and if the structure is a simple one it may then be completely determined by the symmetry elements alone.

In general, this is not the case and the precise atomic positions can only be found by a detailed analysis of the relative intensities of the various diffracted beams. When the positions of the atoms in the unit cell are known it is always possible to calculate the intensities of the reflections from the various crystallographic planes. The converse is not generally true.

The X-rays are scattered mainly by the extra-nuclear electrons and the important characteristic of the molecule is its distribution of electron density. The scattering power of an atom therefore depends upon its atomic number Z but, since it occupies a definite region of space, the electron density falls off in a particular manner.

Hence

$$F_{hkl} = \sum_{n=1}^{N} f_n \exp\{2\pi i(hx_n + ky_n + lz_n)\} \tag{8.3}$$

x is the co-ordinate and f_i the scattering power of the ith atom and the summation is over all atoms of the unit cell, and F_{hkl} is the structure factor.

Usually relative values of $|F|$ are derived from the appropriate spots on the X-ray photograph.

The electron density $\rho(xyz)$ is usually represented by a Fourier series. With the non-centrosymmetric structures the Fourier series is

$$\rho(x, y, z) = (1/V_0) \sum_h \sum_k \sum_l F(hkl) \cos 2\pi[\{hx_n + ky_n + lz_n - \alpha(hkl)\}] \qquad (8.4)$$

where $\alpha(hkl)$ is the phase angle.

The particular difficulty in solving the complete structure lies in the determination of the phase angles. As yet, there is no general solution for this and so methods have been devised for circumventing the phase problem. This has been done by (*a*) trial and error methods, (*b*) the heavy atom method, (*c*) isomorphous replacement, and (*d*) Patterson methods.

The first method, (*a*), involves trying various sets of atomic positions in the unit cell until some agreement is obtained between observed and calculated structure amplitudes. The second method, (*b*), involves structures containing an atom of relatively high atomic number. The X-rays scattered from the heavy atom dominate the situation and the sign of the structure factor is likely to be the one obtained if this atom only was present. The position of the heavy atom is readily found and the signs easily calculated. This method is particularly successful with centrosymmetric structures but more difficult with non-centrosymmetric structures. The third method, (*c*), is isomorphous replacement. Here the corresponding atoms in two isomorphous crystals occupy very nearly the same positions in the unit cell, but the interchangeable atoms differ in atomic number and in scattering power. With centrosymmetric crystals the structure factor will differ simply by the difference between the contributions made to that reflection by the replaceable atoms. The method is more difficult to apply to a non-centrosymmetric crystal.

In each method, once the phases of a number of the strongest structure factors are determined, the Fourier series provides the approximate positions for some of the atoms. From the approximate structure, structure factors are calculated, both amplitude and phase. The calculated phases are then used with the observed amplitude in a second synthesis to give a more exact structure. The terms included at each stage are those which give good agreement between observed and calculated amplitudes. The repetitive operation is continued until all observed reflections are included in the series.

The fourth method is due to Patterson [4] and is particularly useful. Here, a Fourier synthesis is performed using F^2 instead of F for the amplitude terms, and the problem of signs or phase angles is disregarded. From the measured structure amplitudes alone, it is possible to produce a vector representation of the crystal structure. Instead of obtaining the position of each scattering centre we obtain a superposition of all the vector distances connecting these centres.

A quantity $A(uvw)$ is introduced which is the weighted average distribution of density if scattering matter about a point (xyz) in the crystal defined by

$$A(u,v,w) = \frac{1}{V}\int_0^a\int_0^b\int_0^c \rho(xyz)\,\rho(x+u,y+v,z+w)\,\mathrm{d}x\,\mathrm{d}y\,\mathrm{d}z \qquad (8.5)$$

Here, $\rho(x+u, y+v, z+w)$ gives the distribution about (xyz) as a function of the parameters, u, v, w and it represents a distribution similar to $\rho(xyz)$ but displaced from the point (xyz) through a distance whose components are (u,v,w). This distribution function is weighted by the amount of scattering matter in the volume element at (xyz).

If the two functions $\rho(xyz)$ and $\rho(x+u, y+V \text{and} z+w)$ are now expanded in terms of a Fourier series and integrated, we obtain

$$A(u,v,w) = \frac{1}{V^2}\sum\sum_{-\infty}^{\infty}\sum F^2(hkl)\exp\{-2\pi i(hu/a+kv/b+1w/c)\} \qquad (8.6)$$

The function $A(u,v,w)$ can therefore be calculated in terms of the squares of the structure factors F^2. Thus a picture of the detailed crystal structure is obtained directly from the measured X-ray intensities in the form of a vector map showing all the inter-atomic vectors of the crystal superimposed.

There are certain limitations on this method due to the possibility of the solutions of the Patterson diagram being non-unique. These are overcome by using the heavy atom method or isomorphous-replacement method.

Once the phases of a sufficient number of the strongest reflections have been determined, or when approximate positions have been found for a sufficient number of atoms, refinement of the analysis takes place.

After each cycle of refinement the agreement between the observed F_o and calculated $|F_c|$ structure amplitudes should improve and it is possible to include more terms in the next synthesis. This is done until all the observations are used.

When the analysis has reached the stage where phases can be assigned to all observed reflections, the electron density maxima may still not be the best co-ordinates possible. This is due to termination of series errors. There are methods for handling this such as the difference synthesis. The Fourier series refinement is continued but, instead of using $|F_o|$ for the amplitude, the algebraic difference $(F_o - F_c)$ is substituted. When the co-ordinates are satisfactory the difference map is flat at the atomic site. When there is a gradient the atom should be shifted in the direction of steepest ascent. Another method is the least-squares refinement in which the computation is set up so as to include the small shifts in co-ordinates which will minimize the sum $\sum (F_o - F_c)^2$.

The refinement of an analysis is usually expressed as R, the agreement index defined as:

$$R \text{ is } \frac{\sum \left| |F_o| - |F_c| \right|}{\sum |F_o|} \tag{8.7}$$

As R falls in value the refinement increases. Other methods of assessing the accuracy are also used.

LOW-ANGLE SCATTERING

In ordinary crystals the separation of the lattice planes is of the same order as the wavelength and the scattering angles are relatively high. When, however, we consider macromolecules, such as proteins or high polymers, the large lattice spacings are of the order of ten to one hundred times the interatomic distance. Thus if the usual wavelength radiation is used (about $\simeq 2$ Å) the diffracting angle θ may be less than 1°. Unfortunately the use of longer wavelength radiation is handicapped by increased absorption in the diffracting material.

To study these large spacings it is necessary to observe diffraction effects extremely close to the primary beam. This makes it necessary to have some special experimental requirements [5]. The cross-section and divergence of the beam-collimating slits have to be reduced and parasitic scattering has to be minimized. Geiger-counter techniques make correction easier. A monochromatic primary beam is required.

When a photographic technique is used it is necessary to prevent the direct beam striking the film. This can be done by using a flat band of metal close to the film and allowing some radiation to penetrate so as to mark the film. When a Geiger-counter detector is used the slit before the counter acts as a beam stop.

Using these experimental techniques, the variation of the intensity scattered by a sample as a function of the scattering direction is determined. When the scattering is symmetric about the axis of incident beam only the scattering angle is involved and it is possible to find $I(h)$

where $$h = \frac{4\pi \sin\theta}{\lambda} \tag{8.8}$$

From a graphical representation of this expression it is possible to derive a model of the scatterer in terms of its nearest neighbours and also to predict the size of the scattering moiety.

This technique has been applied to proteins in solution, high polymers, fibres, finely dispersed solids and colloidal solutions [6]. Low-angle diffraction patterns of nerves have also been studied [7]. The technique may be particularly useful for studies of lipoprotein systems such as the soluble lipoproteins.

LONG-CHAIN CRYSTALS AND SUB-CELL THEORY

Many lipids are long-chain compounds and, because of the length and regularity of the chain, certain simplifications are introduced in the

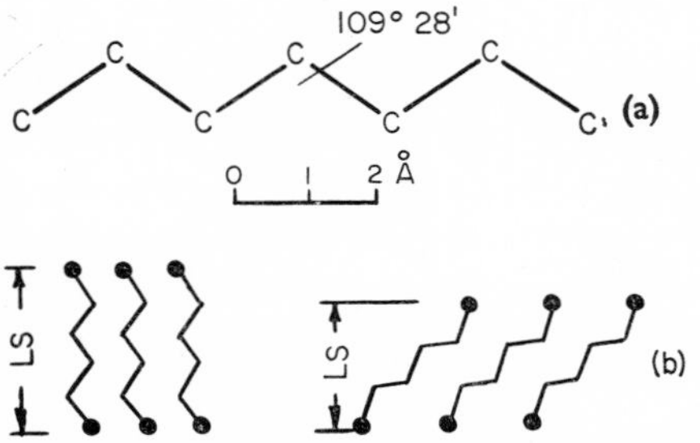

Fig. 96. Zig-zag carbon chain (a) and (b) long spacings of polymethylene chains.

interpretation of both the X-ray powder photographs and also in single crystal structure determinations.

The X-ray powder patterns of these compounds show that the spacings lie in two groups [8] and these are usually referred to as long and short spacings. Within an homologous series the long spacing varies with the number of CH_2 groups in the chain. The short spacings are associated with the manner of packing of the hydrocarbon chains whilst the long spacing is related to integral multiples of the chain length (Fig. 96). With paraffinic hydrocarbons the long chains pack so as to obtain the highest possible van der Waals interaction and the chains pack parallel to each other. The molecular end groups associate with each other to form planes. The chains are usually in the extended *trans* configuration and may be either vertical or tilted to these planes. In an homologous series the molecules are all tilted at the same angle with respect to these planes, and the long spacings are a linear function of the carbon content of the chain [9, 10] (Fig. 97).

Long-chain compounds are particularly prone to polymorphism and this may occur as a consequence of different packing arrangements or differing tilts with respect to these basal planes. The polarity of the molecule determines whether the long spacing corresponds to single or multiple chain lengths. The X-ray powder photographs for crystals with a single molecule between successive reflecting planes show that the lines of successive orders of reflection decrease in intensity with a natural decline with increasing order. For crystals with double molecules between successive layers there is an alternation superposed on this usual decline. In the first eight or nine lines strong odd and weak even orders appear. This alternation tends to disappear when a very heavy atom is present in the molecule [11]. The particular observed intensity

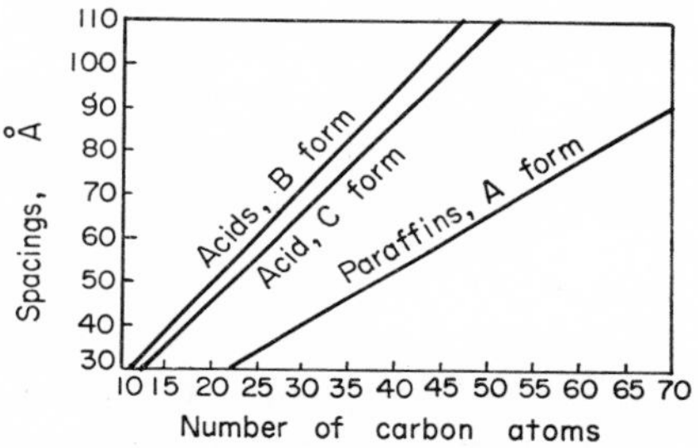

Fig. 97. Variation in spacing values as a function of the number of carbon atoms in the normal paraffins and the two forms of fatty acids.

distributions can be useful for locating groups of high scattering power. This has been nicely illustrated by Shearer [12] who showed that with ketones the exact location of the carbonyl group could be easily determined, since when the carbonyl group was on the nth carbon atom the nth, $2n$th, $3n$th, etc., order disappears and there is corresponding maxima of intensity at the $n/2$, $3n/2$, $5n/2$ order. Similar variations in intensity of lines have been observed with n-aliphatic alcohols [13]. The intensity variation observed with a number of long-chain compounds are shown in Fig. 98.

From the long spacings it is possible to determine whether they correspond to single or multiple chain lengths. This is done by assuming that the chains pack in a zig-zag manner with an angle of 109° 28′. In this arrangement the average distance between carbon atoms is about 1·26 Å. Thus if the uniform increase in the long spacing per CH_2 of the chain is approximately this value the members of the series crystallize with a single molecule between planes, whilst if it is larger than this they crystallize with two or more. Once this is decided, the angle of tilt of the chains can be decided using the relation

$$\sin\beta = \frac{\text{increment per } CH_2 \text{ tilted}}{\text{increment per } CH_2 \text{ perpendicular } (2{\cdot}52)} \qquad (8.9)$$

Schoon [14] made the suggestion that the polymorphic forms of the long-chain compounds may fall into a few groups depending on the angle of tilt between the carbon chains and the plane of the end groups.

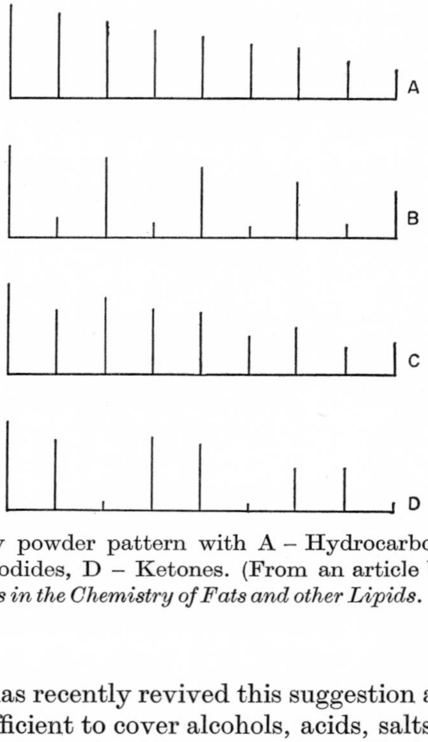

Fig. 98. X-ray powder pattern with A – Hydrocarbons, B – Acids, Alcohols, C – Iodides, D – Ketones. (From an article by T. Malkin in Vol. 1 of *Progress in the Chemistry of Fats and other Lipids*. 1952, Pergamon Press Ltd.)

Gunstone [15] has recently revived this suggestion and considers that five groups are sufficient to cover alcohols, acids, salts, alkyl esters and mono-, di- and tri-glycerides. Using the relationship $L = na + c$, where L is the long spacing, n the number of carbon atoms and c a constant, he finds that by comparison with the experimental data the values for (a) fall into groups corresponding to the different angles of tilt of the chains. (The crystalline forms frequently contain double molecules lying head to head so that the value for n is twice the number of carbon atoms in a single molecule.) The five groups with appropriate symbols occur at angles 90° (V), 68° (U), 64° (T), 57° (S) and 52° (R). This has some uses in resolving certain discrepancies in the data on saturated triglycerides but is apparently not useful with the unsaturated glycerides. It has to be remembered that a long-chain compound can have the same tilt but different chain packing, so that a knowledge of both is required to define a particular form. With triglycerides of markedly different chain length or with unsaturated chains one may have more than one angle of tilt and even more than one type of packing. See the discussion on the branched-chain carboxylic acids.

A particular feature of long-chain compounds is that the same, or very similar, short spacing is often observed at 4·1 to 4·2 Å. This was first observed by Muller [16] with hydrocarbons and was interpreted to indicate that the hydrocarbon chains were arranged in an hexagonal array with the chains rotating or in random orientation about these axes [17]. The chain axes are usually perpendicular to the basal planes. Strong spacings at 3·8 and 4·2 Å with additional weaker lines are often observed, and less frequently a strong – usually the strongest – spacing at 4·6 Å. The hydrocarbon chain packings in these two types is very probably of the orthorhombic O$\perp$ and triclinic T$\parallel$ type (see later discussion).

Occasionally attempts have been made to deduce more structural information than is justified from X-ray powder photographs and errors ensue. There is little doubt, however, of the enormous value of such photographs for analytical studies and for studying changes in crystal structure. The use of this technique to study the packing of lipids in biological systems may be particularly informative.

Sub-cell concept

For single-crystal studies a particularly useful concept has been introduced – this is the sub-cell [18, 19]. When the hydrocarbon chains pack in the crystal lattice they do so with a regular or almost regular plane zig-zag conformation. The periodicity of the chain gives rise to a small unit of repetition in space within the main cell. For a particular chain packing there exists a characteristic sub-cell describing the translation between equivalent positions within one chain and in adjacent chains. The sheets of end groups are regarded merely as faces of a sub-cell. It is useful for the calculation of structure-factors and from the few carbon atoms of the sub-cell it is possible to calculate the contribution to the structure factors of all the atoms of the sub-cell region. The dimensions of the sub-cell can be obtained from the reciprocal lattice, and if the dimensions fit the sub-cell data for a structurally known chain arrangement, this chain packing probably occurs in the compound and it is relatively easy to obtain information about the main arrangement of the hydrocarbon chains. There are, however, some snags in this and care has to be taken not to start a false structure refinement.

Patterson projections along the shortest axes provide information about the chain direction. This is useful when the chain is severely distorted, but otherwise only confirms the direction found from the

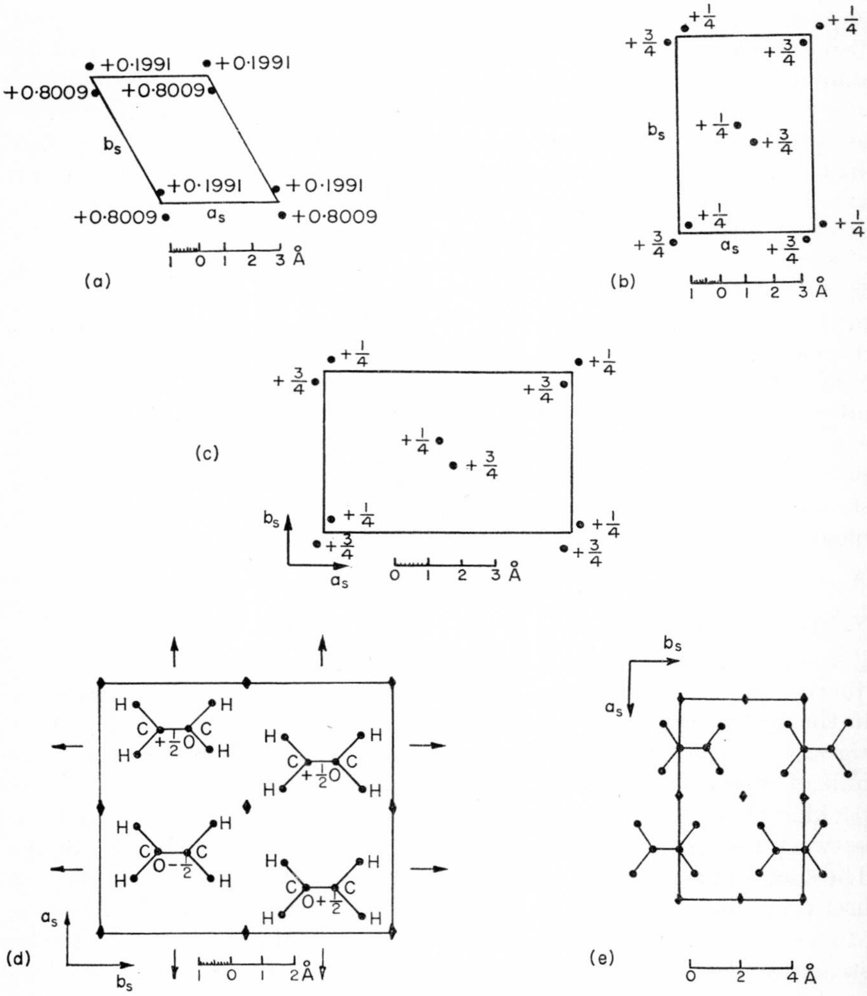

Fig. 99. Types of sub-cell observed with long hydrocarbon chains: (*a*) T‖. (*b*) O⊥ sub-cell. (*c*) O′⊥ sub-cell. (*d*) O‖ sub-cell. (*e*) O′‖ sub-cell. (Adapted from von Sydow, E. *Arkiv Kemi*, **9**, 231, 1956.)

orientation determination of the sub-cell within the main cell. Information about atoms which do not belong to the sub-cell region is obtained only in special cases; and these atoms are placed in the most probable position for the first trial structure [20].

As well as the sub-cell being a useful concept in this way, it is also a convenient method for describing the essentials of the hydrocarbon chain packing. Because the van der Waals energy is insensitive to slight changes of the mutual orientation of the chain planes of the neighbouring molecules a large number of structures with minor differences of lattice energy occur. Usually the chains pack parallel to one another and many of the structures can be classified by means of the sub-cell concept. Two main types have been observed, the triclinic T|| and the common orthorhombic O⊥; but recent work has shown the existence of other types.

Triclinic T|| packing

The triclinic sub-cell is shown in Fig. 99a. It contains two CH_2 groups and belongs to the space group $P\bar{1}$. In the triclinic packing of hydrogen chains all chain planes are parallel. A chain packing very similar to this occurs in the triclinic form of *n*-hydrocarbons [21], and is found in the *A* and *A'*-form of *n*-fatty acids [22, 23] and in β_L-trilaurin [24], as well as many methyloctadecanoic acids [25, 26]. Data for various compounds are given in Table 36.

Table 36. *Data for the triclinic T|| sub-cell*

Long-chain compound	a_s Å	b_s Å	c_s Å	α	β	γ	Vol./CH_2 Å^3
Trilaurin β_L-form	4·287	5·40	2·45	74° 45′	108° 2′	117° 24′	23·7
n-C_{12}, *A*-form acid	4·42	5·41	2·63	74°	109°	122°	25·0
n-C_{15}, *A'*-form acid	4·25	5·82	2·61	66°	106°	122°	25·0
2 DL-Me—C_{18} acid	4·33	5·27	2·50	72°	109°	117°	23·6
3 DL-Me—C_{18} acid	4·22	5·18	2·52	75°	107°	119°	22·8
9 DL-Me—C_{18} acid	4·20	5·27	2·55	81°	103°	118°	24·2
14 DL-Me—C_{18} acid	4·47	5·16	2·57	72°	109°	117°	24·5
16 DL-Me—C_{18} acid	4·49	5·40	2·56	73°	107°	123°	24·5

Common orthorhombic packing O⊥

The orthorhombic O⊥ sub-cell is shown in Fig. 99b. It is observed in a variety of long-chain compounds, including paraffins, esters and fatty acids. The four CH_2 groups of the cell are arranged according to the space group *Pbnm*. It can be seen that every second chain is approximately perpendicular to the neighbouring planes. Data for this sub-cell are given in Table 37.

Table 37. *Data for the common orthorhombic O⊥ sub-cell*

Long-chain compound	a_s Å	b_s Å	c_s Å	b_s/a_s	Vol./CH_2 Å^3
Polyethylene [27]	4·93	7·40	2·534	1·50	23·1
n-Hexatriacontane [28]	4·95	7·42	2·546	1·50	23·4
n-Paraffins [29]	4·96	7·41	2·54	1·49	23·3
Racemic *trans*-9,10-methylene octadecanoic acid [30]	4·98	8·12	2·60	1·63	27·1
Racemic *cis*-11,12-methylene octadecanoic acid [31]	5·10	7·55	2·53	1·48	24·4
14-Heptacosanol [32]	4·95	7·8	2·58	1·58	24·9
3,1-compound of *n*-C_{18} and 14-DL-Me—C_{18} acid [20]	4·95[a]	7·38[a]	—	1·49	—
n-C_{11}, acid *C′*-form [33]	4·92	7·95	2·52	1·62	24·7
n-C_{12}, acid *C*-form [34]	4·97	7·80	2·52	1·57	24·4
n-C_{15}, acid *B′*-form [35]	5·02	7·59	2·51	1·51	23·9
n-C_{18}, acid *C*-form at 70° C (extrapolated) [36]	4·92[a]	7·58[a]	—	1·54	—
n-C_{18}, acid *C*-form at 23° C [37]	4·96[a]	7·49[a]	—	1·51	—
n-C_{18}, acid *B*-form [38]	4·99	7·40	2·53	1·48	23·3

(*a*) Section perpendicular to the *c*-axis.

New orthorhombic packing O′⊥

This sub-cell is shown in Fig. 99c. It contains four CH_2 groups and the space group is *Pbnm*. The dimensions of the sub-cell are $a_s = 7{\cdot}43$ Å, $b_s = 5{\cdot}01$ Å and $c_s = 2{\cdot}50$ Å. The chain packing is similar to the common orthorhombic type with the same sub-cell symmetry, while every second chain plane is roughly perpendicular to the other planes. Both sub-cells are identical in shape and volumes per CH_2 are also identical (23·3 Å^3) and the interaction along the carbon chains is the same. The essential difference is that equivalent chains make the closest approach in the b_s-direction.

This sub-cell has only been observed with one compound, 2-D-methyl octadecanoic acid [39].

New orthorhombic packing O||

This is a further unusual type of sub-cell (Fig. 99d). It has symmetry $P2_12_12$ and contains eight CH_2 groups. All the chain planes are parallel in this packing. The volume per CH_2 group is slightly larger (24·0 Å) than in the other orthorhombic types. It has dimensions $a_s = 8{\cdot}150$ Å, $b_s = 9{\cdot}214$ Å and $c_2 = 2{\cdot}55$ Å. This sub-cell has only been observed in (−)2-methyl-2-ethyl eicosanoic acid [40].

Orthorhombic packing O′||

With oleic acid a further type of hydrocarbon chain packing has been observed [41]. This has been designated an O′|| packing. It is orthorhombic with four CH_2 groups and has the symmetry $P2_122$. The dimensions are $a_s = 7{\cdot}93$ Å, $b_s = 4{\cdot}74$ Å and $c_s = 2{\cdot}53$ Å. All chain planes are parallel, as in the orthorhombic packing O||, but the planes of chains repeated along the b_s-axis coincide, whereas two adjacent chains in O|| are about 1 Å displaced when seen in the corresponding direction (see Fig. 99e).

Hexagonal packing

The hexagonal packed form was first observed by Muller [16] with paraffins. Paraffins with an odd number of carbon atoms and chain length greater than seven, and even numbered paraffins with a chain

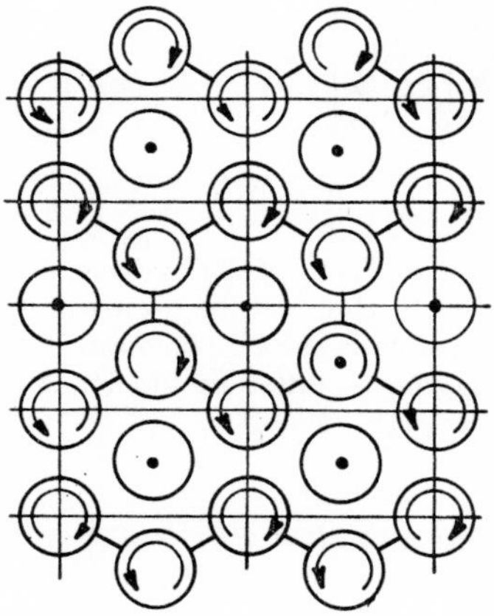

Fig. 100. Hexagonal type of sub-cell showing possible molecular motion.

length greater than twenty, undergo a phase transition to a hexagonal form at a certain temperature just below their melting point. The form is usually recognized by the presence of a single short spacing of about 4·2 Å on the X-ray powder photograph. It is observed with long-chain alcohols, ethyl esters and glycerides. It is considered that at least some of the molecules in this form can rotate about their long axes (Fig. 100), and this is supported by n.m.r. and dielectric studies [42, 43]. The form is generally called alpha and is often indicated by the symbol α. Various theories concerning the molecular rotation in this form have been presented [44, 45, 46].

Factors affecting polymorphism

As we have indicated, polymorphism with lipids is particularly prevalent and can arise from different types of hydrocarbon chain packings or from different angles of tilt with respect to the end-group planes. The production of a particular form depends upon the number of carbon atoms in

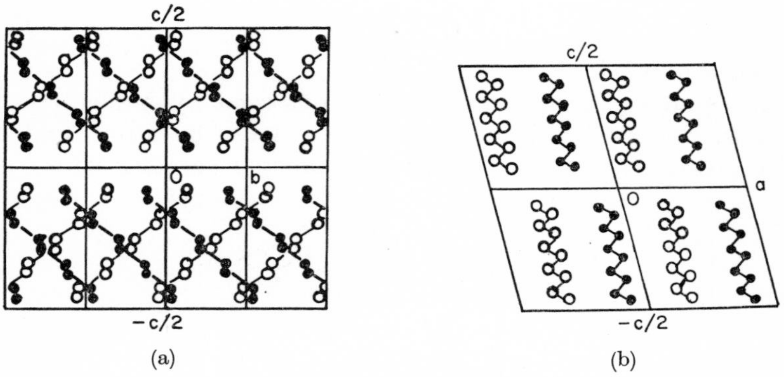

Fig. 101. Typical configuration of the hydrocarbon chains in potassium soaps and amides showing the cross-chain arrangements. (*a*) Projection along the *a* axis. (*b*) Projection along the *b* axis. Black and white circles represent atoms belonging to different blocks of sub-cells. (Sukarai, T. *J. Phys. Soc., Japan*, **10**, (12), 1955.)

the chain, temperature and purity. Purity is particularly important. The existence of a particular polymorphic form can depend completely on the presence or absence of impurities. Transition points can be depressed and the temperature range over which the hexagonal lattice occurs extended. Different forms can also be produced by changing the method of crystallization by using different solvents or by varying the temperature.

With amides [47, 48] and potassium soaps [49] a radically different chain arrangement is observed, so that the adjacent chains pack with their axes crossed (Fig. 101). The interaction between chains is small compared with the forces between the polar groups in these compounds.

Hydrocarbon packing in the liquid

X-ray diffraction studies of some *n*-paraffins, *n*-alcohols and carboxylic acids in the liquid state were studied more than thirty years ago [50]. This work showed that a main diffraction peak occurs at 4·6 Å with all these long-chain compounds. This peak was explained in terms of the radial distribution function of cylindrically shaped chains packed in an hexagonal manner with an interchain distance of 5·0 Å. An additional weak peak is observed with the fatty acids and alcohols [51, 52]. This occurs at smaller angles as the number of carbon atoms in the chain increase and is considered to measure the distance from the heavy end-group to the centre of the gap between this molecule and the next. For sufficiently long chains this distance equals the chain length. It is concluded that the chains remain essentially straight in the liquid state.

More recent studies of liquid *n*-pentane, *n*-hexane, *n*-heptane and *n*-octane have concluded that the major part of the molecules are in the extended *trans* configuration [53]. The total radial distribution functions are dominated by the packing of the molecules and the distance between nearest-neighbour molecules seem to be a little larger for pentane than for other paraffins. It has also been suggested that the chains rotate with the rotations coupled in a gear-like fashion and in a rhomboidal rather than hexagonal array [54].

If these conclusions are correct, and infra-red spectroscopic studies are not consistent with them (page 95), this may be particularly important for interpreting X-ray data on lipid–water systems and the structure of lipoproteins and membranes. At present the view taken by the author is that the hydrocarbon chains take up more of a chaotic configuration and that this is why the long spacings decrease as the temperature increases (page 296). A study of rotational isomerism of hydrocarbon molecules, using electron-diffraction techniques [55], in the vapour state has shown that with *n*-heptane only a small fraction of the chains is in the *trans* configuration.

Applications to lipids

ALCOHOLS

Of the early members of the aliphatic alcohols only methyl alcohol has been studied in detail [56]. This study has shown that it exists in two structures; a low-temperature form (− 160° C) and a high-temperature form (− 110° C). The high-temperature form has a space group *Cmcm*; it is hydrogen bonded throughout in zig-zag rows; the C—O bond length is 1·43 ± 0·03 Å. In the low-temperature form the hydrogen-bonded zig-zags become more puckered and the C—O ... O angle more nearly tetrahedral.

The long-chain alcohols exhibit polymorphism and this has been investigated by a number of workers. Malkin showed that some of the normal long-chain primary alcohols can exist in two polymorphic modifications, one having vertical chains and the other having tilted chains [57]. He suggests that the first of these is the most stable form for the odd-numbered carbon series of alcohols whilst the tilted-chain modification is the most stable for the even-numbered carbon series. When the long spacings are plotted against the number of carbon atoms in the chain, two straight lines are obtained, one for the odd members and the other for the even members. However, for the even members of chain length below C_{16} the spacings lie on the line for the odd members whilst the C_{16} alcohol gives two spacings, one for each curve. All the alcohols crystallize in bimolecular layers.

Wilson and Ott [13] did not find two modifications for the odd members but otherwise agree in general with these findings.

Kolb and Lutton examined *n*-hexadecanol and *n*-octadecanol and showed that they can exist in three modifications which they term alpha, sub-alpha and beta [58]. The beta form is obtained by crystallization from solvent or by transformation from the alpha form. It is the most stable form and crystallizes with tilted chains. The alpha form has short spacings of 4·17 vs similar to forms of other long-chain molecules in which rotation of the hydrocarbon chains can occur. It is obtained from the melt. The chains are vertical in this form. The sub-alpha form is obtained by rapid chilling of the melt to room temperature. The chains are vertical in this form. The X-ray data for these forms are shown in Table 38. It may be observed that there is a distinct analogy between these polymorphic forms and those observed with certain glycerides.

No complete X-ray structure of cholesterol has yet been published but studies of some cholesterol esters, e.g. cholesteryl stearate are at present in progress [59]. The structure of cholesterol iodide has been studied [60].

Table 38. *X-ray data for some long-chain alcohols*

	LONG SPACING Å			SHORT SPACING Å		
Alcohol	Alpha	Sub-alpha	Beta	Alpha	Sub-alpha	Beta
n-Octadecanol	49·0	49·7	41·8	4·19	4·09 vs 3·73 m 3·64 s	4·30 m 4·08 vs 3·62 s
n-Hexadecanol	44·3	44·9	37·2	4·17	4·09 vs 3·73 m 3·64 s	4·30 m 4·08 vs 3·60 s

CARBOXYLIC ACIDS

A considerable number of aliphatic carboxylic acids have been examined both by single-crystal X-ray studies and powder-photography methods. By this means a considerable amount of information has been obtained about the orientation of the carboxyl groups, the packing of the hydrocarbon chains and the polymorphism displayed by the longer-chain compounds.

(*a*) *Saturated acids*

Single-crystal studies of the early members such as formic acid and acetic acid show that, unlike the longer chain compounds, they crystallize in a polymeric form – rather than in a dimeric form. Formic acid has a unit cell containing four molecules [61] and the space group of the unit cell is *Pna*. The long spacing and short spacing for this acid is given in Table 40.

An unusual splitting of the line at 5·14 Å occurs just as crystallization takes place. This is also observed with other acids and is attributed to a stacking fault similar to that observed in metals or alloys, rather than due to the appearance of an additional phase.

Acetic acid also crystallizes [62] with the molecules linked together in chains as in formic acid. The space group is $Pna2_1$ with $a = 13{\cdot}32 \pm 0{\cdot}02$ Å, $b = 4{\cdot}08 \pm 0{\cdot}01$ Å, and $c = 5{\cdot}77 \pm 0{\cdot}01$ Å. The four heavy atoms of each molecule lie in a plane. The bond distances are C—C, 1·54 Å; C=O, 1·24 Å; C—O, 1·29 Å; and O—H, 2·61 Å.

X-ray powder photographs of a great number of the simple monocarboxylic acids have been obtained [63]. The occurrence of fairly large spacings between the long and short spacings is common with the acids of five or less carbon atoms. Here the terminal groups affect the molecular packing whilst with the longer chain acids the packing is influenced only by the aliphatic chain.

X-ray powder photograph studies of the long-chain fatty acids show that they exhibit polymorphism. The even members crystallize in any of three forms which are designated *A*, *B* and *C*, whilst the odd members may also crystallize in three forms *A′*, *B′* and *C′*. A fourth form, a *D′*-form considered to exist at one time, is now thought to have been an artefact associated with impurities.

The transitions from one polymorphic form to another have been particularly well studied for these acids. With the even members crystallization from the melt and rapid crystallization from solution at room temperature gives a *C*-form. Crystallization from solution can give *A*, *B* and *C* forms either singly or two together, but less seldom are *A* and *B* together. Slow crystallization, except when the solvent molecules are strong dipoles such as with acetic acid, favour formation of *A*- or *B*-

Table 39. *X-ray data for short-chain acids* [63]

Carbon atoms	Name	Long spacing Å	Short spacing Å	
1	Formic	5·14	4·52 (10)	3·92 (25)
			3·68 (100)	3·32 (10)
2	Acetic	6·65	4·35 (100)	3·91 (20)
			3·67 (40)	3·46 (70)
			2·88 (40)	
3	Propionic	7·05	5·52 (10)	4·70 (50)
			4·19 (100)	3·89 (10)
			3·66 (10)	3·44 (5)
			2·85 (60)	2·65 (50)
			2·63 (30)	2·14 (5)
			1·579 (10)	
4	Butyric	9·45	7·60 (40)	4·07 (1000)
			3·93 (70)	3·78 (100)
			3·69 (40)	
5	Pentanoic	12·63	7·25 (50)	4·82 (50)
			4·44 (100)	3·88 (40)
			3·65 (50)	3·60 (100)
			3·46 (20)	
6	Hexanoic	14·25	4·05 (100)	
			3·90 (25)	3·67 (30)
				3·42 (35)
7	Heptanoic	16·23	4·36 (50)	3·88 (50)
			3·75 (100)	3·65 (40)
				3·43 (40)
8	Octanoic	18·65	4·10 (100)	3·91 (20)
			3·67 (10)	
9	Nonanoic	20·73	4·40 (40)	4·27 (70)
			4·00 (100)	3·89 (65)
			3·43 (30)	
10	Decanoic	23·10	4·13 (90)	3·87 (25)
			3·78 (100)	

Long spacing $= 2{\cdot}22N + 0{\cdot}86$ where N is the number of carbon atoms in the acid.

forms. With odd members crystallization from the melt for *n*-heptadecanoic acid and longer acids gives the B'-form, but with smaller chain length the A'-form becomes more common. Lowering the rate of crystallization by lowering the temperature of crystallization also helps crystallization of the A'-form. The crystal forms obtained by crystallization under different conditions are shown in Table 40 [64].

Table 40. *Forms of acids obtained by various treatments*

Even numbered acids	SOLVENT Glacial acetic acid	Light petroleum	Melt
12	*C*	*A*	*C*
14	*C*	*A*	*C*
16	*C*	*A*	*C*
18	*A*+*C*	*B*+*C*	*C*
20	*B*+*C*	*B*+*C*	*C*
22	—	*A*+*C*	*C*
24	—	*B*+*C*	*C*
26	—	*B*+*C*	*C*
28	—	*B*	*C*
Odd numbered acids			
13	*A′*	*A′*	*A′*
15	*A′*+*B′*	*A′*	*B′*
17	*B′*	*B′*	*B′*
19	*B′*	*B′*	*B′*
21	—	*B′*	*B′*
23	—	*B′*	*B′*
27	—	*B′*	*B′*
29	—	*B′*	*B′*

The transitions of one polymorphic form to another by heating have been studied for the acids from C_{12} to C_{29} in chain length. These data [65] are given in Table 41. The odd-numbers containing 15 or more carbon atoms show a reversible *B′* to *C′* transition whilst the C_{13} acid shows a reversible *A′* to *C′* transition. The C_{15} acids and C_{19} acids undergo an *A′* to *B′* transition. Just below the melting point of the acids the crystal form is the *C′*-form. This is the solid phase in equilibrium with liquid phase. With the even-numbered acids the transitions are not reversible and no *A* to *B* transitions are observed. It is suggested that the *A*-form is the stable one up to 22 carbon atoms and the *B*-form stable for the longer chain numbers.

Examination of the *C*-form of the even-numbered acids using the Guinier powder method show that the unit cell dimensions vary with the chain length. The series is therefore not strictly homologous. The c_s dimension, the distance between alternate carbon atoms, decreases with

Table 41. *Thermal and X-ray data for monocarboxylic acids*

Number of carbon atoms	Melting point °C	LONG SPACINGS Å			TRANSITION POINT ON HEATING °C		
		A	*B*	*C*	*A* → *C*	*B* → *C*	*A* → *B*
12	44·0	32·1	—	27·4	32	—	—
14	54·2	36·7	—	31·7	44	—	—
16	62·9	41·7	—	36·0	59	—	—
18	69·7	46·5	44·1	40·0	54	46	—
20	75·1	—	48·8	43·0	—	52	—
22	79·9	55·5	—	48·3	63	—	—
24	83·9	—	57·8	52·9	—	65	—
26	87·5	—	62·2	57·1	—	72	—
28	90·7	—	67·5	61·6	—	79	—
13	41·4	35·1	—	29·6	34	—	—
15	52·1	40·2	36·4	34·5	—	46	45
17	61·1	—	40·3	38·5	—	56	—
19	68·5	49·2	44·7	43·0	—	66	52
21	74·8	—	49·1	46·9	—	72	—
23	79·1	—	53·6	51·0	—	77·5	—
25	83·2	—	58·0	56·2	—	81·5	—
27	87·5	—	62·7	60·0	—	85	—
29	90·4	—	66·6	65·2	—	89	—

increasing chain length, probably in an asymptotic manner. The variation of the cell dimensions of the *B*- and *C*-forms of stearic acid with increasing temperature have also been studied [36, 37]. The changes in the *c* dimensions are very small, i.e. the length of stearic acid is almost independent of temperature. Considering the sub-cell, the shortest dimension (4·95 Å) is almost unchanged whereas the large one ($\sim$ 7·40 Å) is very variable. It is clear that the sub-cell tends to approach the hexagonal type of packing as the melting point is approached, similar to the behaviour of hydrocarbons and ethyl esters.

With decanoic acid the short spacing near 3·7 Å has a thermal expansion of 28×10^{-4} $A/°$C, whilst the spacing near 4·1 Å has a thermal expansion of 7×10^{-4} $A/°$C.

The first single-crystal study of a monocarboxylic acid was that of Muller with the *B*-form of octadecanoic acid [16]. Many other studies on both odd and even members have been reported in recent years. Information has been obtained on the hydrocarbon packing and general arrangement of the chains in each of the polymorphic forms. Only two types of sub-cell are observed with these acids, the common orthorhombic O$\perp$

and the triclinic T||. Information on the various polymorphic forms of the simple monocarboxylic acids is as follows:

FORM A′. This form has the chains packed roughly in the triclinic T|| manner. With *n*-pentadecanoic acid the only symmetry element is a centre of symmetry and the main unit cell is triclinic.

$$a = 4{\cdot}25\ \text{Å} \qquad b = 5{\cdot}01\ \text{Å} \qquad c = 42{\cdot}76\ \text{Å}$$
$$\alpha = 89^\circ\ 50' \qquad \beta = 111^\circ\ 5' \qquad \gamma = 112^\circ\ 10'$$

The cell contains two molecules and the space group is C_c'–P. The carboxyl groups are arranged in the dimeric form to allow for hydrogen

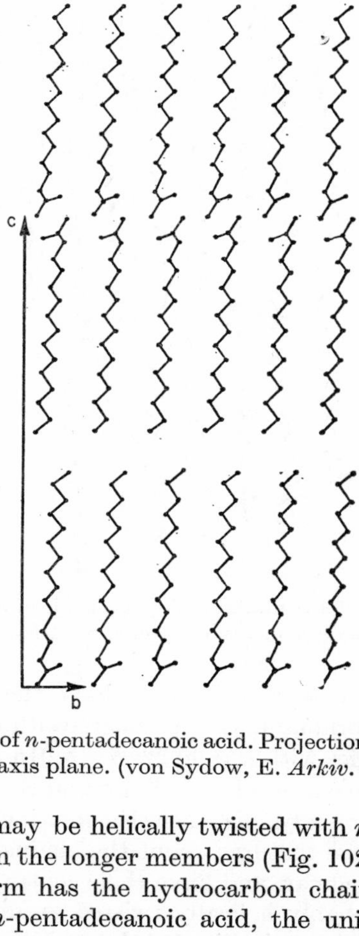

Fig. 102. A′-form of *n*-pentadecanoic acid. Projection along the shortest axis on the largest axis plane. (von Sydow, E. *Arkiv. Kemi*, **9**, 1956.)

bonding. The chain may be helically twisted with *n*-pentadecanoic acid but is probably less in the longer members (Fig. 102).

FORM B′. This form has the hydrocarbon chains orthorhombically packed O⊥. With *n*-pentadecanoic acid, the unit cell has the same symmetry as form *A*′. It is triclinic with $a = 5{\cdot}543$ Å, $b = 8{\cdot}061$ Å and

$c = 42{\cdot}58$ Å, $\alpha = 114°\ 18'$, $\beta = 114°\ 13'$ and $\gamma = 80°\ 37'$. The cell contains four molecules and has space group C_1–$P1$ or C'_i–$P\bar{1}$. The packing may be deformed near the carboxyl groups, but even at this chain length the hydrocarbon chains dominate the structure (Fig. 103).

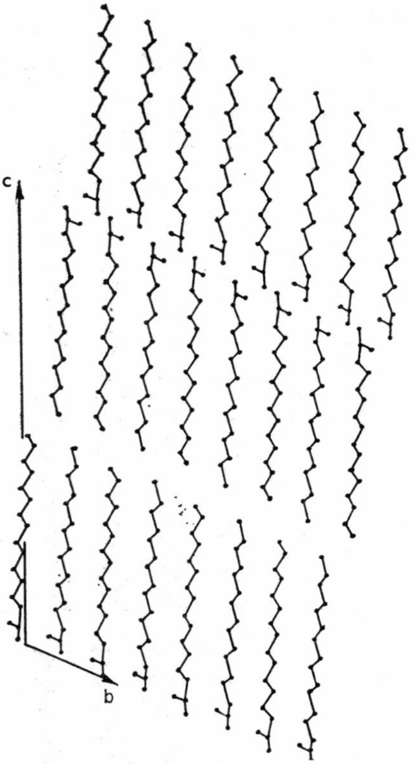

Fig. 103. B′-form of *n*-pentadecanoic acid. Projection along the shortest axis on the largest axis plane. (von Sydow, E. *Arkiv. Kemi*, **9**, 1956.)

FORM C′. This form is considered to have the hydrocarbon chains arranged in the orthorhombic O⊥ manner. With hendecanoic acid the unit cell is monoclinic, with $a = 9{\cdot}622$, $b = 4{\cdot}915$ and $c = 34{\cdot}18$ Å and $\beta = 131°\ 17'$. The space group is C^5_{2h}–$P2_1/a$ and there are four molecules per unit cell. This form only exists near the melting point of the acid and there are some unusual features about the chains. They are said to be neither straight nor planar, and have their centre lines bent whilst the chain planes are probably helically twisted around their centre lines. The chain packing is shown in Fig. 104. It may be that the hydrocarbon chains are quite near to a hexagonal-type sub-cell and involved in considerable motion, somewhat analogous to that observed with the α-form of hydrocarbons and ethyl esters. As the chain is lengthened they may arrange themselves more strictly in an orthorhombic sub-cell.

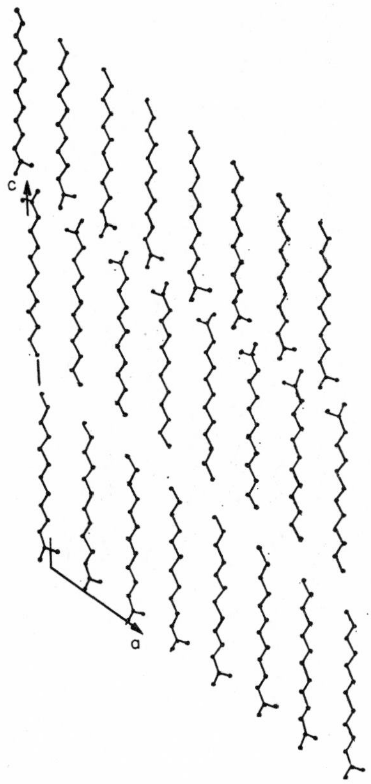

Fig. 104. C′-form of *n*-hendecanoic acid. Projection along the shortest axis on the largest axis plane. (von Sydow, E. *Arkiv. Kemi*, **9**, 1956.)

FORM A. This form has triclinic packed chains T||. With dodecanoic acid the unit cell is triclinic and there are six molecules in the primitive unit cell. The centred cell, however, contains twelve molecules (space group C_c'–$A\bar{1}$). The structure can be regarded as a six-fold superstructure with regard to the chain packing. The dimers are arranged so that carboxyl and methyl groups appear in the same planes in the crystal. As a consequence of this the usually strong odd long spacing reflections disappear. The cell dimensions are $a = 5{\cdot}41$ Å, $b = 26{\cdot}27$ Å and

$c = 35{\cdot}42$ Å, $\alpha = 69° 36'$, $\beta = 113° 9'$ and $\gamma = 121° 21'$. A similar arrangement is observed with *n*-tetradecanoic acid [66]. An arrangement without superstructure has been found for these acids but a full structural determination has not been carried out. It is presumed that in this

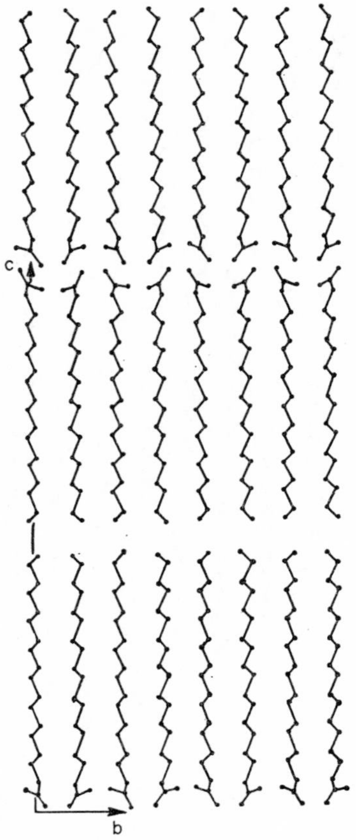

Fig. 105. B-form of *n*-octadecanoic (stearic) acid. Projection along the shortest axis on the largest axis plane. (von Sydow, E. *Arkiv Kemi*, **9**, 1956.)

form the dimers are arranged with carboxyl and methyl groups in alternate layers. An additional form has recently been observed with dodecanoic acid designated an A_1-form which is closely related to the *A* super form [67]. There are two molecules per unit cell and the sub-cell is triclinic.

FORM B. This form has orthorhombic packed chains $O\perp$. With *n*-octadecanoic acid the unit cell is monoclinic with $a = 5{\cdot}591$ Å, $b = 7{\cdot}404$ Å and $c = 49{\cdot}38$ Å and $\beta = 117° \; 22'$. The carbon atom in the carboxyl group is forced from its place in the sub-cell to allow the dimerization. The cell contains four molecules. The space group is $C_{2h}^{5}\text{–}P2_1/a$. This form was first investigated by Muller (1927) and the

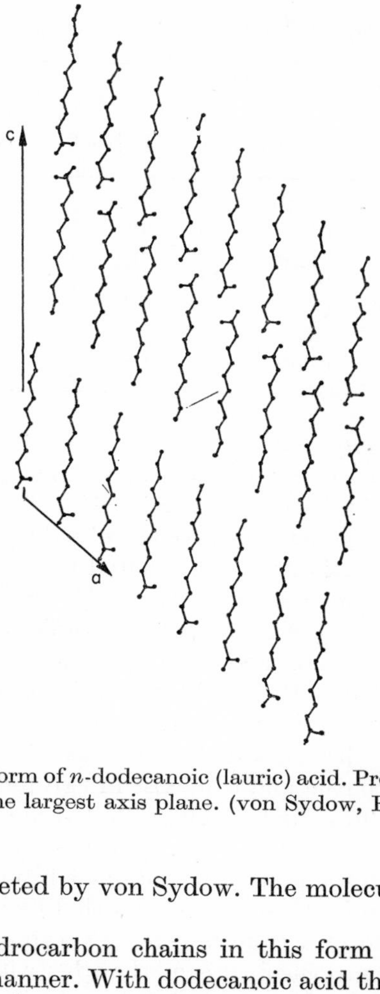

Fig. 106. The C-form of *n*-dodecanoic (lauric) acid. Projection along the shortest axis on the largest axis plane. (von Sydow, E. *Arkiv Kemi*, **9**, 1956.)

structure was completed by von Sydow. The molecular arrangement is shown in Fig. 105.

FORM C. The hydrocarbon chains in this form are packed in the orthorhombic O⊥ manner. With dodecanoic acid the unit cell is monoclinic with $a = 9{\cdot}524$ Å, $b = 4{\cdot}965$ Å and $c = 35{\cdot}39$ Å, $\beta = 129° \; 13'$. The cell contains four molecules and space group $C_{2h}^{5}\text{–}P2_1/a$. The chains appear to be regular in the short axis projection but in the bounded projection along the medium axis the chains are bent. It is expected, however, that with the longer members the chains will be packed in the strictly orthorhombic manner. The molecular arrangement is shown in Fig. 106.

The structures of the different crystal forms of the monocarboxylic acids are summarized in Table 42.

Table 42. *Crystallographic data*

Crystal form	Acid examined	Space group	Sub-cell	No. of moles/unit cell	Angle of tilt
A	12	$A\bar{1}(P\bar{1})$	T∥	12 (2)	64°
A_1	12	$P\bar{1}$	T∥	2	67°
B	18	$P2_1/a$	O⊥	4	66°
C	12	$P2_1/b$	O⊥	4	56°
A′	15	$P\bar{1}$	T∥	2	66°
B′	15	$P\bar{1}$	O⊥	4	61°
C′	11	$P2_1/b$	O⊥	4	59°

(*b*) *Branched-chain fatty acids*

The methyl branched-chain fatty acids are of biological importance and are fairly common in nature. Several acids of this type have been observed as trace components in various animal fats. The acid (−)10-D-methyl octadecanoic acid has been isolated from the lipids of tubercle bacilli and other branched-chain acids are also present.

A considerable amount of X-ray powder studies have been carried out with these branched acids and long spacings determined. The data appear to indicate that in these acids the hydrocarbon chains are tilted more towards the end group planes than are the normal chain acids. A recent study [20, 68] has shown that the racemic methyl octadecanoic acid shows polymorphism and can exist in two forms. This is observed with 6-DL-Me-C_{18}, 10-DL-Me-C_{18}, 11-DL-Me-C_{18} and 12-DL-Me-C_{18} acids. The low melting form is obtained by rapid crystallization from the melt, whereas the other form is usually obtained from slowly evaporating solvent. A plot of the $d(001)$ spacings show that two modifications occur, one designated a τ-form with long spacing varying with the position of the branch (the high melting form) and the other with an almost constant value of the long spacing irrespective of the substituent position (the low melting ν-form).

Single-crystal studies of 9-DL-Me-C_{18}, 16-DL-Me-C_{18} and 17-Me-C_{18} acids in their τ-crystalline form have been made. These show that the branched methyl groups are given space between the methyl end-groups of the acid molecules. The hydrocarbon chains pack in the triclinic T|| manner. This forces a large tilt on the molecules; thus the 17-Me-C_{18} acid has the chains tilted at an angle of 46° compared with the angle 60° of the normal acid. The molecules become more tilted as the branch shifts closer to the carboxyl group.

The carboxyl groups are forced into the chain packing but cause distortions. With 9-DL-Me-C_{18} the distortion is large but localized and the neighbouring chains bend into the space between the chain ends leaving other parts of the chain unaffected. With the other acids the distortions are smaller but affect the whole chain packing. With the17-Me-C_{18} acid the carboxyl groups have a slightly different orientation and the atoms of the two hydrogen-bonded carboxyl groups are not co-planar. With the other acids, the dimerized carboxyl groups are parallel.

Single-crystal studies of 14-DL-C_{18} and 2-DL-Me-C_{18} acids in the ν-form have been made. These show that the shape of the molecule is different from that of the τ-form. Here the branching methyl group constitutes the end of a straight carbon chain starting from the carboxyl group. The remaining carbon atoms form a side chain which is at an angle of about 110° with the main chain. The main chain becomes shorter and the side chain longer as the branch approaches the carboxyl group. This explains why the long spacing remains almost constant with the acids in this form.

The hydrocarbon chain packing may be different for the main chain and the branch chain. With 14-DL-Me-C_{18} acid the main chain has triclinic T|| packing, whilst the packing of the side chain is quite imperfect. When the side chain becomes longer it may dominate the crystallization. With 2-DL-Me-C_{18} acid it has almost perfect triclinic packing. The main chains are arranged in the orthorhombic O$\perp$ manner with the 15-DL-Me-C_{18} acid. The molecules in this form have the lowest possible tilt for methyl branched octadecanoic acid which increases the disturbing influence of the carboxyl groups. It has a lower density corresponding to less effective filling of space than with the τ-form.

The 3-DL-Me-C_{18} acid has a crystal structure which does not fit into the τ- and ν-series.

Single-crystal studies of some optically active methyl octadecanoic acids have also been made [20]. The acid 3-D-Me-C_{18} in its high melting form shows two sub-cell directions in the structure. The unit cell is monoclinic containing eight molecules: $a = 8{\cdot}92$ Å, $b = 52{\cdot}2$ Å and $c = 9{\cdot}93$ Å, $\beta = 123°$. The dimensions of the sub-cell do not fit those of any known sub-cell. ($a_s = 5{\cdot}18$ Å, $b_s = 8{\cdot}92$ Å and $c_s = 2{\cdot}70$ Å, $\alpha_s = 133°$, $\beta_s = 73°$ and $\gamma_s = 129°$.) The arrangements in the carboxyl region is uncertain. The low melting form has not been studied. The high melting form of 2-D-Me-C_{18} acid is interesting since the chains pack in the unique packing O′|| arrangement. The carboxyl group branches are accommodated between the ends of the molecules. Instead of being dimerized, as with most other methyl octadecanoic acids, this acid has infinite helices of hydrogen bonds through the structure parallel to the *b*-axis. This hydrogen bond system is similar to that observed with formic and acetic acid. There is very efficient molecular packing in this crystal. The structure of the low melting form of this acid is similar to that of the 2-DL-Me-C_{18} acid.

(*c*) *Unsaturated acids*
One of the earliest studies of unsaturated acids was due to Muller and Shearer [69] who investigated unsaturated acids of the same chain length, e.g. oleic, elaidic, iso-oleic, erucic and brassidic acids and showed that different isomers, although of the same chain length, can have different long spacings.

Polymorphism with unsaturated acids was first investigated by Lutton [70], who investigated the two forms of oleic acid. The lowest melting form crystallizes in a normal tilted double molecule structure whilst the higher melting form is apparently somewhat unusual and there is some uncertainty as to whether it contains four molecules in length or two. The usual alternation of strong intensities of the odd order of reflection are missing with this form. (An infra-red spectroscopic examination of this form may be of value in providing further information on the dimerism or chain packing.)

Trans-octadecanoic acids with the double bond varying from the sixth to the twelfth position have been investigated [71]. They do not exhibit polymorphism. The acids with the double bond at an odd-numbered carbon atom have greater long spacings and lower melting points than those having a double bond at an even-numbered carbon atom. The former crystallize with the hydrocarbon chains vertical, the latter with the hydrocarbon chains tilted. Their short spacings at 4·13 *vs* and 3·74 s; and 4·16 s, 4·43 s, and 3·17 s perhaps indicate that the hydrocarbon chain packing is common orthorhombic O⊥ in the former and triclinic T|| in the latter. The individual acids can be differentiated by their X-ray powder patterns. Vaccenic acid has been studied [72] and shown to give long and short spacings very similar to those given by elaidic acid.

A single-crystal study of the low melting form of oleic acid has been completed [41]. This shows that the chains about the *cis* double bond are tilted in opposite directions. The chain packing is of a new type O′||. The acid dimers are held together by hydrogen bonds around centres of symmetry. There are four molecules per unit cell and the space group is

$P2_1/a$. The molecular arrangement along the *a*- and *b*-axes are shown in Fig. 107. The cell dimensions of erucic and *cis*-nervonic acids have also been determined.

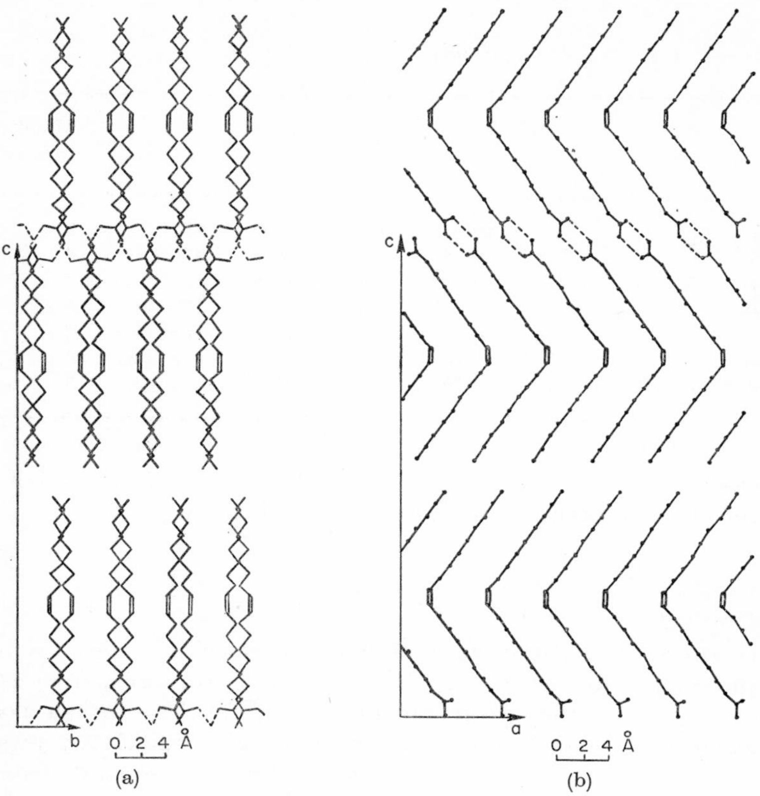

Fig. 107*a*. Molecular arrangement of oleic acid seen along *a* axis. (Abrahamsson, S. and Ryderstedt-Nahringbauer, I. *Acta Cryst.*, **15**, 1261, 1962.)

Fig. 107*b*. Molecular arrangement of oleic acid seen along *b* axis. (Abrahamsson, S. and Ryderstedt-Nahringbauer, I. *Acta Cryst.*, **15**, 1261, 1962.)

(*d*) *Dicarboxylic acids*

Dicarboxylic acids are amongst some of the earliest acids to be investigated [73, 74] and single-crystal studies were carried out as early as 1928. The values of the sub-cell dimensions for a number of these acids are given in Table 43. The crystals can be divided into two classes according to whether there are odd or even numbers of carbon atoms in the molecule. The *c*-axes of the even carbon series are nearly proportional to the number of carbon atoms, whilst in the odd series they are proportional to twice this number. The former contain two molecules per unit cell, whilst the latter contain four molecules per unit cell.

Table 43. *Unit cell dimensions*

Acid	*a*	*b*	*c*	β	Moles in unit cell
Adipic	10·27	5·16	10·02	137° 5′	2
Pimelic	9·93	4·82	22·12	130° 40′	4
Suberic	10·12	5·06	12·58	135° 0′	2
Azelaic	9·72	4·83	27·14	129° 30′	4
Sebacic	10·05	4·96	15·02	133° 50′	2
Brassylic	9·63	4·82	37·95	128° 20′	4
Hexadecane dicarboxylic	9·76	4·92	25·10	131° 10′	2

These acids have been shown to exhibit dimorphism; azelaic and pimelic acid can occur in two different modifications [75].

ESTERS

(a) Ethyl esters

Ethyl esters can exist in at least two polymorphic forms. From the palmitate upwards, they solidify from the melt into a transparent α-form which on cooling changes to an opaque β-form. The former possess vertical rotating chains, and the latter tilted chains. Malkin suggests [76] that ethyl myristate and lower members of the series separate from the melt into the stable β-form and no α-form exists.

Smith suggests that three kinds of polymorphism occur [77]. Up to ethyl myristate the opaque β-forms of both even and odd numbers are stable and the transparent α-forms are metastable. From the myristate to the eicosanoate the α-forms are stable near the melting point and change enantiotropically to the β-forms on cooling; α-forms of the even members are metastable and change monotropically to the β-forms. Above ethyl eicosanoate the α-forms of both the odd and even numbers are stable near the melting point. The α-form shows a single short spacing near 4·2 Å whilst the β-form show strong spacings at 3·7 and 4·1 Å. A single crystal study has been completed with ethyl stearate [78]. The structure is shown in Fig. 108, along the *a*-axis. The chain packing is common orthorhombic O$\perp$.

(*b*) *Methyl esters*

The methyl esters, according to Malkin [8], show dimorphism with the odd numbers whilst the even numbers do not exhibit polymorphism. The odd numbers separate from the melt in a form which consists of layers of single molecules. It is suggested that the chains are tilted at an angle of

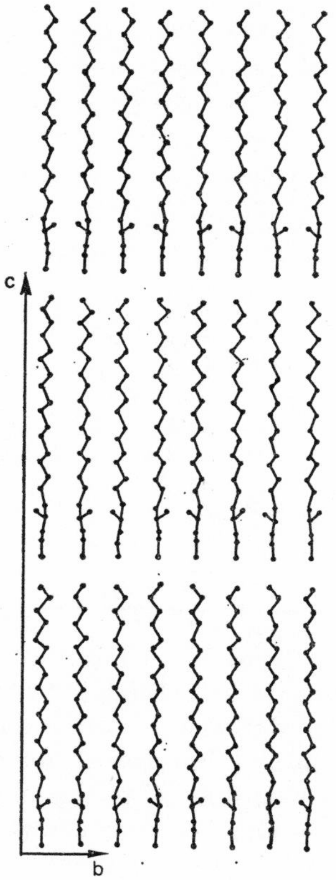

Fig. 108. Schematic view of ethyl stearate seen along the *a* axis. (Aleby, S. *Acta Cryst.*, **15**, 1248, 1962.)

75° but there is some uncertainty concerning this form. It may be a rotating form as with the hydrocarbons.

The most stable form crystallizes in double molecules which are tilted across the (001) planes.

The long and short spacings of the ethyl and methyl esters [79] are given in Table 44.

A single crystal structure of methyl stearate [80] shows that the unit

Table 44. *Long and short spacings of ethyl and methyl esters*

Ester	Short spacings Å				Tilt
Ethyl stearate	3·69 s	4·08 s	4·28 w	4·46 vw	62° 45'
Ethyl nonadecylate	3·68 s	4·12 s	4·28 vw	4·44 w	62° 45'
Methyl stearate	3·69 s	4·05 s	4·28 w	4·46 vw	61° 40
Methyl nonadecylate	3·68 s	4·09 s	4·30 w	4·45 w	61° 40

Long spacings Å

Carbon atoms in acid	Methyl esters α	Methyl esters β	Ethyl esters α	Ethyl esters β
14	—	38·8	—	—
15	23·6	41·8	—	—
16	—	43·45	—	22·9
17	26·0	46·3	27·1	24·75
18	—	47·95	—	25·80
19	28·4	50·8	29·8	26·95
20	—	52·3	—	27·6
21	30·9	55·25	32·4	29·35
22	—	—	—	29·90
23	—	—	—	31·50
24	—	—	—	32·15

cell is monoclinic, the hydrocarbon chains are packed in the common orthorhombic O⊥ manner. The cell contains eight molecules and the space group is $A2/a$. In a similar way to the monocarboxylic acids the molecules form double sheets (dimerize) although, of course, there is no possibility of hydrogen bonding with this molecule. The molecular arrangement along the a- and b-axes is shown in Fig. 109. This is in contrast to the ethyl esters and the higher esters. The closest distance between the ester carbon atoms is 3·3 Å, which is unusually short. The polar forces between oxygen and carbon atoms are presumably the cause of the dimerization. X-ray powder photographs of the material obtained from different solvents and the melt are found to be identical, except for rapid crystallization from chloroform or the melt. The powder diagram, whilst similar, is somewhat more simple. The melting points of the two forms are very nearly the same. This is consistent with the observations of Francis and Piper [79] who state that the long-chain methyl esters have two crystal forms with different melting points only a few tenths of a degree apart.

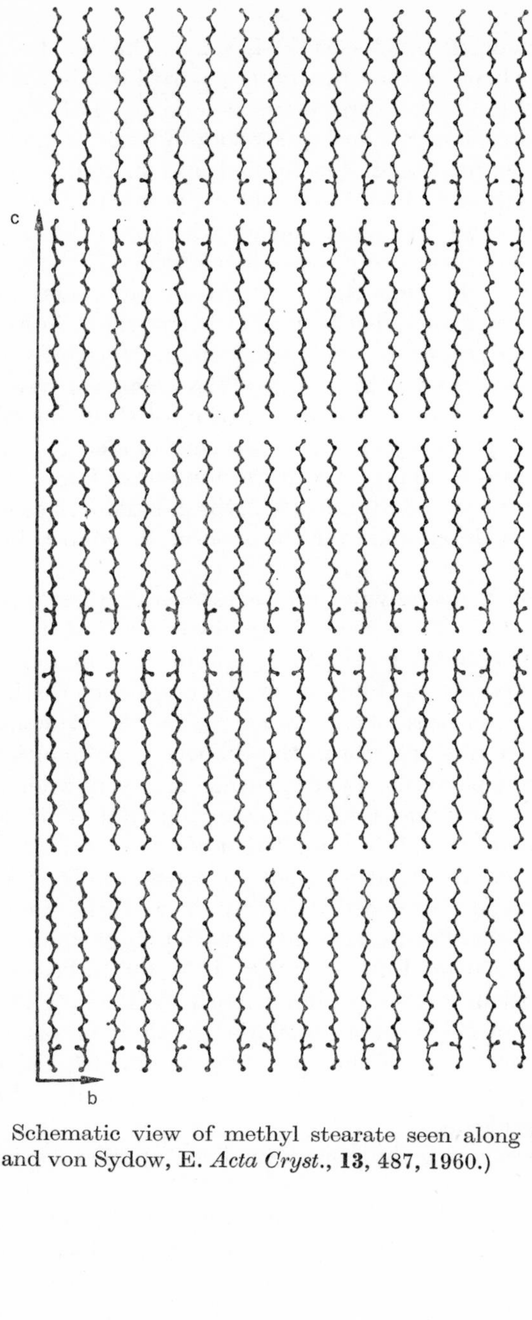

Fig. 109. Schematic view of methyl stearate seen along the *a* axis. (Aleby, S. and von Sydow, E. *Acta Cryst.*, **13**, 487, 1960.)

GLYCERIDES

Introduction

The multiple melting of glycerides has been known for more than a century and has been studied by numerous workers, but it has long been a field for confusion and controversy. As long ago as 1849 tristearin was observed after melting [81] and quick solidification to melt at 51–52° C, whilst on further heating it resolidified and melted at 62–62·5° C. In 1853 it was shown [82] to have three melting points 52°, 64·2° and 69·7° C. The highest melting point was identical with that of the solvent crystallized glyceride and the lowest practically coincided with the setting point. It was assumed at this time that this melting behaviour was due to the occurrence of some form of isomerism. Other workers, however, reported only two melting points for tristearin, tripalmitin and trimyristin [83, 84, 85]. Later the three melting points of tristearin were rediscovered [86] and this was supported by the observation of three melting points for tripalmitin [87]. The subject was again confounded in 1930 when only two melting points were reported for a number of triglycerides thought to be of high purity [88]. Later, in 1932, the existence of as many as seven different forms were claimed for the saturated mono-acid triglycerides [89].

As a result of X-ray powder photograph investigations, Malkin and colleagues [90, 91] demonstrated conclusively that the basis of the multiple melting behaviour is actually polymorphism, i.e. the occurrence for a given compound of different crystalline forms distinguishable by X-ray diffraction pattern. Later workers [92, 93, 94] came to the conclusion that there was an error in this association of melting points with X-ray diffraction patterns. Lutton, using X-ray powder photography, was particularly prominent in this assertion [95]. This, however, was vigorously denied by Malkin [96]. This unfortunate controversy spread to a wide area of the field and led to considerable confusion in the literature. It was further accentuated by the use by these workers of the same symbols with differing association with polymorphic form. Reviews of the field in 1950 by Lutton and in 1954 by Malkin emphasize the confusion and dichotomy of opinion, both workers standing rigidly on the correctness of their differing views. Some attempts were made to arrive at a compromise of the two view-points [97, 98] but were not accepted. Disagreement also occurred over the polymorphism of the di- and monoglycerides.

In recent years new techniques have been applied to this field, notably dielectric measurements, the use of differential heating apparatus, some X-ray single-crystal studies, infra-red spectroscopy and nuclear-magnetic resonance spectroscopy, and the deadlock appears to be finally broken. A recent review has examined this controversial field, particularly in the light of this new evidence, and assessed the main areas of controversy [99]. Here we shall point out the main features of the controversy and show how it has recently been resolved.

Nomenclature of glycerides

The nomenclature for designating the different polymorphic forms of glycerides is extremely confusing. This is due to the fact that the same symbols are used with different association with polymorphic form by different workers. The nomenclature used by Malkin [96] is based on melting points, the highest melting form is called β, the intermediate melting forms marked with a prime (β', β'') and the form having a single X-ray short spacing of 4·1 Å is designated α or alpha. The lowest melting form for triglycerides was said by this author to be vitreous. Lutton, on the other hand [95], uses X-ray data as a basis for his nomenclature. This is shown in Table 45.

Table 45. *Lutton nomenclature for glyceride forms*

Form	Short spacing pattern characteristics
Alpha	A single strong line corresponding to approximately 4·15 Å
Beta prime	Usually two (but occasionally more) strong lines corresponding to approximately 4·2 and 3·8 Å
Beta	A strong (usually strongest) line corresponding to approximately 4·6 Å

Presumably to try to prevent confusion, the full name is written by Lutton, e.g. alpha rather than α- and beta prime rather than β'-, but confusion nevertheless occurred. The subtle distinction was apparently not always obvious, and when the terms are spoken they sound the same. To designate an alpha form having long spacings equivalent to two lengths of fatty-acid chains the term alpha-2 is used and similarly beta-3 is used to indicate triple chain length structures, etc.

The existence of these two alternative schemes of nomenclature leads to unusual situations, e.g. the highest melting form of 2-stearodipalmitin is referred to correctly as beta or β' (pronounced beta-prime), depending upon the author or on which side of the Atlantic one is writing. Recently it was suggested that the use of a suffix M or L would be useful in order to give a more precise designation of a particular form and the short symbol α- for alpha, β'- for beta prime and β- for beta could otherwise be retained. Hence the highest melting form of 2-stearodipalmitin can be referred to correctly as either a β_M-form or a β'_L-form without resultant confusion. This is used wherever possible throughout this chapter.

Both systems used, however, have their limitations. The weakness of the Malkin scheme apart from the introduction of a vitreous form, (see later discussion) is that it does not give any indication of marked crystal similarities between one family of glycerides and another. On the other hand, that due to Lutton, whilst revealing crystal similarities, almost certainly over-simplifies the variations possible in glyceride crystal structures. It has also become cumbersome and terms such as sub-alpha, sub-A-beta, sub-B-beta, and super alpha-1 are used. Furthermore, it is not clear how far crystal similarities are indeed being picked out and indicated in the nomenclature. The hydrocarbon chain packing in the sub-alpha form is almost certainly the same (common orthorhombic O$\perp$) as in the β'_L-form of the triglycerides, yet the nomenclature does not indicate this. The nomenclature gives no clue as to whether the chain packing in the super-alpha form is similar to the alpha or to the sub-alpha modification.

The new types of sub-cell or chain packing observed with amides, soaps and branched chain fatty acids (see page 240) show that caution is needed in attempting to provide a simple nomenclature based on crystal structure to cover the enormous variation possible in all glycerides. However, if the nomenclature based on X-ray data is regarded as an approximation and used as such it can be useful. The use of one or other of the two systems with the suffix M or L seems the best at this stage.

(*a*) *Mono-acid saturated triglycerides*

Although this group of glycerides is probably the most complete homologous series of glycerides that have been studied it is around these compounds that most disagreement and controversy has raged [95, 96, 100]. Disagreement centres on the association of X-ray diffraction patterns with melting point, the existence of a vitreous form and the precise number of forms possible for these compounds.

With regard to the latter, most workers in the field now generally agree that an early claim for the occurrence of seven polymorphic forms for glycerides such as tristearin is incorrect. With pure mono-acid saturated triglycerides only three, or at best four, distinct X-ray patterns have ever been observed.

(i) THE MAIN CONTROVERSY. The disagreements in this field can be best illustrated by considering the polymorphism of tristearin (see Table 46).

Malkin claimed on the one hand, that this compound has four melting points between 54·5° C and the final melting point, whilst Lutton, on the other hand, claimed that there are only three. Both workers found three distinct X-ray powder patterns but, unfortunately, associated them with different melting forms. Indeed, it is only with the highest melting form that there is agreement on association of X-ray powder patterns.

Table 46. *X-ray and melting data for tristearin according to Malkin and Lutton*

	MALKIN		LUTTON	
Tristearin m.p. °C	X-ray short spacing Å	Name	X-ray short spacing Å	Name
54·5	Diffuse 4·15	Vitreous	4·15	Alpha (α)
65·0	4·15	α	3·8 and 4·2	Beta prime (β')
70·0	3·8 and 4·2	β'	—	—
72·0	4·6	β	4·6	Beta (β)

Malkin claimed that the form melting at 54·5° C gives a diffuse short spacing at 4·15 Å and calls it a vitreous form, stating it to be not fully crystalline and having some characteristics of a glass. Lutton, on the contrary, stated that this form gives a sharp single spacing at 4·15 Å and concluded that the form is crystalline and analogous to the α-forms of hydrocarbons and other long-chain compounds.

(The fogging on the film due to general X-ray scattering can affect the decision on whether a line is sharp or diffuse.)

Malkin claimed that it is the next highest melting form at 65° C which was associated with the powder pattern having a sharp single short spacing at 4·15 Å and that this is the crystalline α-form. He pointed out that only small amounts of this form need be present in a predominantly vitreous form and yet give rise to a sharp X-ray diffraction pattern and thus lead to erroneous conclusions.

One might have expected that the correct association of the X-ray pattern with short spacings at 3·8 and 4·2 Å and melting point would be a comparatively easy matter to decide. However, one of the short spacings is close to that of the lower melting form and transitions can occur before the capillary melting point is reached. The average time for an adequate exposure on the X-ray equipment is, moreover, quite long, and during this time such a transition may occur.

Both workers repeated their original observations but also, unfortunately, their original arguments.

Malkin supported the correctness of this experimental work with a number of points:

(*a*) The α-form is distinguished from the vitreous only by the presence of sharp lines due to long spacings. It is to be remembered that there is no sharp dividing line between the crystalline and the non-crystalline state. With very small units the X-ray diffraction becomes more diffuse. As the layer structure falls below a certain size the long spacings disappear; a diffused short spacing still persists, owing to lateral diffraction by the hydrocarbon chains, which does not necessarily depend on a layer structure.

(*b*) When the most stable form of a triglyceride is obtained from solvent it has a higher melting point (say 72·0° C) than the form (regarded by Lutton as the most stable form) obtained by thermal transformation (say, 70° C). With a pure compound, the same crystallographic form cannot have two different melting points.

(*c*) Consideration of the methyl group packing in long-chain crystals leads to an association of alternation of the melting points of an homologous series with the tilting of the hydrocarbon chains, i.e. where the melting points alternate the hydrocarbon chains are tilted and where they are non-alternating the chains are vertical. As the long spacings associated with the short spacings at 3·8 and 4·2 Å are consistent with tilted and not vertical chains, this pattern cannot be associated with a series of non-alternating melting points, as Lutton would have it.

Arguments put forward against these points were:

(*a*) The problem is not whether a form actually crystalline is called a glass but what properties are truly associated with the lowest melting point. The form is, moreover, not a glass in the usual sense anyway. It has (1) a sharp melting point, (2) discontinuity in specific volume on melting, (3) discontinuity in heat content on melting, (4) anisotropy, (5) sharp diffraction lines not in the position of the typical diffuse lines of a liquid fat.

(*b*) A pure long-chain compound can give rise to a spread in melting level according to the degree of stabilization of the form (see later discussion).

(*c*) The relationship between alternation and tilting of hydrocarbon chains is only a theory (due to Malkin). If the experimental facts show the theory to be not completely valid, so much the worse for the theory.

American workers [92, 93] other than Lutton also considered that Malkin had mistakenly associated X-ray diffraction pattern with melting points. Against this, however, Russian workers [101] supported Malkin in his claim for the existence of a vitreous form for glycerides, adducing optical evidence to do so. Since the same considerations apply to all the triglycerides, including simple saturated, mixed saturated and unsaturated in character, a massive deadlock occurred in this field which has lasted for some years. This was further confused by the use of the two alternative systems of nomenclature which we have already discussed.

This deadlock was at last broken by the introduction of a new technique for studying the polymorphism of glycerides, namely, infra-red spectroscopy. A study of the various spectral changes observed with the polymorphic forms of hydrocarbons, ethyl esters and alcohols showed infra-red spectroscopy to be useful for studying polymorphism [102, 103]. Marked changes occur between one polymorphic form and another. Certain significant similarities are also apparent between the spectra of related forms from one class of long-chain compound to another. Thus when these molecules are obtained by thermal treatment in the hexagonal α-form (rotator form) a strong single band is observed in the infra-red spectrum at 720 cm^{-1} corresponding to the main CH_2 rocking mode. The spectra of the more stable crystalline forms (non-rotator forms) show usually a doublet for this mode at $\sim$ 727 and 719 cm^{-1} of approximately equal intensity, although occasionally with certain hydrocarbons only a strong single band at 717 cm^{-1} is observed. There are other significant band changes but these are particularly prominent.

When the technique is applied to triglycerides, e.g. tristearin, three distinct spectra are obtained. These were compared with the three distinct X-ray diffraction patterns obtained for this compound. Further discussion of the spectra appear in the chapter on infra-red spectroscopy.

By comparison with other long-chain esters, fatty acids, hydrocarbons and alcohols the polymorphic forms of the simple triglycerides are classified into three crystallographic types according to their hydrocarbon chain packing or the symmetry of their sub-cells. Thus the α_L-form has hexagonal sub-cell, the β'_L-form orthorhombic $O\perp$ sub-cell and the β_L-form triclinic $T\|$ sub-cell symmetry. This throws light on to the classification of the triglycerides by means of their X-ray short spacings proposed by Lutton. The short spacing classification is possible because of the underlying symmetry of the sub-cell.

Further support for these considerations has been provided by discussions of the relationship between X-ray short spacings and the hydrocarbon chain packing in long-chain crystals [104]. It should be emphasized that the classification into three types is related not to the crystal symmetry but to the sub-cell symmetry or hydrocarbon chain packing of the glyceride.

All the evidence shows that rejection of Malkin's interpretation of his X-ray data produces (*a*) consistency of pattern of infra-red spectra of the triglycerides with those of other long-chain compounds, (*b*) an internal consistency of the pattern of infra-red spectra of one type of triglyceride

Table 47. *Collected data on the three main crystallographic forms for mono-acid triglycerides*

Property	α_L-Form	β'_L-Form	β_L-Form
MELTING	Sharp melting point Non-alternating	Sharp melting point Non-alternating	Sharp melting point Alternating
X-RAY DIFFRACTION	Sharp diffraction line at 4·1 Å	Strong short spacings at 3·8 and 4·2 Å	Strong short spacing near 4·6 Å
CHAIN PACKING	HEXAGONAL	ORTHORHOMBIC Probably monoclinic crystal	TRICLINIC Also triclinic crystal
DILATOMETRIC DATA (Tristearin) g/ml (−38° C)	Least dense (1·014)	Intermediate density (1·017)	Greatest (1·043)
HEAT OF CRYSTALLIZATION	44 cal/g	Undetermined	62 cal/g
DIELECTRIC BEHAVIOUR (tristearin)	Different from that with glass (2·684) at 52° C	—	(2·340) at 65·1° C
Infra-red spectrum	Characteristic spectrum evidence of considerable crystallinity. A single band at 720 cm^{-1}	Characteristic spectrum. Doublet at 727 and 719 cm^{-1}	Characteristic spectrum Single band at 717 cm^{-1}
N.m.r. spectrum	Considerable proton mobility. The second moment of the line width is similar to that obtained with hydrocarbons in their rotator form, i.e. 11·1 for tristearin	Slight degree of proton mobility as in the β_L-form	A slight degree of proton mobility. Second moment for tristearin 22·2 (293° K)

to another, and (*c*) consistency of X-ray and infra-red data. Conversely, acceptance of Malkin's interpretation produces inconsistency of spectral characteristics within the glycerides themselves and also with the other long-chain compounds. Other studies of the lowest melting form of the triglycerides are consistent with this conclusion.

Dielectric studies of tristearin and tripalmitin also show that orientational freedom occurs in the lowest melting α-form of these compounds. The dielectric constant is lower than that of the liquid but high enough to show orientational freedom [105].

Microscope investigations of these glycerides are unfortunately not too definitive, in that a variety of crystal habits may occur for the same basic crystal form. An examination of the lowest melting form, however, shows that it exhibits strong birefringence inconsistent with this form being glassy or vitreous [106].

A further interesting fact of relevance to the discussion of existence of a vitreous form is that the kinetics of crystal nucleation in some normal alkane liquids, e.g. $C_{16}H_{34}$, $C_{17}H_{36}$, $C_{18}H_{38}$, $C_{24}H_{50}$ and $C_{32}H_{66}$, shows that such molecules have very weak glass-forming tendency and this is attributed to the hypothesis of nucleation of small segments of molecules [107]. Information relating to the properties of three main forms of the even mono-acid triglycerides are shown in Table 47.

The unfortunate consequence of Malkin's error was that it is perpetuated in all of his work on triglycerides. This means that a large part of the work requires re-examination. In some cases the correct association of X-ray and melting data may be comparatively easy to make, in other cases it will be more difficult. The correct association of X-ray data and melting points for the even numbers are shown in Table 48. The corrected association for the odd numbers are also given with the suspect additional melting points given in brackets. Further work is required to check this.

(ii) ADDITIONAL FORMS. Whilst there is little doubt about the incorrect association by Malkin of X-ray data and melting point with the simple saturated triglycerides the question still remains as to how many polymorphic forms are possible with these compounds. It is an experimental fact observed by many authors that the stable form obtained from solvent has a higher melting point than the same form obtained by thermal transformation, yet the X-ray powder photographs are often the same.

An attempt to provide a rationalization of microscope data, melting-point and X-ray data for tristearin is shown in Table 49.

Attempts have been made to explain this variation in melting point by considering variations in crystalline size and crystalline perfection. It is

Table 48. *X-ray and melting data for the mono-acid triglycerides*

Glyceride	MELTING POINTS °C			LONG SPACINGS			SHORT SPACINGS								
	α_L	β'_L	β_L	α_L	β'_L	β_L	α_L			β'_L		β_L			
Tristearin	54	64	73·1	50·6	47·2	45·0	4·2	3·8 s	4·22 s	—	—	3·7 m	3·9 m	4·6 s	5·3 m
Tripalmitin	44·7	56·6	66·4	45·6	42·6	40·6	4·2	3·8 s	4·22 s	—	—	3·7 m	3·9 m	4·6 s	5·3 m
Trimyristin	33	46·5	57·0	41·2	37·6	35·8	4·2	3·8 s	4·22 s	—	—	3·7 m	3·9 m	4·6 s	5·3 m
Trilaurin	15	35·0	46·4	35·6	32·9	31·2	4·2	3·78 s	4·18 vs	—	—	3·7 m	3·9 m	4·6 s	5·3 m
Tridecylin	−15	18·0	31·5	—	—	26·8	4·2	—	—	—	—	3·7 m	3·9 m	4·6 s	5·3 m
Trimargarin	50	61·0 (62·5)	64·0	48·5	43·7	43·5	4·2	3·79 s	4·02 w	4·19 s	4·37 w	3·65 m	4·0 m	4·6 s	5·3 m
Tripentadecylin	40·0	51·5 (53·0)	54·0	42·9	39·1	38·9	4·2	3·81 s	4·12 s	4·3 s	—	3·65 m	4·0 m	4·6 s	5·3 m
Tritridecylic	25·0	41·0 (42·5)	44·0	37·7	34·2	34·1	4·2	3·85 m	4·04 w	4·26 s	4·43 w	3·65 m	4·0 m	4·6 s	5·3 m
Triundecylin	1·0	26·5 (29·0)	30·5	33·0	29·5	29·6	4·2	3·88 s	4·25 s	4·52 w	—	3·65 m	4·0 m	4·6 s	5·3 m

certainly true that small particles of a substance may have different properties than larger particles of the same material, such as lower melting point, higher solubility. Very thin layers of tristearin can give a lower melting point than thicker layers. The large differences of 2 or 3° seem rather high to be explained on this basis. The effect of variation of chain alignment or of the methylene groups within the chain may provide the basis for a better explanation. Comparison has been made with similar behaviour in polymers, but there is as yet no generally accepted explanation for this behaviour.

Table 49. *The relationship of the seven forms of tristearin using microscopy with X-ray data*

Weygand and Gruntzig symbol	Probable X-ray pattern	Microscope appearance	Melting points (for tristearin) °C
I C	β_L	Beta rhombs	71·0
I B	β_L	Beta spherulites	70·5
I C	β_L	Often alpha mosaic may be hazy	69·5
II A	β'_L	Bright beta prime	65·5
II B	β'_L	Dull to bright beta prime	65·0
II C	β'_L	Dull beta prime	65·0
III C	α_L	Alpha mosaic	55·0

Note: Beta crystals have oblique extinction.
Beta prime crystals have parallel extinction and spherulites positive and/or negative.
Alpha crystals have spherulite elongation always negative.

There is, however, experimental evidence for a further form of the simple triglycerides. The presence of this form was first observed in some behenyl mixed triglycerides and subsequently in tristearin. It transforms reversibly from the α_L-form at low temperature (−50° C) without melting. Its short spacings are similar to those of the β'_L-form (∼ 3·7 and 4·2 Å) and it was designated a sub-alpha (sub-α_L-form). With tristearin a diffuse darkening in the 3·8 Å region is observed at −50° C. Malkin threw doubt on the correctness of this interpretation, pointing out that at such low temperatures ice condenses on the specimen, giving rise to a spacing in this region.

A phase change is confirmed, however, by means of infra-red spectroscopy. If the glyceride is obtained in the α_L-form in an evacuated low-temperature cell and the temperature lowered the specimen remains generally the same although bands narrow and sharpen. As the temperature approaches $-50°$ to $-70°$ C the main CH_2 rocking mode in the 720 cm^{-1} region gradually changes from a single band to a doublet. The doublet is similar to that observed with the spectrum of the intermediate β'_L-form and the chains in this sub-α_L-form are probably orthorhombically packed. This spectral change is observed with other triglycerides such as trimargarin and 1-oleodistearin. It is analogous to the changes observed with 1-monoglycerides. Examination of differential heating curves of the triglycerides reveal no heat changes in the -50 to $-70°$ C region. Examination of curves showing the variation of dielectric constant with temperature for the α_L-form show a region of anomalous dispersion consistent with a phase change taking place. The dispersion behaviour is similar to that observed with the sub-α-form of monoglycerides. When n.m.r. measurements are made on the α_L-form of tristearin the second moment is observed to be $11{\cdot}1 \pm 0{\cdot}3$ at 293°K and $24 \pm 0{\cdot}2$ at 90°K showing a considerable reduction in proton mobility. (The second moment for the stable β_L-form at this temperature is $24{\cdot}7 \pm 0{\cdot}6$.) The infra-red and n.m.r. data are consistent with the idea that as the temperature is lowered the chains rotate less rapidly and pack together more tightly.

(iii) SINGLE CRYSTAL STUDY. Single crystal data are available for the β_L-form of trilaurin [24]. This shows that the unit cell is triclinic and that it contains two molecules per unit cell $a = 12{\cdot}31 \pm 0{\cdot}10$ Å, $b = 5{\cdot}40 \pm 0{\cdot}06$ Å, $c = 31{\cdot}77 \pm 0{\cdot}10$ Å, $\alpha = 94°\ 16'$, $\beta = 96°\ 52'$ and $\gamma = 99°\ 12'$.

The sub-cell is also triclinic and contains two CH_2 groups per unit cell. The dimensions of the sub-cell are given in Table 37. The angle of tilt between the chains and the a–b plane of the main unit cell is 62° 7′ in good agreement with the angle predicted from the long spacing of the even series of triglycerides (61° 35′). Later studies of trilaurin [107] have shown good agreement with this work but it is suggested that there are small errors in the sub-cell dimensions. A structure of the β_L-form of tricaprin has also been published [108, 109].

The general manner of arrangement of the glycerides in the lattice is shown in Fig. 110. This shows that the glyceride packs in a type of tuning-fork configuration but rather different from that conventionally accepted. The central and one of the two extreme alkyl groups are along the same axis. Two glyceride molecules pack in such a way that the third remaining alkyl groups also lie along an axis parallel to the first. It can be seen from this arrangement that the structure very much resembles that of a long-chain hydrocarbon, the perturbation due to the presence of the glyceryl residue being made rather small in its effect. It can be

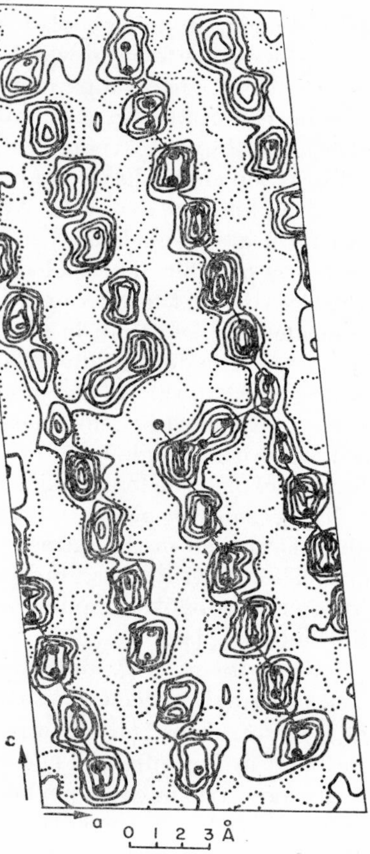

Fig. 110. X-ray structure of trilaurin. (Vand, V. and Bell, I. P. *Acta Cryst.*, **4**, 465, 1951.)

appreciated from this structure why the crystallization behaviour is similar to that of long-chain paraffins.

Re-examination of the long spacings of mixed saturated triglycerides can be made on this basis but it is rather dangerous to try to predict too much detail from long-spacing data alone. A single-crystal study of the β'_L-polymorphic form of the simple saturated triglycerides would be particularly valuable to provide additional evidence on their polymorphism.

(iv) THE PRESENT PICTURE. The present picture of the polymorphic transitions which occur with saturated mono-acid-triglycerides is the following:

A triglyceride, e.g. tristearin, on being cooled from the melt to below room temperature crystallizes in a form in which the long hydrocarbon chains are hexagonally packed with chains normal to the basal plane and in which the chains can rotate in a manner analogous to that observed in the rotator form of hydrocarbons. Essentially, in the undercooled liquid, the hydrocarbon chains have arranged themselves parallel over small distances and this has extended over more than, say, a hundred molecules to form an α_L-nucleus. The terminal groups move into a single plane as far as possible. The molecules in this form do not fit into each other very tightly and the entropy decrease in the formation of an α_L-nucleus is considerably less than in the formation of the more densely packed β_L-nucleus. The formation of an α_L-nucleus is hence much more easily undergone than that of the more stable modifications. This form gives rise to X-ray short spacings near 4·2 Å and a characteristic infra-red spectrum with a single band at 720 cm^{-1}.

If the α_L-form is further cooled the long chains rotate more slowly and pack more tightly. X-ray short spacings at 3·8 and 4·2 Å are now observed and a doublet is formed in the infra-red absorption spectrum near 727 and 719 cm^{-1}. The transition is a gradual one and is reversible. The packing of the chains is probably common orthorhombic, O$\perp$ with the chains normal to the basal plane.

On heating the α_L-form to its melting point (with very pure saturated triglyceride) a rapid transformation occurs with evolution of heat to the most stable form, the β_L-form. There is now a strong X-ray short spacing at 4·6 Å and a single band in the infra-red spectrum at 717 cm^{-1}. The hydrocarbon chains are now triclinically packed T$\parallel$ and tilted to the basal plane. (With some mixed saturated triglycerides transitions can occur directly from the $\alpha_L \rightarrow \beta'_L \rightarrow \beta_L$-form.)

If, alternatively, the liquid melt is cooled to a temperature of a few degrees above the melting point of the α_L-form and held at this temperature until crystallization occurs, the intermediate β'_L-form is produced. This form has X-ray short spacings at 3·8 and 4·2 Å and a distinctive infra-red spectrum with bands near 727 and 719 cm^{-1} in the 720 cm^{-1} region. The hydrocarbon chains are probably packed in the common orthorhombic O$\perp$ manner and tilted with respect to the basal planes. (The crystal structure is probably monoclinic.) On heating up to the melting point of this form some melting occurs and evolution of heat and a transition occurs into the stable β_L-form. These transitions are demonstrated for tristearin [110] and its homologues in Fig. 111.

The melting points are lower and transformation rates are faster as the chain length is decreased. A variety of pathways are available for the formation of stable β_L-crystals, depending upon the particular glyceride

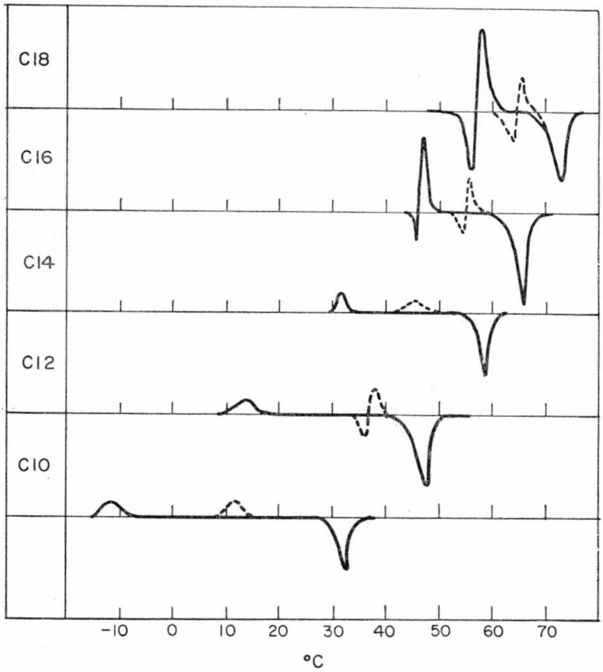

Fig. 111. Differential heating curves of a series of triglycerides.

and the conditions. The stable β_L-form is also readily obtained from solvent.

With the odd numbers of the series, e.g. trimargarin, the transitions are similar but the β'_L-form appears to be rather more stable and can be relatively easily obtained by heating the α_L-form. The stable β_L-form is obtained from solvent and also slowly by heating. A sub-α_L-form has been detected with these compounds by infra-red spectroscopy, and analogous spectra obtained for α_L-, β'_L- and β_L-forms to those observed with the even numbers. These glycerides, however, require a full examination before anything more definite can be said about their behaviour.

(*b*) *Diacid saturated triglycerides*

The diacid triglycerides, whilst having similar behaviour to the simple saturated triglycerides, vary quite considerably, depending upon the chain length of the acids concerned and upon their symmetrical or unsymmetrical nature. A considerable amount of work has been done on the polymorphism of the mixed saturated glycerides by Malkin and his associates [111, 112, 113, 114, 115]. The different groups of glycerides shown have been examined.

(*a*) $C_{12}C_{10}C_{12} \ldots C_{18}C_{16}C_{18}$
(*b*) $C_{10}C_{12}C_{10} \ldots C_{16}C_{18}C_{16}$
(*c*) $C_{10}C_{12}C_{12} \ldots C_{16}C_{18}C_{18}$
(*d*) $C_{12}C_{10}C_{10} \ldots C_{18}C_{16}C_{16}$

It is unfortunate that the vitreous form is assumed to occur in all of them, so that an incorrect association of melting point and X-ray data

Table 50. *A comparison of data relating to the mixed triglycerides of palmitic and stearic acid*

Glyceride	Vitreous	MELTING POINTS (MALKIN) °C α_M	β'_M	β_M	MELTING POINTS (LUTTON) °C α_L	β'_L	β_L
1-stearodipalmitin (SPP)	46·5	55	59·5	62·5	47·4	57·7–61·7	62·7
1-palmitodistearin (PSS)	50	57	61	65	50·6	61·1–65·0	65·2°
2-stearodipalmitin (PSP)	49	59	65	68	46·5	68·6	—
2-palmitodistearin (SPS)	50	56	64	68	51·8	—	68·5

Glyceride	LONG SPACINGS (MALKIN) Å α_M	β'_M	β_M	LONG SPACINGS (LUTTON) Å α_L	β'_L	β_L
1-stearodipalmitin (SPP)	47·8	43·9	42·5	47·6	43·8	42·1
1-palmitodistearin (PSS)	48·8	44·7	46·5	48·5	45·1	44·7
2-stearodipalmitin (PSP)	50·2	44·7	43·2	46·65	42·75	—
2-palmitodistearin (SPS)	50·5	47·5	44·2	29·2	—	43·1

has taken place. Whilst in some cases the correction of this may be straightforward this may not be so in other cases. This is seen where a re-examination of some of these glycerides has already been made. This is illustrated in Table 50 with the mixed triglycerides of palmitic and stearic acids. Different associations of X-ray pattern and melting form are made, different melting points are observed and there are differences in long-spacing data.

It can be seen that 2-stearodipalmitin can exist in four polymorphic forms according to one group [114] but only two according to the other group [116]. This is also the case with 2-palmitodistearin. An infra-red spectroscopic investigation confirmed the conclusions of the latter workers [117]. (The existence of a third form for 2-palmitodistearin may, however, be directly related to the presence or absence of small impurities.)

The strong X-ray short spacings for the most stable form of the glycerides in group (*b*) are the same as those of the intermediate β'_L form of tristearin. This probably indicates that for these glycerides the most stable forms crystallize with common orthorhombic $O\perp$ rather than triclinic $T\|$ packed chains. By analogy with tristearin the form is designated a β'_L-form. The infra-red spectrum of a member of this series, 2 stearodipalmitin, in its most stable form shows spectral resemblance to the spectra of the β'_L-form of tristearin and tripalmitin. A doublet occurs for the main CH_2 rocking mode in the 720 cm^{-1} region.

The considerable individuality shown by quite closely related isomers of the C_{16} and C_{18} saturated acids is shown in Table 51. Dielectric

Table 51. *Polymorphic behaviour of closely related isomers of palmitic and stearic acids*

Glyceride	Forms
1-stearodipalmitin (SPP)	α_L, β'_L and β_L(β_L-stable)
1-palmitodistearin (PSS)	α_L, β'_L from melt; β_L from solvent (β'_L and β_L equally stable)
2-stearodipalmitin (PSP)	α_L, β'_L
2-palmitodistearin (SPS)	α_L, β_L, (β'_L – possibly)

measurements on some of these glycerides have been made [118]. The dielectric properties and dispersion characteristics of the α_L-form are observed to be similar to that of the α_L-forms of tristearin and tripalmitin, showing that molecular freedom occurs. The sharpness of the

α_L-solidification point of this glyceride aroused the comment that this could not possibly correspond to a glassy form.

The infra-red spectra of these compounds are very similar to those of tristearin and tripalmitin, differing from them in the 1250 cm^{-1} region. The polymorphic modifications show a single band at 720 cm^{-1} for the α-forms, a doublet at 727 and 719 cm^{-1} for the β'_L-forms and bands at 890 and 717 cm^{-1} for the stable β_L-forms.

Other triglycerides have also been re-examined, 2-myristodistearin, 2-myristodipalmitin, 1-stearodimyristin and 1-palmitodimyristin and corrections made [119, 120]. Whilst three forms are observed rather than four (including a vitreous form) for three of these glycerides, 2-myristodistearin was found to occur in four forms. The four forms, however, do not include a vitreous form. The additional form is designated a β'_L-4 form on the basis of its similarity in short spacings to the β'_L forms, but has long spacing consistent with a chain length multiplicity of four. Infra-red spectroscopy and differential heating curves have confirmed the general conclusions of this work [119].

Four forms are also observed with 1-stearodilaurin: α_L-2, β'_L-2, β'_L-3 and β_L-3. When the chain length difference is two or less, three forms are usually observed, but with greater chain length difference the polymorphism becomes more complex. Close similarity between mixed triglycerides occur when the chain length differences within the similar glycerides are equal, as with 2-myristodipalmitin and 2-palmitodistearin. The behenyl mixed triglycerides, 2-behenyldipalmitin, 2-behenyldistearin, 1-palmitodibehenin, and 1-stearodibehenin have also been examined [121]. Whilst their behaviour is somewhat similar to that of the mono-acid saturated triglycerides, the behenyl glycerides all show a great stability for the β'-form, and with some of them stable β_L-forms could not be obtained from the melt. The glyceride 1-palmitodibehenin crystallizes from the solvent in a β'_L-form, this being its most stable form. A sub-α_L-form is also clearly observed with these compounds (see Table 52).

The crystal forms of glycerides containing both long and very short chains exhibit unusual properties. The glycerides 1-stearodiacetin, 1-palmitodiacetin, 1-stearodipropionin, 1-stearo- and 1-palmito-dibutyrin have been examined [122] and the unusual stability of the α_L-form observed. The α_L-form appears to be indefinitely stable between its melting point and a sub-α_L transformation. The glyceride 1-stearodiacetin normally solidifies into a soft waxy polymorphic form (α_L-form) from the melt which transforms reversibly into a sub-α_L-form on cooling. The β_L-form is obtained from solvent. The α_L-form of this glyceride can be stretched in length some 200–300 times [123, 124]. The highest melting

Table 52. *X-ray and thermal data of some behenyl triglycerides*

Glyceride	MELTING POINTS °C			LONG SPACINGS Å				SHORT SPACINGS Å							
	α_L	β'_L	β_L	sub-α_L	α_L	β'_L	β_L	sub-α_L		α_L	β'_L		β_L		
2-Behenyldistearin (SBS)	56·0	64·0	70·6	—	53·2	49·4	75·1	—	—	4·14	4·18 vs	3·78 s	4·58 s	3·78 vs	
2-Behenyldipalmitin (PBP)	47·4	61·5	66·6	—	50·0	46·0	70·4	—	—	4·14	4·19 vs	3·76 s	4·58 s	3·79 vs	
1-Palmitodibehenin (BBB)	55·9	66·1	—	58·9	57·4	52·4	—	4·2 s	3·72 m	4·15	4·20 vs	3·78 s	—	—	—
1-Stearodibehenin (SBB)	61·3	71·5	73·5	61·4	59·1	53·3	54·6	4·2 s	3·77 m	4·15	4·20 vs	3·78 s	5·49 s	3·87 s	3·70 s

form does not exhibit this property. The dilatometric properties of 1-palmitodiacetin, 1-palmito- and 1-stearo-dibutyrin have been reported and some polymorphic transformation points observed which had been missed by earlier workers [125].

A study of the glycerides 2-aceto-, 2-butyro- and 2-caproyldistearin and dipalmitin has been made using thermal and X-ray data [126]. These glycerides are found to exhibit marked individuality of behaviour, although the glycerides, having in common a given acyl short chain, behave similarly. Three of the compounds exhibit an α_L-form (2-butyrodistearin and dipalmitin and 2-caproyldistearin). The long spacing is compatible only with a single palmito or stearo chain. All of these glycerides exhibit a sub-α_L-form. Particularly unusual is the observation of a super-α_L-form. This is a polymorphic modification having the characteristic short spacing near 4·2 Å with a melting point 10–12° C higher than the α_L-form. The super-α_L-form is observed with 2-butyrodistearin and dipalmitin. The caproyl glycerides show a multiplicity of β_L-type forms. Thus 2-caproyldistearin exhibits sub-A-β_L-forms and sub-B-β_L-forms as well as a β_L-form.

It is clear that the nomenclature is particularly cumbersome with these glycerides, matching the greater complexity of their polymorphic behaviour.

(*c*) *Triacid saturated triglycerides*

The melting point data for a series of triacid triglycerides have been reported [127, 128]. The chain lengths extend from $C_{10} \ldots C_{18}$. Three forms are observed but X-ray data for only two forms are reported. The two forms are called β'- and β-forms and it was observed that the β'-form could be readily obtained from solvent. A selection of the data is given in Table 53. It is suggested that forms I and II correspond to β- and β'-forms.

Examination of the data suggests that the reported correspondence of forms I and II to β- and β'-forms may not be correct with the 1-stearoyl-2-acyl-3-caproyl glycerides (these are marked with an asterisk in the table). Instead, it seems that 1-stearoyl-2-palmitoyl-3-caproyl glyceride can exist in two β'_L-forms rather than a β- and β'-form as shown. (There is nothing extraordinary about a long-chain compound existing in two forms having orthorhombic or approximately orthorhombic packing.) Also the triglyceride 1-stearoyl-2-lauroyl-3-caproyl glyceride appears to have its X-ray diffraction patterns in the wrong order. The typical β'_L-diffraction pattern is here designated as a β-form. The diffraction pattern associated with the β'-form of 1-stearoyl-2-myristoyl-3-capryl, on the other hand, has a strong short spacing at 4·58 Å, whilst the pattern

Table 53. *Melting points of triacid triglycerides Long and short spacings of triacid triglycerides*

	MELTING POINTS °C			LONG SPACINGS		SHORT SPACINGS							
Glyceride	I	II	III	β	β′	β				β′			
C_{18}–C_{10}–C_{14}	52·5	50·1	14	57·3	—	3·82 vs	4·3 m	4·62 s	4·82 m				
								5·18 s	5·35 m				
C_{18}–C_{16}–C_{12}	52·0	47·0	33·4	62·4	43·3	3·82 vs	4·34 m	4·62 vs	5·2 m	3·82 s	4·11 s	4·29 vs	
C_{18}–C_{14}–C_{12}	49·4	45·5	27·5	59·6	40·1	3·82 vs	4·32 s	4·61 vs		3·81 vs	4·26 vs	4·45 m	
							4·82 s	5·02 m	5·42 m				
C_{18}–C_{10}–C_{12}	—	41·8	22·3	54·9	—	3·82 vs	4·6 vs	5·28 m					
C_{18}–C_{16}–C_{10}*	50·0	46·5	26·1	38·5	59·0	3·85 vs	4·14 vs	4·33 s		3·76 s	3·86 s	4·22 vs	5·14 m
							4·82 m	5·35 m	5·55 m				
C_{18}–C_{14}–C_{10}*	45·0	42·0	21·5	56·1	54·3	3·83 vs	4·2 vs	4·45 s	5·6 s	3·73 s	3·84 s	4·05 s	4·19 s
												4·45 s	4·58 s
C_{18}–C_{12}–C_{10}*	44·0	40·0	14·5	35·6	53·0	3·81 s	4·19 vs			3·83 s	4·16 vs	4·29 s	4·46 s
C_{16}–C_{14}–C_{12}	49·0	44·0	37·0	35·7	—	3·74 s	3·83 s	4·57 vs		—			
							5·08 m	5·33 m					
C_{14}–C_{12}–C_{10}*	37·0	34·0	22·0	33·4	—	3·82 s	4·13 vs	4·33 vs		—			
								4·6 m					

associated with the β-form has strong spacings at 3·83 vs, 4·2 vs (and 4·45 vs).

Further work is required with the triacid triglycerides.

Unsaturated triglycerides

Glycerides containing unsaturated acids have very similar polymorphic behaviour to that of the saturated glycerides. Those containing *trans*-unsaturated acids are thought to be very similar in behaviour and structure to glycerides of the corresponding saturated acids. Those containing *cis* groups have a tendency to crystallize in a way which gives rise to long spacings indicative of a triple chain length structure. The controversy over the existence of a vitreous form and the association of X-ray diffraction pattern and melting point also exists with these compounds.

(i) SIMPLE TRIGLYCERIDES. Little additional work has been reported on these compounds since the review by Malkin [96]. A corrected association of X-ray pattern and melting point is shown in Table 54. Further work may be required for trierucin, where four melting points are given but only three distinct X-ray diffraction patterns are observed and tribrassidin, where three melting points are observed but only two distinct X-ray patterns.

(ii) MIXED TRIGLYCERIDES. A considerable amount of work has been carried out in recent years on these glycerides, mainly because of their practical importance in confectionary fats such as cocoa-butter. The variety of results obtained on nominally the same compounds is disturbing and must be related to variations in the purity of the compounds examined. The effect of acyl migration occurring at some stage of the synthesis of the compounds may partly explain some of the differences.

Daubert and Clarke [129] used cooling and heating curves to examine the 2-oleo-disaturated glycerides of capric, lauric, myristic, palmitic and stearic acids and suggested there are four polymorphic forms; later X-ray data for some of the glycerides were also reported [130]. Another examination of 2-oleodistearin by thermal and X-ray methods led to the suggestion that there are only three forms for this glyceride. A later investigation of 2-oleodimyristin, dipalmitin and distearin then led to the proposal that there are five forms for these glycerides, but this includes a vitreous form. Further examinations followed of 1-oleo-disaturated glycerides, oleodipalmitin, distearin, palmitostearin, and stearopalmitin as well as 2-oleopalmitostearin, using capillary melting point, X-ray photography, differential heating apparatus and, with some of the glycerides, dilatometry. The number of possible polymorphic

Table 54. *Melting and X-ray data for unsaturated simple triglycerides*

Glyceride	MELTING POINTS °C			LONG SPACINGS Å			SHORT SPACINGS Å							
	α_L	β'_L	β_L	α_L	β'_L	β_L	α_L	β'_L			β_L			
Triolein	−32°	−12°	4·9°	45·2	45·8	43·3	4·36s	4·35s	3·87m	—	5·28m	4·57 s	3·97m	3·84 3·74
Trielaidin	15·5	37 (?)	42	—	—	44·1	4·15s	—	—	—	5·3m	4·6 s	3·9m	3·7
Trierucin	6	17 (25)	30	—	54·7	51·1	—	4·53	4·28	3·88	5·24	4·6 s	4·03 3·7	3·84
Tribrassidin	43	50	59	59·3	—	53·6	—	—	—	—	5·3	4·6 s	3·9	3·7

forms for these glycerides is still, however, in doubt and there is wide diversity of melting point data [95, 129, 131, 132, 133]. Further work is required on these glycerides provided that some adequate check on purity can be devised.

The most stable forms of the 2-oleo- and 1-oleo-disaturated glycerides have different crystal structures. The short spacings for the 2-isomer are consistent with this being a β_L-form, whilst for the 1-isomer they are consistent with it being a β'_L-form. The long and short spacings are given in Table 55 for the most stable forms of the isomers of oleodistearin and

Table 55. *Long and short spacings for the most stable forms of* 2-*oleo-* 1-*oleo-disaturated glycerides*

Glyceride	Long spacing Å		Short spacing Å	
2-oleodistearin	64	4·59 s 3·79 ms	3·68	4·02 ms
1-oleodistearin	70·8	4·06 s 4·39 m	3·79 ms	4·64 m
2-oleodipalmitin	60·2	4·56 vs 5·40 w	4·05 m	3·73 m
1-oleodipalmitin	65·0	4·03 s	3·78 vs	4·68 m

oleodipalmitin. The long spacings for all the isomers appear to be consistent with a triple-chain length structure [94].

A dielectric study of this glyceride shows that the stable β_L-form has a lower dielectric constant than the sub-β_L-form and that the low-temperature dispersion of the α_L-form is less pronounced than with 2-oleodipalmitin [118].

Diglycerides

(i) THE 1,3-DIGLYCERIDES. The polymorphism of simple 1,3-diglycerides was first investigated by Malkin, Shurbagy and Meara [113], who suggested that they were similar to the triglycerides and exist in α_M-, β_M- and β'_M-forms. They also considered that a discontinuity occurred in the even homologous series. Other authors [134] found only two forms which they termed, on the basis of the X-ray short spacings, β_L-*a*- and β_L-*b*-forms for the series dilaurin to distearin. They found no evidence for the occurrence of an α_L-form. The β_L-*a*-form was characterized by short spacings at 4·6, 3·9 and 3·7 Å and the β_L-*b*-form by spacings at 4·6 and 3·75 Å. These authors did not agree that a discontinuity occurred in the even homologous series. The β_L-*a*-form is usually the first form obtained from the melt but it transforms to β_L-*b*- near its melting point. Both forms are obtainable from solvent, high purity favouring the β_L-*b*-type. Although they exhibit different stability both are considered to have the same melting points.

Disagreement still exists with these glycerides [96, 135]. Malkin suggests:

(*a*) that an α_M-form exists and gives definite melting points;

(*b*) that the two stable forms have different melting points, e.g. dilaurin 54° and 56·5° C;

(*c*) that the X-ray short spacings for the stable forms can be classified into three groups *a*, *b* and *c*. The *a*-type is observed with the β_M-forms of all odd acid diglycerides and the β'_M-forms of dipalmitin and distearin; the *b*-type with the β'_M-forms of all diglycerides except dipalmitin and distearin and the *c*-type with the β_M-forms of all even acid diglycerides (i.e. a discontinuity does occur with the β'-forms of the even diglycerides). Note that the *c*-type corresponds to the β_L-*b*-type of pattern.

(*d*) The fact that both the β'_M- and β_M-forms of the diglycerides give rise to diffraction patterns with a strong spacing at 4·6 Å shows the difficulty of attempting to classify the polymorphic forms of glycerides according to the type of short spacing.

Whilst a judgement on this classification into three types would require an examination of the original diffraction photographs, an examination of the quoted data shows that such a distinction rests on very slender evidence. The X-ray short spacings for the even-acid diglycerides is said to fall into two groups. Thus whilst tristearin has short spacings at 4·6 s, 3·88 s and 3·68 s, dimyristin, on the other hand, of supposedly a different type, has spacings at 4·64 s, 3·88 m, 3·68 s and 3·53 vw. The data for dimyristin given by the other group of workers is 4·58 s, 3·91 m, 3·73 s, 2·53 w and 2·24 w.

The most reliable data is given in Table 56 for the even-acid diglycerides.

An infra-red spectroscopic examination of some even-acid diglycerides shows two very similar spectra for the forms corresponding to the β_L-*a*- and the β_L-*b*-forms [136]. No evidence for an α_L-form was observed.

The spectrum of the β_L-form obtained from solvent shows two carbonyl frequencies and two hydroxy frequencies, consistent with the hydrogen bonding being different for one carbonyl group than for the other. A recent X-ray single-crystal structure of the 1,3-diglyceride of 3-thiododecanoic acid supports this and shows that the hydrogen bond links from the hydroxyl group of the one molecule to a carboxylic oxygen in a neighbouring molecule [137]. The repetition in the structure is such that one carboxylic oxygen always participates in the hydrogen bond whilst the

Table 56. *Melting and X-ray data for 1,3-diglycerides*

Glyceride	Melting point °C	LONG SPACINGS Å		SHORT SPACINGS Å								
		$\beta_L - a$	$\beta_L - b$	$\beta_L - a$				$\beta_L - b$				
Distearin	78·2	50·2	52·8	4·61 vs	3·90 s	3·71 s+	2·55 w+	4·59 vs	4·14 w	3·74 vs	2·52 w	2·44 w
Dipalmitin	72·9	44·7	47·4	4·60 vs	3·88 m	3·72 s+	2·50 m	4·58 vs	3·75 vs	2·45 m	—	—
Dimyristin	66·5	40·6	42·4	4·58 s	3·91 m	3·73 s	2·33 w	4·55 s	3·74 s	—	—	—
					2·53 w	2·44 w						
Dilaurin	56·8	35·4	37·5	4·48 s	3·89 m	3·68 s	3·39 w	4·55 m	3·70 s	—	—	—
				2·75 w	2·50 w	2·41 w	2·30 w					

other carboxylic group never does so. The two carbon chains are oppositely directed but are not parallel. The X-ray structure of a 1,3-diglyceride of the 3-thiododecanoic acid is shown in Figs. 112a and b.

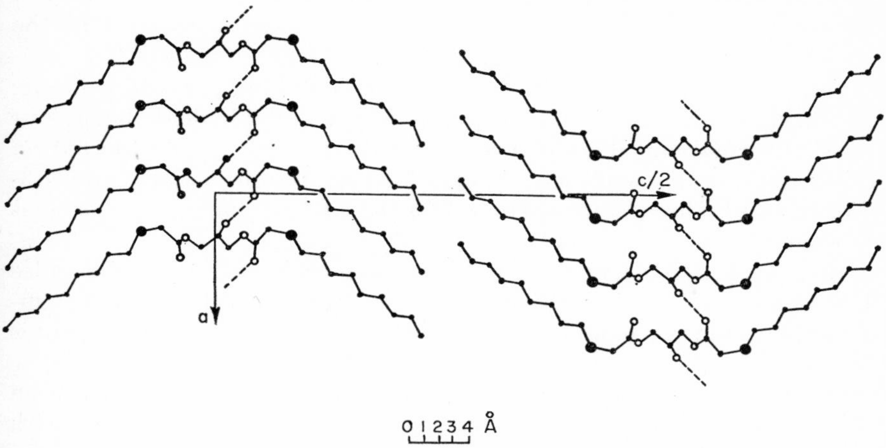

(a)

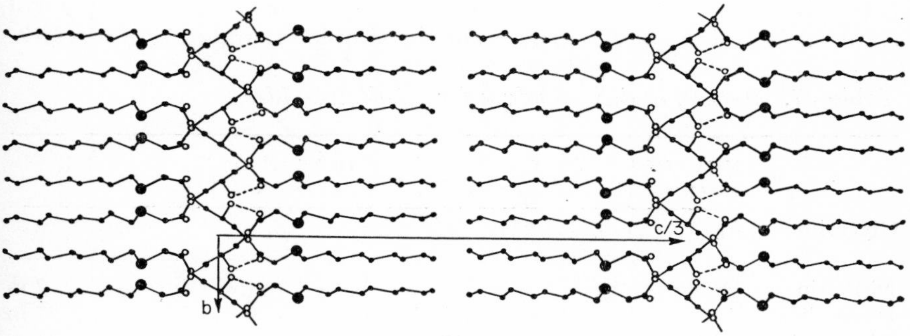

(b)

Fig. 112*a*. Projection along the *b* axis showing the molecular arrangements of the 1 : 3-diglyceride of 3-thiododecanoic acid. (After Larsson.[137].)
Fig. 112*b*. Projection along the *a* axis showing the molecular arrangement of the 1 : 3-diglyceride of 3-thiododecanoic acid. (After Larsson, K.[137].)

Nuclear-resonance spectra of the two forms of the 1,3-diglycerides show that both forms have similar second moments ($\sim$ 20 gauss^2) and the chains undergo only slight freedom of torsional motion. Additional evidence confirming the absence of an α_L-form with these diglycerides was obtained by a study of the variation of the dielectric constant with temperature for distearin and dipalmitin.

X-ray studies of mixed-chain 1,3-diglycerides such as 1-aceto-3-stearin show differences in polymorphic behaviour. This glyceride exists in three polymorphic forms α_L-, sub-α_L and, the most stable form, a β'_L-form. The infra-red spectrum of the stable form of 1-aceto-3-palmitin shows a doublet near 720 cm^{-1} analogous to that observed with the β'_L-form of saturated simple triglycerides.

Some unsaturated diacid diglycerides have been examined, e.g. 1-stearyl-3-olein, and found to exhibit rather individualistic behaviour [138]. Thermal and dilatometric data have recently been reported on other diglycerides such as 1-butyro-3-olein, 1-aceto-3-olein, and 1,3-diolein [139]. Three forms are found for the latter compound, in contrast to earlier investigators [140].

(ii) THE 1,2-DIGLYCERIDES. The polymorphism of 1,2-diglycerides has been investigated by thermal and X-ray methods [135]. These compounds exist in two modifications α_M and β_M. The material from solvent is in the β_M-form; on melting it re-solidifies at the α_M melting point. The transition $\alpha_M \rightarrow \beta_M$ is very slow. These glycerides have also been examined by thermal and infra-red spectroscopy [141]. By analogy with the short spacings of the polymorphic forms of other glycerides the forms are designated α_L- and β'_L-forms (see Table 57). The α-form has spectral similarities to that of the α_L-form of the simple saturated triglycerides.

Table 57. *Melting and X-ray data for* 1,2-*diglycerides*

	MELTING POINTS °C		LONG SPACINGS Å		SHORT SPACINGS Å			
Glyceride	α_L	β'_L	α_L	β'_L	α_L	β'_L		
Distearin	59·9	71	54·5	48·3	4·12	3·81 s	4·05 vs	4·27 m
Dipalmitin	47·7–50	61	49·3	43·5	4·10	3·76 s	4·03 vs	4·27 m
Dimyristin	37·1	51·7	44·4	38·8	4·12	3·82 s	4·06 vs	4·31 m
Dilaurin	19·7	38·2	39·2	34·1	4·13	3·79 s	4·0 vs	4·31 m

Monoglycerides

(i) 1-MONOGLYCERIDES. The first report of the double melting of 1-monostearin and palmitin [142] was in 1920. In 1930 a systematic study of the even-acid 1-monoglycerides from monolaurin to monostearin was carried out and they were shown to exist in two distinct forms [143]. The work was extended by Malkin and Shurbagy [144] who found three modifications for the 1-monoglycerides from monodecoin to monostearin. These were a low melting α_M-form and two higher melting modifications β'_M and β_M. The X-ray pattern of the α_M-form shows only one strong side spacing at 4·12 Å. Lutton and Jackson [145] also examined some 1-monoglycerides and suggested that the α_L-form is reasonably stable down to a lower transition temperature, at which point it changes reversibly into a new crystalline modification, sub-α_L, giving a distinctive set of short spacings. Some differences in the long spacings were also observed. A similar nomenclature to that used for the triglycerides was adopted, i.e.

sub-alpha (sub-α_L-form)	– a single strong short spacing at 4·15 Å with other medium lines at 3·9, 3·75 and 3·55 Å
alpha (α_L-form)	– a single strong short spacing at 4·15 Å
beta-prime (β'_L-form)	– a strong spacing at 4·15 Å and at 3·65 Å; a medium line which is the strongest between 4·2 and 2·6 Å
beta (β_L-form)	– a strong short spacing at 4·55 Å and the highest melting form

Large unexplained density differences were observed for slowly and rapidly chilled sub-α_L-forms.

Malkin did not agree with some of the conclusions of this work, repeated that the α_M-form was only stable near the melting point, and he stated that the sub-α_L-form was a semi-vitreous solid rather than a crystalline modification. The reversible character of the sub-α_L- to α_L-form was also doubted.

An infra-red spectroscopic examination [102, 146] showed that the α_L-form is stable down to a lower transition temperature and changes into a form giving a spectrum of crystalline modification, the sub-α_L-form. A doublet occurs in the 720 cm^{-1} region at 727 and 719 cm^{-1}. The reversible nature of the sub-α_L- to the α_L-modification was also confirmed. The bands in the spectrum of the sub-α_L-form were rather broad and suggestive of some orientational freedom. The spectra of the β'_L- and β_L-forms give bands which are narrow and sharp and typical of some crystalline materials without orientational freedom. The spectrum of the β'_L-form was at first thought to have only a single band at 719 cm^{-1} but further work showed that a doublet occurs at 727 and 719 cm^{-1} as with the β'_L-form of other glycerides. It may be that the β'_L- and the sub-α_L-form have common orthorhombic O$\perp$ packed chains, whilst the β_L-forms have triclinic T$\|$ packed chains as with the triglycerides.

Changes in hydrogen bonding for the glyceride from the liquid state through the variety of polymorphic forms have been determined. The carbonyl stretching frequency shifts from 1706 cm^{-1} in the liquid to 1721 cm^{-1} in the α_L-form, 1730 cm^{-1} in the sub-alpha form and 1736 cm^{-1} in the β-forms. The OH stretching frequency shifts to lower frequencies in the order liquid → α_L → sub-alpha → β'_L → β_L. This has been interpreted to show that the hydrogen bonding is increasing in this order but that the bonding is occurring preferentially between hydroxyl groups rather than between hydroxyl and carbonyl groups.

Nuclear-magnetic resonance measurements of 1-monoglycerides, e.g. 1-monostearin, show (see page 168) that the sub-alpha form gives rise to a large second moment ~ 20 gauss. The α_L-form, however, gives rise to rather small second moments, showing that for this form the chains have considerable freedom of motion not only about the chain axes. Some lateral and longitudinal motion of the chains seems to occur.

Dielectric studies [43] show similar effects. The dielectric constant increases normally in the liquid until the freezing point of the α-form is reached; at this point it increases sharply. Just below the α → sub-α transition point the dielectric constant is still reasonably high, indicating considerable orientational freedom in this form, but the frequency dependence of the dielectric constant and the conductivity decrease rapidly below the transition temperature. The abnormally high conductivities of the α-forms are suggested to be the result of the transfer of protons through the sheets of hydroxyl groups in the crystals. The dielectric constants of the stable β- and β_L-forms are low enough for them to be considered as non-rotators whilst in the sub-α-form the dipole orientation process is thought to be probably segment orientation. Thermal and X-ray data relating to the 1-monoglycerides are given in Tables 58 and 59.

It is of interest that the α_L-forms show additional weak lines compared with other glycerides. This may be related to the large amount of freedom

Table 58. *Long spacings and thermal points for the 1-monoglycerides* (80)

	THERMAL POINTS				LONG SPACINGS Å			
Monoglyceride	Transition to α_L	α_L	β'_L	β_L	sub-α_L	α_L	β'_L	β_L
Decoin	8	27	49	53	—	37·2	32·9	32·9
Undecoin	3	36·5	52	56·5	—	40·2	35·2	35·2
Laurin	15	44	59·5	63	—	43·2	37·3	37·3
Tridecoin	9	50	61	65	—	46·2	39·6	39·6
Myristin	24	56	67·5	70·5	—	—	41·5	41·5
Pentadecoin	17	62	68	72	—	51·3	43·8	43·8
Palmitin	34 (39)	66·5	74	77	(45·5)	(45·6)	45·8	45·8
Heptadecoin	28	70	74·5	77	—	—	48·2	48·2
Stearin	47·5 42 (49°)	74	79	81·5	50·3	58·3 (50)	50·0	50·0

Table 59. *Characteristic short spacings for* 1-*monopalmitin and* 1-*monostearin*

Sub-α_L	α_L	β'_L	β_L
4·14 vs	4·64 w	4·15 vs	4·55
3·92 m	4·18 vs	3·87 vw	4·37 s
3·75 m	3·99 vw	3·65 w+	3·86 s+
3·56 m	3·81 w	3·30 w	3·74 w

of the hydrocarbon chains in this form detected by the n.m.r. measurements. The sub-α_L to α_L change can be readily followed by dilatometry [147]. The density of the stable β_L-form is between that of the α_L- and the sub-α_L-forms.

Some recent X-ray single-crystal studies on monoglycerides [148] have been reported. Optically active 1-monoglycerides are said to exist in four polymorphic forms and have different polymorphic behaviour from the racemates. Crystallization from solvents gives rise to two stable modifications, both with orthorhombic O$\perp$ chain packing. Further details concerning these studies will be useful in relating the crystallization of these compounds to those of the di- and triglycerides.

(ii) THE 2-MONOGLYCERIDES. These glycerides appear to be free of polymorphism and the same form is obtained from solvent and by cooling the melt [129, 130]. The following lines are common to the various homologues, 4·60 s, 4·4 vs and 3·9 vs. It will be noted that a strong line occurs at 4·6 Å. It is possible that the hydrocarbon chains pack here in an analogous manner to that of the β_L-form of 1-monoglycerides, but this is not certain. No single-crystal studies have yet been made of a 2-monoglyceride. Infra-red spectra have been reported and show distinctive differences from the stable forms of the 1-monoglycerides. Thermal and X-ray data relating to these forms are shown in Table 60.

Table 60. *Melting and X-ray data for* 2-*monoglycerides*

Glyceride	Melting point °C	Long spacing Å	Short spacings Å		
Monostearin	75·2	43·9	3·86	4·43	4·60
Monopalmitin	69·0	40·4	3·88	4·52	4·60
Monomyristin	61·3	36·2	3·92	4·42	4·60
Monolaurin	51·0	32·8	3·96	4·40	4·58
Monocaprin	40·2	29·4	4·07	4·38	4·58

The melting points are some 10° C lower than the corresponding 1-monoglyceride and the long spacings are much smaller.

Summary of glyceride crystallization behaviour

Similar polymorphic behaviour is not to be expected to occur merely because the tri-, di- and monoglycerides are all derivatives of glycerol. Similarity in behaviour is determined by the fact that with the long-chain derivatives the hydrocarbon chains are common to all of them and that fairly long chains will tend to dominate the crystallization processes. For a given chain length the balance of polar and non-polar forces involved differs with a triglyceride, diglyceride and monoglyceride and this requires consideration. With fairly long chain derivatives, say greater than 10 carbon atoms, similarities in crystallization behaviour are expected to occur, but with shorter chain lengths, where the polar properties are becoming more important, there will be less similarity. The effect of the polar forces is illustrated by the amides and soaps, where unusual crossed-chain packing is observed.

Without more definite X-ray single-crystal data it requires caution in picking out similarities in crystal form between one glyceride and another and from one type of glyceride to another.

When both the X-ray data and the infra-red data on the glycerides are taken into consideration it is clear that the two support each other well and it is concluded that similarities can indeed be picked out. As a first approximation the β_L-forms are considered to have triclinic T$\|$ packed chains, the β'_L-forms to have orthorhombic O$\perp$ packed chains and the α_L-form to have hexagonal packed chains. The sub-α_L-forms are also considered to have orthorhombic O$\perp$ chains but the chains are vertical to the basal plane whereas the chains are usually tilted with the β'_L-forms. (It must be emphasized that this is only an approximation and that this says nothing of the symmetry of the actual crystals.) If we use this approximation we should not be surprised to find a glyceride having two forms with triclinic packed chains of different tilt, and hence two β_L-forms, or two forms with orthorhombic packed chains of different tilts, and hence two β'_L-forms. The n.m.r. results show how the molecular mobility can vary from one α_L-form to another, again emphasizing that such a designation implies similarity and not identity of behaviour. Deductions based on long spacing data must also be considered with considerable caution at present.

It seems certain that exceptions to the simple classification of Lutton will be observed when complete structures are determined. The variety of sub-cells observed with the long branched chain fatty acids makes it clear that the overall generality of the classification is bound to fail when applied to the enormous variations possible with glycerides. At the present stage of development of structural determinations of glycerides the classification is still useful as an approximation, particularly with the limited chain-length range of the glycerides at present examined.

Applications of polymorphism

The characterization of naturally occurring compounds is usually rather difficult and this is true of oils and fats. Polymorphic behaviour can, however, assist this identification. A number of melting points corresponding to those of a glyceride is more conclusive than a single value. This also applies to other physical data, such as X-ray pattern or infra-red spectra. For example, whilst the infra-red spectrum of a molecule has frequently been likened to a fingerprint and has been used to assist unique identification of many simple molecules, glycerides may give a regular 'handful of fingerprints'. Polymorphic study has already been useful for determining a number of glycerides in natural fats, including 2-oleodistearin and 2-oleodipalmitin and various isomers of palmitic and stearic acids. A great deal of work has been carried out on the polymorphic behaviour of cocoa-butter because of its importance in chocolate manufacture. The lowest melting form is said to be a glassy or vitreous form and a critical assessment of the polymorphism seems to be required. The identification of the major glyceride of cocoa-butter followed from the fact that two closely related isomers such as 1-oleo- and 2-oleo-disaturated glycerides, e.g. 2-oleodistearin and 1-oleodistearin, have different crystallographic stable forms, β'_L and β_L respectively, hence giving rise to considerable difference in X-ray patterns and infra-red spectra [149].

PHOSPHOLIPIDS

At present no single-crystal X-ray study of a phospholipid has been reported. Studies up to the present on phospholipids have been made entirely using X-ray powder photographs. Polymorphism can be expected with the long-chain derivatives and it is indeed observed.

X-ray diffraction studies have been made with nerve lipids [150, 151]. Lecithin, cephalin, sphingomyelin, kerasin and phrenosin isolated from beef spinal cord and other pure specimens were examined. Long-spacing data are said to agree with the assumption that the molecules in these lipids are packed in bi-molecular leaflets. The polar groups are thought to form a layer whilst the hydrocarbon chains lie parallel to each other, similar in packing to the fatty acids and soaps. Short spacings were found at 4·2 Å with all long-chain derivatives. Mixtures of the lipids were also examined, and it is claimed that it is possible to detect the presence of cholesterol, lecithin or cephalin in a preparation of sphingomyelin or cerebroside. When the phospholipid preparations are stirred with two volumes of water various changes in the X-ray spacings are observed. The short spacings merge to a single line at 4·2 Å when water is added to a cephalin. The line is sharp until amounts of water in excess of 20% are added and changes gradually to a diffuse spacing at about 4·6 Å. The spacings of the cerebrosides change little with wetting: the long spacings of the sphingomyelin increase by about 23% and those of lecithin some 60%. The cephalin preparation, which probably contained acidic phospholipids, showed a large increase of about 270%. Mixtures of histone or globin with preparations of phosphatidyl ethanolamine have been examined. In the absence of added protein or water the phospholipid is oriented in bimolecular layers with a long spacing of 43·8 Å. This spacing increases when histone is present by 13–15 Å whilst with globin it increases by 7–9 Å. The phospholipid–histone complexes take up water sparingly, and the long spacing increases by only 5–10 Å. As addition of water to the phospholipid alone produces large increases in the spacings it is suggested that the phospholipid and protein are fixed together.

X-ray data have also been obtained for some pure sphingolipids [152] and some α-lecithins [153]. It is suggested that with the lecithins the hydrocarbon chains are approximately perpendicular to the bimolecular leaflet and the end group is 10 Å long in the chain direction.[1]

A number of other pure synthetic phospholipids have also been examined.

(*a*) *Phosphatidic acids*

X-ray powder studies have been carried out on a series of (±) 1,2- and 1,3-Di-O-acyl-glycerol-(dihydrogen phosphates), i.e. a series of isomeric glycerophosphatidic acids [154]. This shows that they occur in α and β polymorphic forms. With the 1,2-di-O-acyl-glycerol-3-dihydrogen phosphates the α-form is obtained from the melt or by crystallization from a polar solvent (e.g. acetone or alcohol). The β-form is obtained by slow crystallization from light petroleum (40°–60°) or ether. The α-form changes slowly at room temperature to the β-form. The long spacings of both forms are linear with carbon content and the intercepts at C=O are 9 Å (β-form) and 13 Å (α-form). The results agree with a bimolecular structure with the long chains vertical to the reflecting planes (α-form) and tilted at an angle of 59° across the reflecting planes (β-form).

With the 1,3-compounds the α- and β-forms melt at different temperatures; the long spacings of both forms are linear with carbon content and

[1] Only diagrams of diffraction rings are given for the α-lecithins. The sphingolipids examined are *n*-acetyl, triacetyl and tribenzoyl dihydrosphingosine.

Table 61. *Thermal and X-ray data for some 1-glycerophosphatidic acids*

Phosphatidic acid	α-FORM			β-FORM				
	m.p. °C	Long spacing Å	Short spacing Å	Long spacing Å	Short spacing Å			
Dilauroyl	45°	44·0	4·14 s	34·6	4·74 vs	4·52 m	4·22 vs	—
					3·94 w	3·82 m	3·68 w	3·57 m
Dimyristoyl	55°	47·5	4·12 s	39·2	4·70 s	4·46 m	4·18 vs	—
					3·87 m	3·63 m		
Dipalmitoyl	62–63°	54·0	4·10 s	43·6	4·64 vs	4·48 m	4·19 vs	—
					3·84 m	3·63 m		
Distearoyl	~71°	59·7	4·12 s	48·1	4·69 vs	4·49 m	4·20 vs	—
					3·86 m	3·63 m		

Table 62. *Thermal and X-ray data for some 2-glycerophosphatidic acids*

Phosphatidic acid	α-FORM m.p. °C	α-FORM Long spacing Å	α-FORM Short spacing Å	β-FORM m.p. °C	β-FORM Long spacing Å	β-FORM Short spacing Å			
Dilauroyl	−12°	—	—	45°	36·3	5·16 w	4·73 vw	4·44 vw	3·94 v
						3·74 vs	3·55 m	3·34 w	
Dimyristoyl	−36°	45·3	4·15 s	56°	41·0	5·16 w	4·82 vw	4·45 vs	3·84 v
						3·61 vs	3·35 w		
Dipalmitoyl	50°	50·1	4·22 s	64°	45·2	5·16 w	4·78 vw	4·38 vs	3·94 v
						3·72 vs	3·57 m	3·41 w	
Distearoyl	59°	55·8	4·12 s	70°	49·5	5·19 w	4·73 vw	4·41 vs	3·89 v
						3·70 vs	3·54 m	3·39 w	

the intercepts are 10 Å (α-form) and 10 Å (β-form). This agrees with a bimolecular structure with the long chains vertical to the reflecting planes (α-form) and tilted at an angle of 57° across the reflecting planes (β-form). The data are given in Tables 61 and 62.

(*b*) *Cephalins* (*Phosphatidyl ethanolamines*)

The synthetic DL-1,2- and 1,3-diacyl cephalins have also been examined [155]; namely dilauroyl, dimyristoyl, dipalmitoyl and distearoyl phosphatidylethanolamines. The data show that they are arranged as double molecules lying across the reflecting planes at angles of 73° 20′ for the 1,2-diacyl compounds and 55° 5′ for the 1,3-diacyl compounds.[1] The short spacings readily distinguish one class from another. These are shown in Table 63.

Table 63. *Data for isomeric cephalins* (*phosphatidyl ethanolamine*)

DL-1,2-diacyl cephalins	m.p.	Long spacing Å	Short spacings Å				
			w	w	vs	m	w
Dilauroyl	210	45·2	5·91	4·91	4·15	3·86	3·59
Dimyristoyl	207	49·9	5·96	4·94	4·18	3·87	3·6
Dipalmitoyl	198	55·3	5·93	4·92	4·16	3·84	3·59
Distearoyl	196	60·0	5·88	4·94	4·2	3·86	3·6

DL-1,3-diacyl cephalins	m.p.	Long spacing Å	Short spacing Å							
			s	vs	m	m	w	m	m	m
Dilauroyl	208	35·9	5·65	4·72	4·31	4·17	3·89	3·70	3·55	3·42
Dimyristoyl	207	40·1	5·65	4·69	4·33	4·20	3·97	3·78	3·60	3·40
Dipalmitoyl	206	44·3	5·59	4·65	4·30	4·25	3·97	3·79	3·57	3·38
Distearoyl	198	48·3	5·59	4·64	4·33	4·23	3·89	3·79	3·63	3·38

Short spacings are also reported for some 1,2-diacyl cephalins, the dimyristoyl, dipalmitoyl and distearoyl derivatives. These compounds give rise to strong lines at approximately 4·6, 4·1 and 3·8 Å and so the optical isomers may, in fact, crystallize in a different modification from the racemate. It has, however, been suggested that 1,3-isomers may also have been present in the preparation [155].

[1] The high melting points of these compounds strongly suggest that the forces of interaction between the polar parts of the molecule are ionic in character. (Contrast these with the values for the phosphatidic acids.) The lecithins, phosphatidyl serines and sphingomyelins also have very high melting points. The presence of unsaturated hydrocarbon chains does not lower the melting point, nor does the number of chains.

The polymorphism of some of these DL-cephalins has been studied. It is suggested that the 1,3-acyl cephalins show three polymorphic forms, as indicated by three sets of long spacings. The three forms give short spacings *A*, 4·35 and 3·95 Å; *B*, 5·65, 4·7 (4·9 and 4·4) Å; and *C* a diffuse halo between 4 and 5 Å. The dilauroyl and dimyristoyl compounds normally occur in the *B*-form at room temperature, but, on cooling give rise to an *A*-form. The dipalmitoyl and distearoyl compounds were obtained in either *A*- or *B*-forms at room temperature by pre-cooling or pre-heating.

Recent unpublished studies have shown that the 1,2-diacyl cephalins (e.g. 2,3-dimyristoyl-DL-α-phosphatidyl ethanolamine) can exist in two polymorphic forms designated A- and A′-forms. They have similar long spacings but distinct X-ray short spacings and distinct infra-red spectra (page 124). The A-form transforms on heating to the A′-form at 90° C and, on further heating, to 120° C to a liquid–crystalline C-form. The C-form shows a diffuse halo between 4 and 5 Å. Other cephalins, such as DL-2-oleoyl-3-stearoyl phosphatidyl ethanolamine have also been shown to exist in two forms. The temperature for transformation and also for transition into the liquid–crystalline phase are now much lower. These thermal transitions are shown clearly by differential thermal analysis (Chapter 4, Fig. 53).

We can speculate that the polymorphic modification arises in part from different types of hydrocarbon chain packing. The 1,2-diacyl cephalins would then occur in a form having orthorhombic O⊥ packed chains with some tendency to form a hexagonal form as the temperatures increase, whilst at even higher temperatures a liquid crystalline modification is formed. The 1,3-diacyl cephalins, on the other hand, may have a triclinic as well as an orthorhombic packed modification. Further studies are required to confirm this.

The effect of temperature on a number of synthetic phospholipids has also been studied by X-ray diffraction [156] (see infra-red studies, page 119). A study of the myelin sheath of peripheral nerve has earlier shown that the diffraction bands, thought to represent the lipid phase, undergo marked changes when the temperature of the specimen is varied [157] and so a study of the phospholipids was made.

The long spacings of the phospholipids exhibited marked changes. The spacing of dipalmitoyl cephalin is 57 Å at 20° C and remains unchanged up to about 70° C. Above this temperature the intensity decreases and the spacing falls slightly to a value of about 54 Å and is too weak to be observed at a temperature of about 110° C. At 70° C a line appears at 45 Å and this also falls off rapidly in intensity below 110° C. A third line appears at a temperature of about 90° C at about 35 Å which remains unchanged up to 150° C. Meanwhile the short spacings remain essentially the same up to about 100° C, until above about 100° C the short spacings form diffuse haloes at about 4·5 Å and 9 Å. It was often found necessary to cool the specimens below 0° C before the long spacing returned to the initial value of 57 Å. Dimyristoyl cephalin showed similar changes but the short spacings become diffuse at a lower temperature. A summary of the variations of diffraction data are given in Table 64 and the variation of the long spacings are shown diagrammatically in Fig. 113.

The changes observed with the lecithins and the specimen of sphingomyelin appear to be more continuous. Their short spacings show gradual increase as the long spacings decrease. With all the phospholipids no new short spacings were observed when the long spacings indicated that a second polymorph may have been produced, and with saturated materials no well-defined short spacing is observed when the initial long spacing disappears.

These changes were interpreted in terms of an increase in the tilt of the long axes of the molecules with respect to the plane of the bimolecular leaflet. The tilting is then produced by separation of the polar portions of the end group. The short spacings were thought to be related to the distances between these groups although with the cephalins these do not change appreciably. A study of a synthetic phosphatidyl L-serine showed similar variation in the long spacings [158].

These interpretations are rather doubtful. It seems more likely that the variation of the long spacing is related to the increase in the random disorder of the chains and this is also probably the reason for the variation in the short spacings. A similar behaviour is observed with the anhydrous sodium soaps and is discussed in the chapter on infra-red spectroscopy (page 95).

The short spacing observed with the sample of linoleoyl–palmitoyl cephalin is of some interest. Only a diffuse line is observed near 4·5 Å and we can interpret this to indicate that at 20° C the hydrocarbon chains are already in a liquid-like condition. (This is of interest in view of the results deduced from infra-red spectroscopic studies discussed on page 119.) Similar studies, but at lower temperatures, could provide further useful information.

Discussion of the meaning of the long spacing data is hampered by the lack of single-crystal data.[1] The common assumption that the two hydrocarbon chains of a 1,2-diacyl phospholipid point in the same direction

[1] A complete X-ray structural study is at present in progress with 2,3-dimyristoyl-DL-1-phosphatidyl ethanolamine. The unit cell is orthorhombic, $a = 7{\cdot}71$ Å, $b = 9{\cdot}52$ Å and $c = 52{\cdot}5$ Å. The probable space group is $Pm2_1b$ with four molecules per unit cell (Shipley, G. G. and Chapman, D.).

Table 64. *Diffraction spacings* (*in* Å) [156]

Lipid	At 20° C	80° C	95° C	110° C
Dipalmitoyl-cephalin[(a)]	57·0 A VS	55·5 S	55·0 S	54·0 W
		45·0 S	45·0 S	
			36·5 W	32·5 M
	24 VW	28·8 W		
	18 W	19·75 W	22·5 W	
		16·85 W	16·85 W	
	6·16 W	6·16 M	6·16 M	
	5·61 W	5·61 W	5·60 W	Diffuse
	5·10 S	5·10 S	5·10 S	
	4·54 S	4·54 S	4·5 W	
	4·15 M		4·2 W	
Dimyristoyl-cephalin[(a)]	51·5 A VS	50·0 S	49·7 M	36·0 W
				30·5 W
		5·99 W		
	4·64 S	4·64 M	4·64 W	
	4·21 M	4·20 M	4·20 W	Diffuse
	3·93 W			
Erucoyl-stearoyl-cephalin	54·5 VS	53·5 S	37·8 S	37·0 W
	26·5 W			
	17·6 S	17·6 W		
	5·58 W	5·58 M	Diffuse	Diffuse
	4·65 S	4·65 S		
	4·07 W			
Linoleoyl-palmitoyl-cephalin	38 A S	37·8 S	37·5 S	37·2 S
	4·5 Diffuse	Diffuse	Diffuse	Diffuse
Hydrolecithin	59·5 A VS	55·5 S	50·5 S	45·5 M
		47·5 M	42·0 S	39·5 S
	32·5 W			
	16·4 S			
	5·10 VW	5·21 M	5·27 M	Diffuse
	4·54 S	4·77 S	4·85 S	
Sphingomyelin	65·5 A VS	62·0 S	59·0 S	55·5 M
			45·0	43·0 S
	17·8 W			
	5·04 VW	5·10 M	5·24 M	5·30 M
	4·54 S	4·63 S	4·70 S	4·82 S

VW = Very weak. W = Weak. M = Medium. S = Strong. VS = Very strong.

(*a*) The long spacings for these phospholipids are greater than those given by Bevan and Malkin. It is not stated whether those discussed here are DL-type cephalins or 1,2- or 1,3-diacyl cephalins.

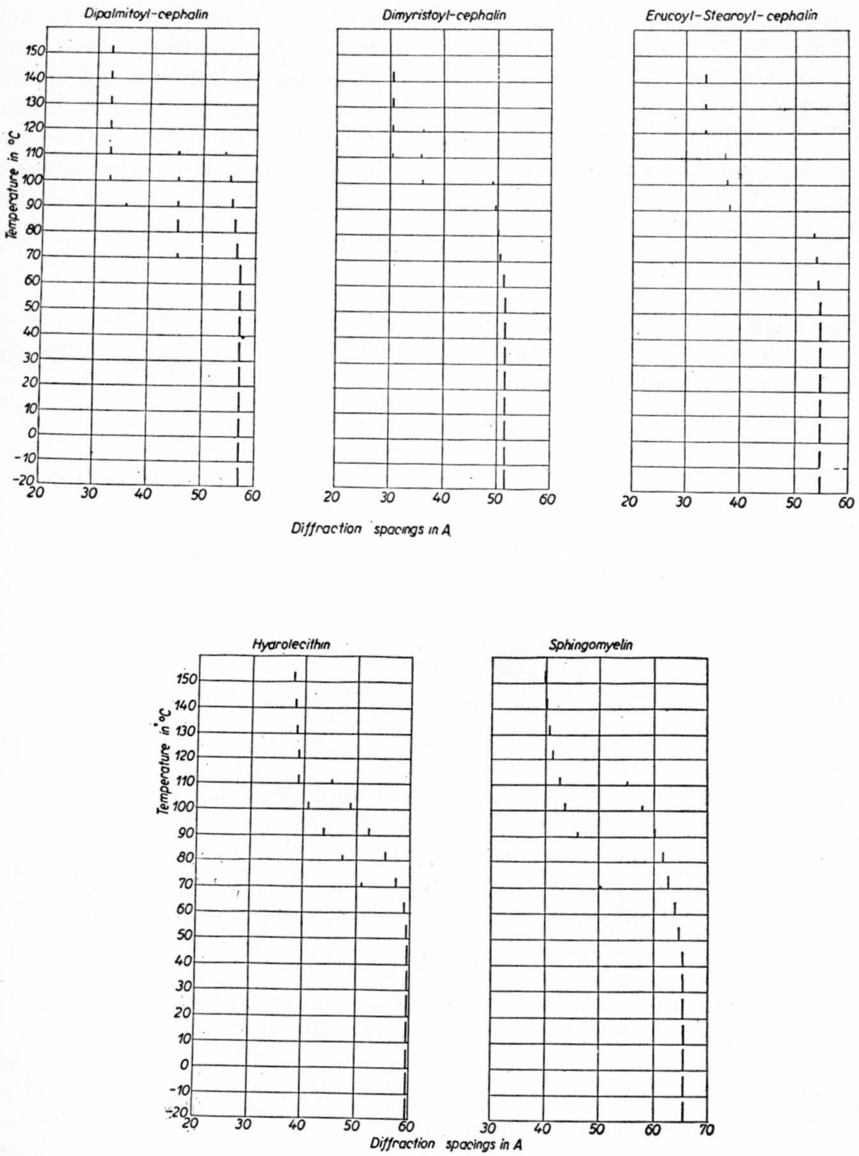

Fig. 113. Summary of changes in long spacing diffraction patterns. (Reproduced from: Finean, J. B. *Biochim. Biophys. Acta*, **10**, 371, 1953.)

need not be correct. As we have seen, this is not the case with trilaurin or tricaprin in their β_L-type polymorphic modification. If it is considered that a better analogous material for comparison is the anhydrous soaps we find, unfortunately, that no single-crystal studies have been reported for long-chain anhydrous sodium soaps although studies of powder diagrams and fibres have led to the suggestion that the chains are in the crossed configuration similar to that observed with potassium caprate [159]. The high melting points appear to rule out internal salt formation and suggest ionic binding of molecule to molecule.

LIPID–WATER SYSTEMS

We shall not review soap systems extensively here, but, in view of their possible important analogy to phospholipid–water systems, point out some of their main features.

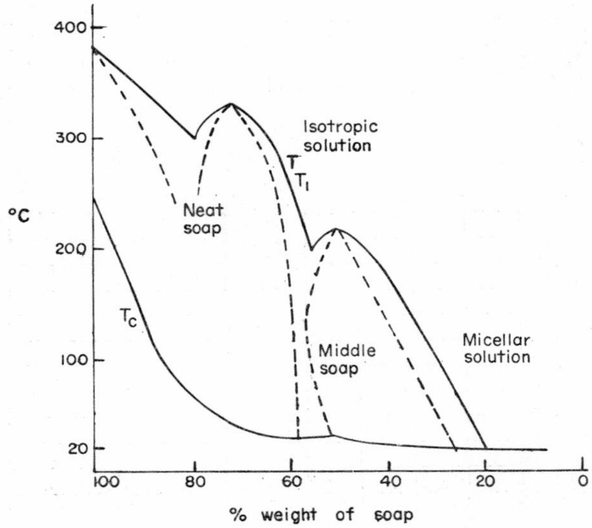

Fig. 114. Phase diagram of the potassium palmitate–water system. (McBain, J. W. and Lee, W. W. *Oil & Soap*, **20**, 17, 1943.)

Lipid–water systems can be described conveniently by reference to their phase diagram [160]. The phase diagram of a potassium palmitate–water system is shown in Fig. 114. The various regions can be identified.

The micellar solution exists above the T_i curve. The viscosity is low and the material is transparent and isotropic in the polarizing microscope. The lipid molecules are associated as micelles at concentrations higher

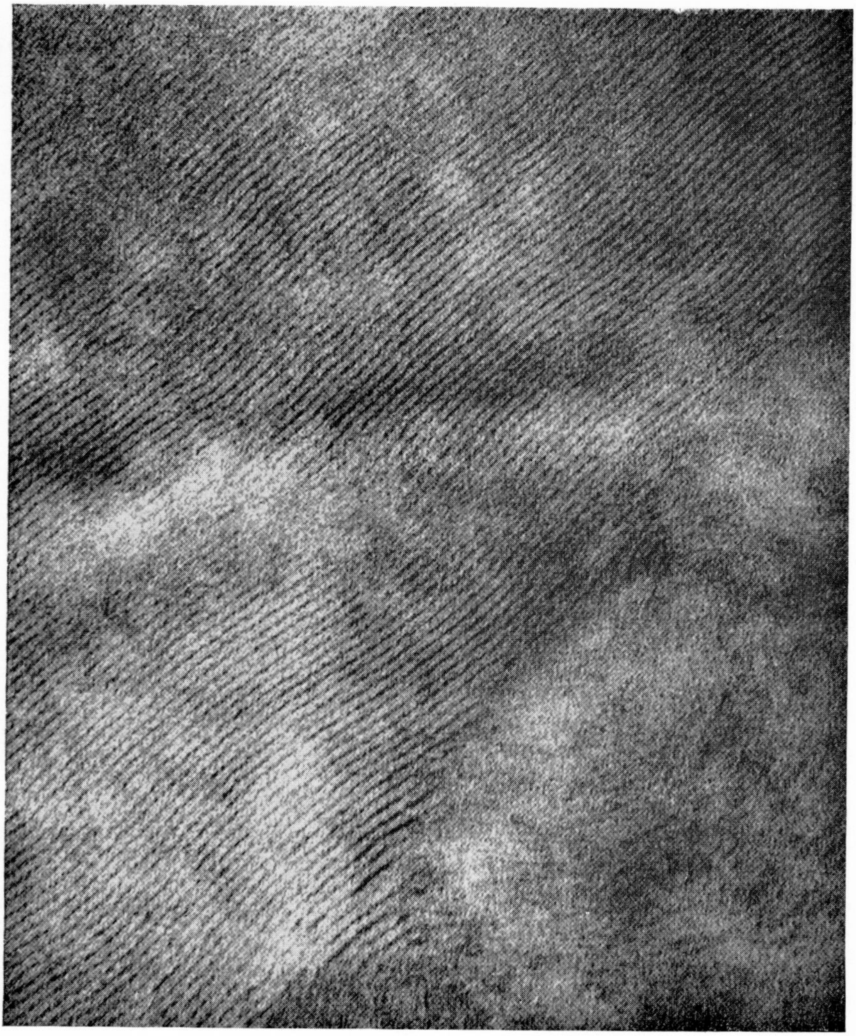

Fig. 115. Phospholipid in the lamellar phase. The sample contained 30% water when fixed with OsO_4. Most of the area in this micrograph shows the band pattern which is seen when the material is cut approximately normal to the plane of the lipid lamellae. × 450,000 (Stoeckenius, W. Reprinted by permission of The Rockefeller Institute Press from *J. Cell. Biol.*, **12**, 221, 1962.)

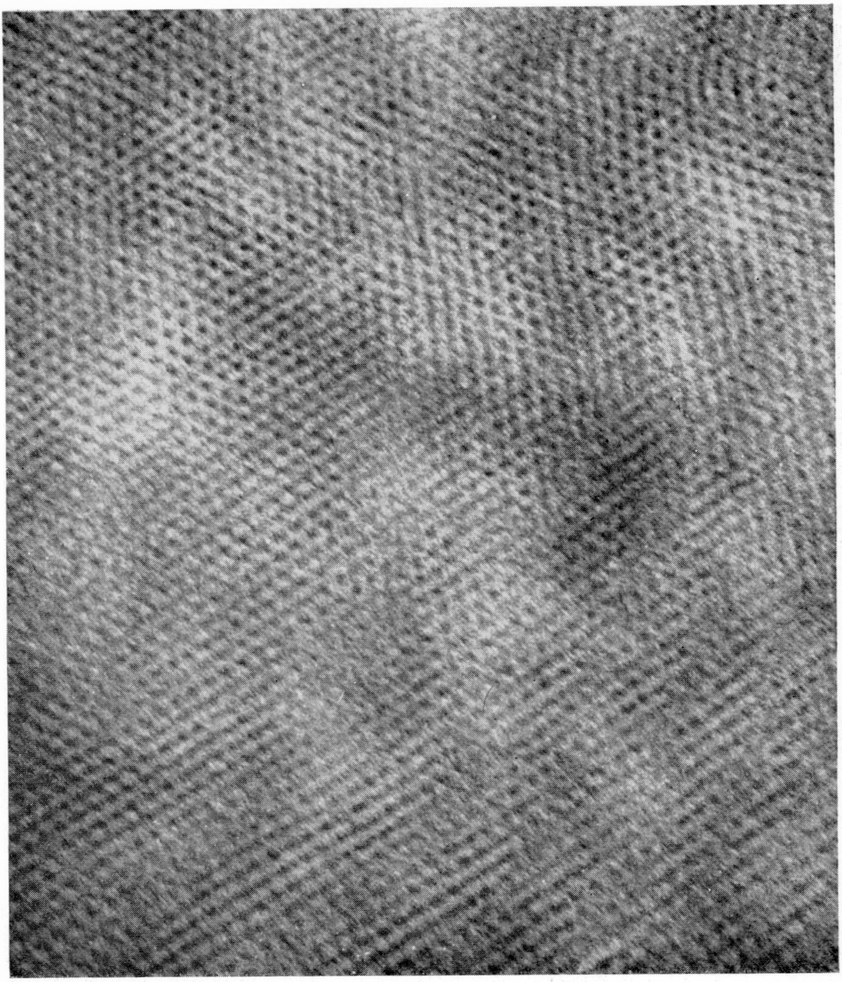

Fig. 116. Phospholipid in the hexagonal phase. The sample contained 3% water when fixed with OsO_4. Most of the area is occupied by hexagonal array of dark dots, which represent cross-sections through cylinders. In other areas a band pattern is visible which probably arises from a slightly different orientation of the cylinders with respect to the direction of view. × 560,000. (Stoeckenius, W. Reprinted by permission of The Rockefeller Institute Press from *J. Cell. Biol.*, **12**, 221, 1962).

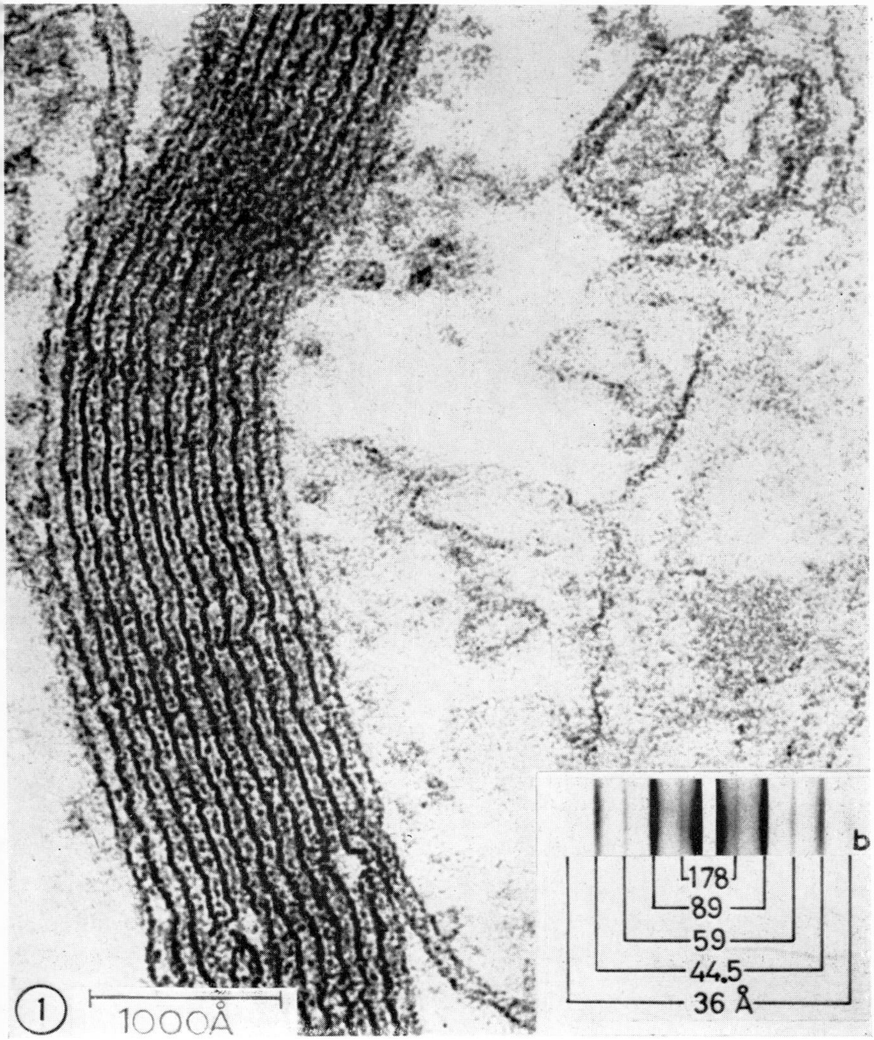

Fig. 117. Electron micrograph of myelin sheath section from a transverse section of osmium fixed rat sciatic nerve. (Fernandez-Moran, H. *Rev. Mod. Phys.*, **31**, 319, 1959.)

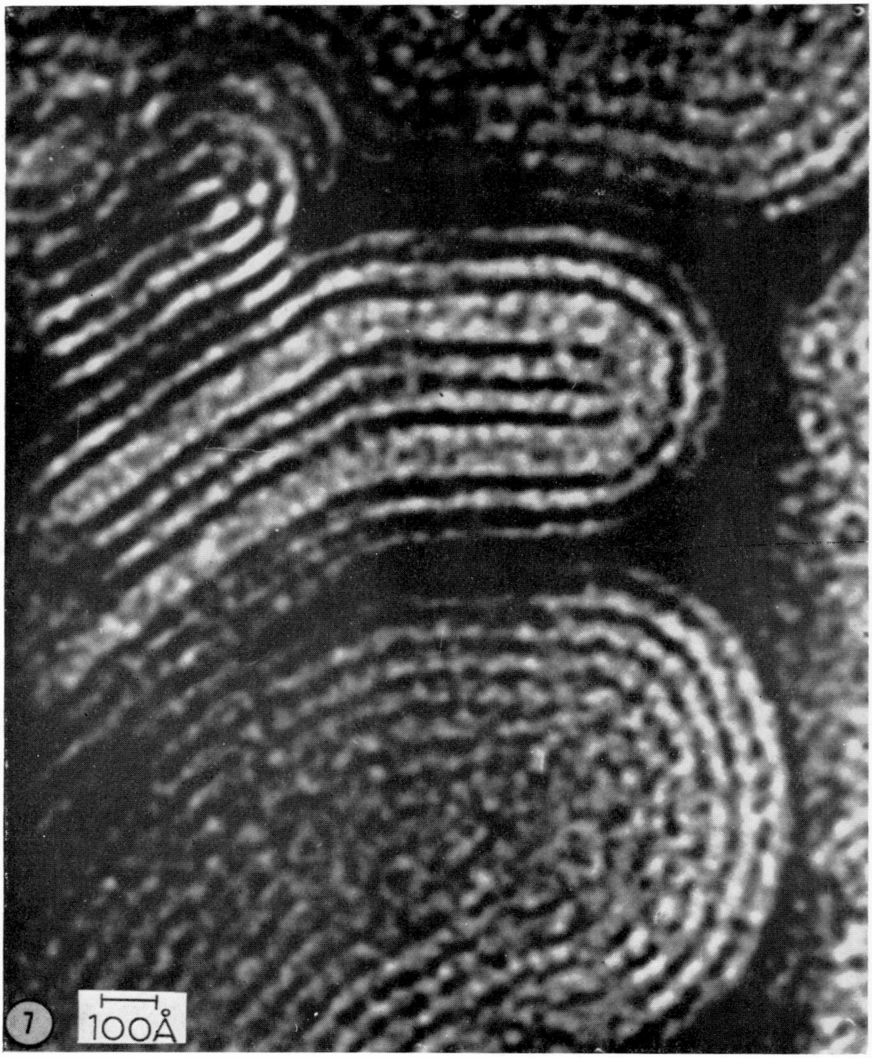

Fig. 118. Electron micrograph of lecithin micelles. (Fernandez-Moran, H. *Royal Microscopical Society Bethesda*, 1964, **83**, 183.

than the critical micellar concentration [161]. Below the T_c curve occurs a gel or coagel. The material is very viscous and equilibrium is often difficult to obtain. Between the T_c and T_i lines the material is liquid–crystalline and obtains equilibrium easily. The material here is very viscous, transparent and optically anisotropic. Several phases exist within this region.

The X-ray patterns [162] show typical features for each of these three regions. The micellar solutions exhibit a few fairly broad bands at large spacings (some 20 to 100 Å) and a diffuse halo at about 4·5 Å. The gels and coagels contain sharp lines at long spacings and a number of sharp lines or narrow bands at spacings smaller than 5 Å. With the liquid–crystalline material there are a few sharp lines at long spacings and a broad band at about 4·5 Å. For each phase the spacings and intensities of the long spacings are characteristic of each phase. The long spacings vary continuously with temperature whilst the short spacing remains constant. This variation in long spacing has been associated with increased disorder of the hydrocarbon chains. The profile of this broad band at ~ 4·5 Å is almost identical with the profile of the band of liquid hydrocarbons. (The infra-red spectra of anhydrous sodium stearate have been obtained at different temperatures (see page 96) and a liquid-like configuration observed above 100° C.) The gel and coagel existing below the T_c line have very different properties. The T_c line is the melting point of the hydrocarbon chains. The liquid–crystalline material can incorporate large quantities of lipid-soluble material and mixtures of lipids behave as one component. The structures deduced for the different phases are shown in Fig. 115. The middle phase diffraction pattern shows that the ratio of the spacings of the sharp line is $1:1/\sqrt{3}:1/\sqrt{4}:1/\sqrt{7}$, typical of equatorial reflections of a hexagonal lattice. The structure is considered to be a hexagonal array of indefinite cylinders. The hydrocarbon chains fill the inside of the cylinders and the water is outside. The hydrophilic groups of the lipid molecules are on the surface. The X-ray spacings give the distance between the axes of the cylinders. The spacings for the neat phase are characteristic of a lamellar structure $1:\frac{1}{2}:\frac{1}{3}:\frac{1}{4}$. The structure is an alternate sequence of the planar layers of lipid and water and the hydrophilic groups of the lipid molecules lie on the surface separating lipid and water. The liquid hydrocarbon chains fill up the lipid layer.

These two phases do not exist in equilibrium. Between the middle and neat phase are the intermediate phases. These are shown in Fig. 119. Some of these are: (i) The deformed middle phase. This is similar to the middle phase but the lattice is orthorhombic. (ii) The rectangular phase. The structure is an orthorhombic two-dimensional lattice of rectangular prisms. (iii) Complex hexagonal. The structure is thought to be one in which the lipids form a cylindrical shell with water filling the inner hole and the external gap between the cylinders. (iv) Cubic phase. The structure is that of close-packed spheres. The hydrocarbon chains are inside the sphere and water is outside.

A brain extract containing 52% cephalin, 35% lecithin and 13% phosphoinositide with known amounts of water was also examined using

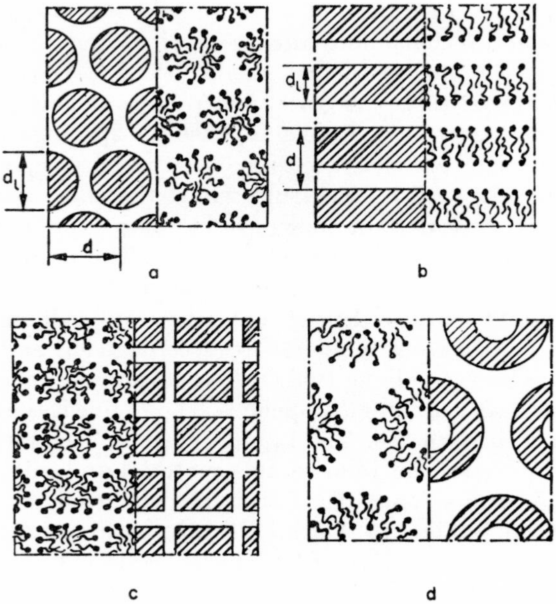

Fig. 119. Structure of some liquid–crystalline phases of simple lipid–water system. (*a*) Middle. (*b*) Neat. (*c*) Rectangular. (*d*) Complex hexagonal. (Luzzati, V. and Husson, F. Reprinted by permission of The Rockefeller Institute Press from *J. Cell. Biol.*, **12**, 207, 1962.)

X-ray scattering techniques [162, 163]. The phase diagram was explored as a function of concentration at two temperatures, 22° and 37° C, and several X-ray patterns were taken with one sample ($c = 0{\cdot}9$) as a function of temperature. The resultant phase diagram is shown in Fig. 120a. Three main phases can be identified. These are the coagel, the hexagonal and the lamellar. Above the dotted line the behaviour is characteristic of liquid–crystalline structures. This material shows a few sharp lines at small angle and a broad band at ~ 4·5 Å. Two phases exist, the lamellar and the hexagonal, which can exist in equilibrium. With the lamellar phase (Fig. 120b) the structure is built up of an alternate sequence of lipid and water layers. (The structure of the hydrocarbon chains is liquid-like.) The suggested structure for the hexagonal phase is shown in Fig. 120b. Here the water is in the interior of the cylinders and the lipid

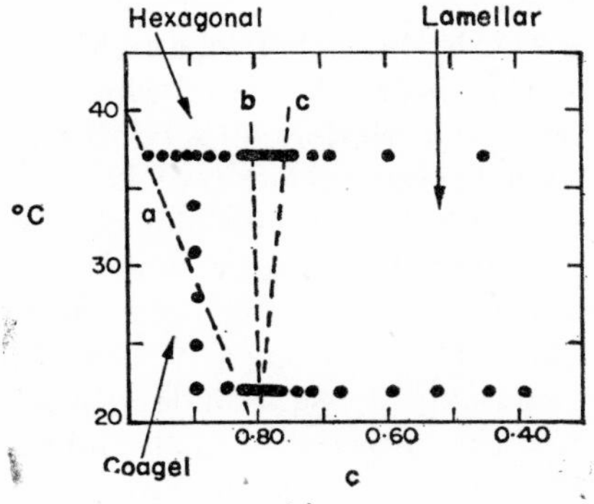

(*a*)

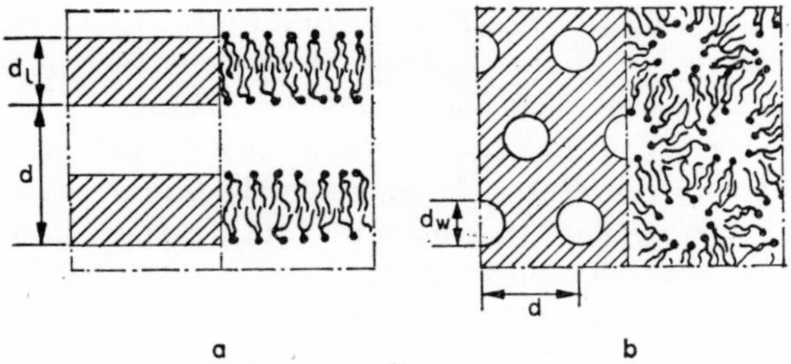

(*b*)

Fig. 120*a*. Phase diagram of phospholipid–water system, and position of the experimental points.
Fig. 120*b*. Structure of the liquid–crystalline phases of the phospholipid water system. (*a*) Lamellar. (*b*) Hexagonal. (Luzzati, V. and Husson, F. Reprinted by permission of The Rockefeller Institute Press from *J. Cell. Biol.*, **12**, 207, 1962.)

molecules fill the gaps between the cylinders. It therefore differs from the structure of the middle phase of the soaps. It is considered that the hydrocarbon chains are also liquid-like. The problem of the shape of the hydrocarbon chains in the liquid is very pertinent (page 241).

Electron microscope observations were made on the same material [164]. By choosing the temperature of fixing the mixture, electron micrographs were obtained corresponding to the known phases as deduced from the X-ray data. The fixation was carried out with osmium tetroxide and dehydration and embedding carried out at room temperature. In this way electron micrographs were obtained of the lamellar phase of the phospholipid–water system. These show alternating light and dense bands with a repeat period of 38 Å (Fig. 115). The dark bands are interpreted to represent layers of hydrophilic groups whilst the light bands are associated with the central parts of the bimolecular leaflets originally containing the hydrocarbon chains of the fatty acids. The electron micrograph of the phospholipid in the hexagonal phase (Fig. 116) shows a hexagonal array of dark dots on a lighter background with the centre-to-centre distance between the dots of 42–45 Å. The dark dots are thought to correspond to the areas containing the hydrophilic groups of the lipid molecules, and are thought to represent cross-sections through cylinders. A line pattern of alternating light and dark bands with a spacing of approximately 36 Å is frequently observed. This is suggested to arise where short pieces of dense cylinders in a section are slightly inclined with respect to the optical axis of the microscope. This has led to the suggestion [162] that for some lipoprotein complexes in a cell membrane the ordinary physiological conditions may not be far from the border line of a phase transition from a liquid–crystalline structure to a coagel. Alteration of the parameters (concentration, temperature, electric potential) causes the hydrocarbon chains to crystallize and some physiological activity of the lipid (perhaps permeability of a membrane) is blocked. The transition from the coagel to the liquid–crystalline region for the brain lipids appears to occur at a temperature close to the body temperature and this may be significant. The fact that the structure and properties of the sodium and potassium soaps are different from each other in the coagel region but identical in the liquid–crystalline region [165] may also be relevant to the selective permeability of membranes to cations if lipoprotein–water systems behave in a similar way.

This is clearly an exciting area for future research and many more studies of lipid systems will help to show whether such speculations can be brought into the realm of proven fact.

LIPOPROTEINS

The myelin sheath of nerve fibres is an example of a multilayered lipoprotein system where the application of X-ray techniques has been particularly useful [166–170]. The myelin sheath is considered to be derived from a multiple folded Schwann-cell surface and may be a model system for the study of cell-membrane structure in general [171].

X-ray diffraction patterns have been obtained from nerve bundles maintained in a physiologically active state in irrigation cells mounted on the X-ray diffraction camera and from nerve bundles sealed in thin-walled glass capillary tubes containing a physiological solution such as Ringer's solution. In both cases the diffraction patterns are observed to be the same.

When the nerve specimens are examined in a direction perpendicular to the fibre axis, using a symmetrically collimated X-ray beam, a meridionally accentuated ring is observed at 4·7 Å and a faint ring is observed at 9·4 Å. These have been shown to be myelin reflections. Other reflections due to myelin also occur at low angles. These low-angle reflections have been accounted for as diffraction orders from a single fundamental repeating unit varying from 150 Å to 180 Å in the different types of nerve examined. Myelin from different sources gives different low-angle reflections. Peripheral nerve from mammals gives five low-angle reflections showing marked alternations in intensities through the orders and indicating a fundamental repeating unit of about 180 Å. The myelin of central origin, such as brain white matter, spinal cord, or optic nerve, gives only two-angle reflections corresponding to a repeat unit of about 80 Å. (The presence of the short spacing near 4·7 Å suggests that the hydrocarbon chains of the lipids present in the myelin sheath are in a liquid-like condition. This does not necessarily preclude some degree of order among the chains.) The variation in the intensities of the low-angle diffractions are interpreted to arise from variations in electron density along the axes of the myelin unit. It has been assumed that the fundamental repeating unit consists of two parts having very similar distributions of X-ray scattering power. From the intensities of the odd-order reflections the magnitude of the difference between the two parts has been estimated. The 'difference factor' is appreciable in peripheral nerve myelin but negligible in optic nerve. Diffraction patterns from the structure along the fibre axis appear as complete rings. This has been interpreted to conclude that the long axis of the rod-shaped unit cell is oriented radially in the myelin sheath.

High-resolution electron micrographs of ultra-thin sections of osmium-fixed peripheral nerve [171, 172] show a series of concentrically arranged dense lines separated by light spaces with an average period of 130 to 140 Å. It is concluded that this corresponds to the fundamental radial unit derived from low-angle X-ray diffraction patterns. The discrepancy of 20 to 30 Å is attributed to shrinkage effects introduced by osmium fixation and other preparative procedures connected with the examination of the thin sections required for the electron microscope. Light intermediate bands which are much narrower (some 10 to 15 Å) are also seen in the electron micrographs. The variation in the densities of the two principal bands of osmium deposition is related to the 'difference factor'.

A high-resolution electron micrograph of myelin-sheath segment from a transverse section of an osmium-fixed rat sciatic nerve is shown in Fig. 117. The low-angle X-ray diffraction pattern of the nerve is also shown. The pattern features a fundamental period of 178 Å with characteristic alternation of the intensities of the even and odd members.

X-ray diffraction experiments have been carried out on nerve after a variety of treatments and useful information obtained [173]. Extraction of fresh nerve with acetone at 0° C removes about 30% of the cholesterol, leaving the other lipid components essentially intact within the still organized residual myelin sheath. The main modifications shown by both X-ray and electron microscopy are expansion of the layered structure with internal rearrangements and formation of collapsed layer systems. Low-angle diffraction patterns of the lipid extract show a strong 34·2 Å reflection, characteristic of cholesterol. A more extensive breakdown of the sheath is observed after alcohol extraction. The breakdown of myelin known to take place during *in vitro* degeneration of nerve has also been studied. The low-angle X-ray diffraction patterns show characteristic changes. There is a marked intensification of the second-order diffraction followed by the appearance of a 70 Å reflection and gradual extinction of the lower orders in later states of degeneration.

Diffraction data has been used to provide information about the molecular organization of myelin. The first ideas about this were based on a polarization optical analysis of freshly isolated nerve fibres before and after treatment with absolute alcohol [166, 174, 175]. This led to the conclusion that the lipid molecules are oriented radially and the non-lipid material arranged in concentric layers (Fig. 121). The layers of oriented lipid molecules alternate with layers of non-lipid material. X-ray data led to the further conclusion that the peripheral nerve consisted of two lipoprotein layers, each of which consists of bimolecular leaflets of 67 Å, sandwiched between protein layers of 25 Å with interposed water layers of about another 25 Å thickness. Further studies by Finean, taking consideration of the contraction of the lipid layers during drying, has led to a more detailed molecular arrangement of the myelin. The changes observed with frog sciatic nerve when dried are that the myelin unit shrinks to about 145–148 Å and at the same time three independently diffraction lipid phases are produced. The residual myelin unit gives X-ray reflections at about 146 Å and 73 Å. X-ray diffraction studies have also been carried out on various types of nerve at different temperatures [157].

The detailed molecular picture for myelin suggested by Finean [176] is shown in Fig. 122. Each lipoprotein is considered to consist of two phospholipid complexes associated with a cerebroside molecule intercalated between monolayers of protein.

The difference factor has been explained by the mechanism of myelin formation. The myelin sheath is formed by an infolding and multiple wrapping of the Schwann-cell membrane around the axon in embryonic

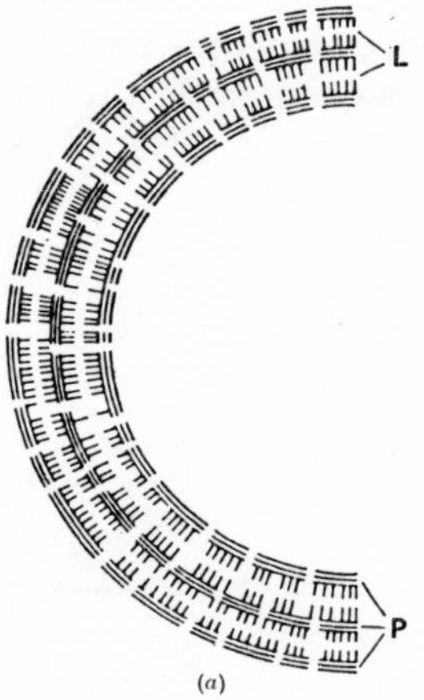

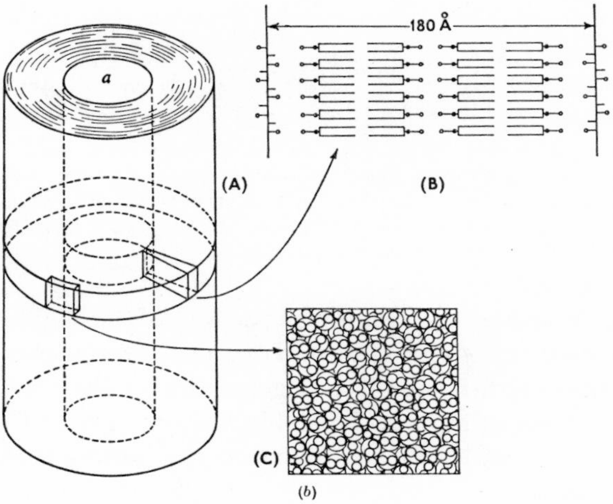

Fig. 121*a*. Orientation of lipid (L) and protein (P) components of the nerve myelin sheath, as deduced from polarized light studies. (Schmitt, F. O. *Rev. Mod. Phys.*, **31**, 455, 1959.)
Fig. 121*b*. Schematic representation of myelin sheath structure showing: A, concentric lipid-protein layers; B, structure in the radial direction (perpendicular to planes of layers); C, structure in the planes of the layers (paraffin chains of lipid molecules shown as open circles).

fibres. If the Schwann-cell lipoprotein membrane is asymmetric the process of rolling on to the axon will produce the symmetry difference observed in successive layers.

The model proposed by Finean has been recently criticized [177] for a number of reasons: (*a*) It does not explain the phosphorus-to-phosphorus distance of about 50 Å without additional assumptions about the arrangement in opposition of a very large number of long chains, which would have to be alternating tilted, or bent interlocking. (*b*) It is incompatible with the occurrence of a considerable proportion of fatty acids with unsaturation starting at C_9 among the phosphatidyl components of

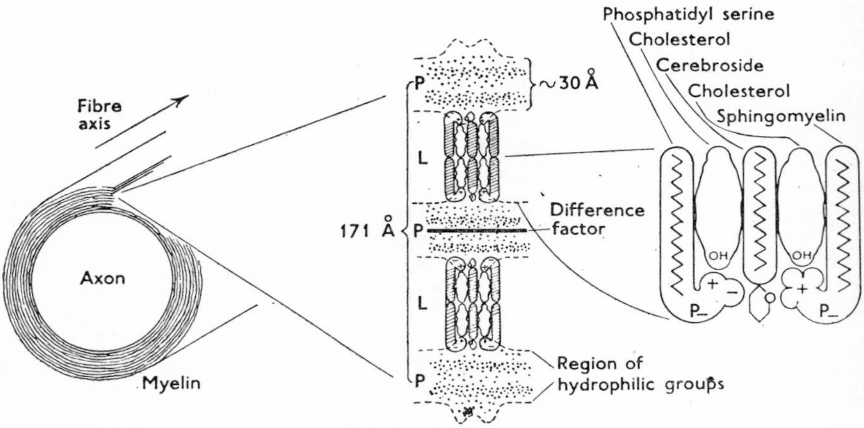

Fig. 122. Drawing showing possible arrangement of molecules (including phospholipid-cholesterol complex) in the structural unit of the myelin sheath of frog peripheral nerve. (Finean, J. B. *Exptl. Cell Res.*, **5**, 18, 1958.)

myelin, as the cholesterol molecule is in the way of the chains. (*c*) A hydrogen bond between the —OH group of the cholesterol and the terminal group of the phosphatidic chain as suggested is unlikely because of lack of colinearity of the atoms involved. (*d*) The position of the cholesterol molecule in the model is not conducive to the largest possible van der Waals interaction.

The similarity in the structure of the phosphatidyl- and sphingolipids has been pointed out (see Fig. 123). The sphingosine molecule is considered to be structurally equivalent to a monoglyceride having a fatty acid chain of 14 carbon atoms. The connection of the fatty acid to C_2 of the sphingosine molecule differs only from that found in the diglyceride moiety of the phosphatidyl lipid with regard to the connecting atom.

Vandenheuvel suggests that the *cis*-vinyl ether linkage of the *phosphatidal* lipids (plasmalogens) does not differ, either in the number of atoms involved or in overall effective dimensions from the corresponding group in phosphatidyl compounds.

He points out that the third chain of these lipids contains a common characteristic sequence indicated in heavy line. Starting from C_1 of glycerol or sphingosine, appear: an oxygen atom, an atom which is either phosphorus or carbon, an oxygen atom, two consecutive carbon atoms,

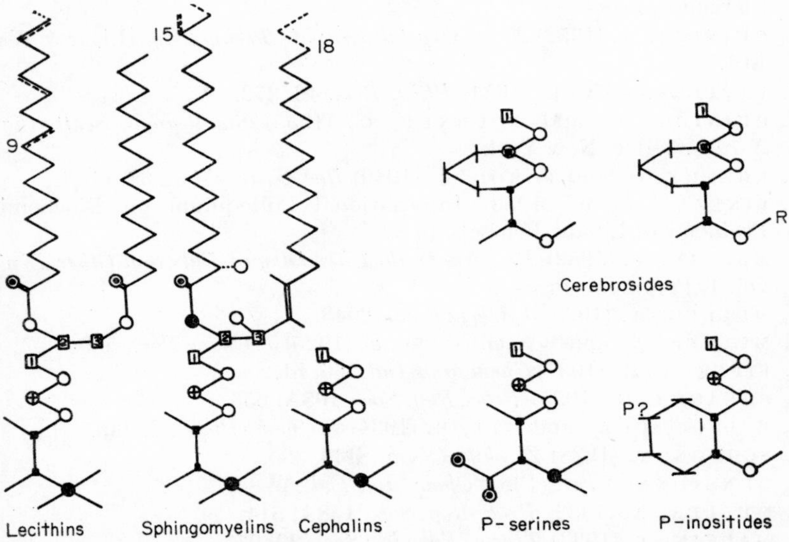

Fig. 123. General similarity of structure of phospholipids. (Vandenheuvel, F. A. *J. Amer. Oil Chemists' Soc.*, **40**, 455, 1963.)

and a polar group. Computations of bond angles and distances of these basic elements predict that a similarity in overall distance and direction is to be expected.

The key to this arrangement of lipids to form a bimolecular leaflet of the observed width is considered to be the group formed by two cholesterol–sphingolipid complex units with either saturated or unsaturated chain of maximum length. When two such units are brought together tail-to-tail with the sphingosine chains in opposition, they interdigitate, resulting in an arrangement which involves considerable van der Waals interaction. In this arrangement, the end of a C_{24} saturated chain fits under the end of opposed cholesterol while the end of the C_{24} monounsaturated chain butts against the end of cholesterol. The distance between phosphorus atoms in the resulting unit is 51·5 Å, which is that observed by Finean for human myelin. Whether this model is consistent with the liquid character of the hydrocarbon chains present in myelin is a question for further experiments.

REFERENCES

1. LONSDALE, K. (1948) *Crystals and X-rays*. G. Bell & Sons Ltd., London.
2. WHEATLEY, P. J. (1959) *Determination of Molecular Structure*, p. 101. Clarendon Press.
3. GUINIER, A. (1952) *X-ray Crystallographic Technology*. Hilger & Watts Ltd.
4. PATTERSON, A. L. (1934) *Phys. Rev.*, **46**, 372.
5. GUINIER, A. and FOURNET, G. (1955) *Small-angle Scattering of X-rays*. Wiley, New York.
6. KRATKY, O. and POROD, G. (1949) *Rev. Trav. chim.*, **68**, 1106.
7. FINEAN, J. B. (1953) International Colloquium on Biochemical Problems of Lipids, Brussels, p. 82.
8. MALKIN, T. (1952) *Progress in the Chemistry of Fats and Other Lipids*, vol. 1. Pergamon Press.
9. MULLER, A. (1923) *J. Chem. Soc.*, 2043.
10. MULLER, A. and SAVILLE, W. B. (1925) *J. Chem. Soc.*, 599.
11. PIPER, S. H. (1937) *Chem. and Ind.*, **56**, 61.
12. SHEARER, G. (1925) *Proc. Roy. Soc.*, **108A**, 655.
13. WILSON, D. A. and OTT, E. (1934) *J. Chem. Phys.*, **2**, 239.
14. SCHOON, T. (1938) *Z. phys. Chem.*, **B39**, 385.
15. GUNSTONE, F. D. (1964) *Chem. and Ind.*, p. 84.
16. MULLER, A. (1932) *Proc. Roy. Soc.*, **138A**, 514.
17. MALKIN, T. (1933) *Trans. Faraday Soc.*, **29**, 977.
18. MULLER, A. (1927) *Proc. Roy. Soc.*, **114A**, 542.
19. VAND, V. (1951) *Acta Cryst.*, **4**, 104.
20. ABRAHAMSSON, S. (1959) *Arkiv. Kemi*, **14**, 65.
21. MULLER, A. and LONSDALE, K. (1948) *Acta Cryst.*, **1**, 129.
22. VON SYDOW, E. (1954) *Acta Cryst.*, **7**, 529.
23. VON SYDOW, E. (1956) *Acta Chem. Scand.*, **10**, 1.
24. VAND, V. and BELL, I. P. (1951) *Acta Cryst.*, **4**, 465.
25. ABRAHAMSSON, S. (1959) *Acta Cryst.*, **12**, 301.
26. ABRAHAMSSON, S. (1956) *Acta Cryst.*, **9**, 663.
27. BUNN, C. W. (1939) *Trans. Faraday Soc.*, **35**, 482.
28. SHEARER, H. M. M. and VAUD, V. (1956) *Acta Cryst.*, **9**, 379.
29. VAINSHTEIN, B. K. and PINSKER, Z. G. (1950) *Doklady Akad. Nauk. S.S.S.R.*, **72**, 53.
30. BROTHERTON, T., CRAVEN, B. and JEFFREY, G. A. (1958) *Acta Cryst.*, **11**, 546.
31. CRAVEN, B. and JEFFREY, G. A. (1959) *Acta Cryst.*, **12**, 754.

32. WELSH, H. K. (1956) *Acta Cryst.*, **9**, 89.
33a. VON SYDOW, E. (1956) *Arkiv. Kemi*, **9**, 231.
33b. VON SYDOW, E. (1955) *Acta Cryst.*, **8**, 810.
34. VAND, V., MORLEY, W. M. and LOMER, T. R. (1951) *Acta Cryst.*, **4**, 324.
35. VON SYDOW, E. (1954) *Acta Cryst.*, **7**, 823.
36. DEGERMAN, G. and VON SYDOW, E. (1959) *Acta Chem. Scand.*, **13**, 984.
37. ABRAHAMSSON, S. and VON SYDOW, E. (1954) *Acta Cryst.*, **7**, 591.
38. VON SYDOW, E. (1955) *Acta Cryst.*, **8**, 557.
39. ABRAHAMSSON, S. (1959) *Acta Cryst.*, **12**, 304.
40. VON SYDOW, E. (1958) *Acta Chem. Scand.*, **12**, 777.
41. ABRAHAMSSON, S. and RYDERSTEDT-NAHRINGBAUER, I. (1962) *Acta Cryst.*, **15**, 1261.
42. ANDREW, E. R. (1950) *J. Chem. Phys.*, **18**, 607.
43. CROWE, R. W. and SMYTHE, C. P. (1950) *J. Amer. Chem. Soc.*, **72**, 4427.
44. HOFFMAN, J. D. and SMYTHE, C. P. (1950) *J. Amer. Chem. Soc.*, **72**, 171.
45. KATIUCHI, Y. (1951) *J. Phys. Soc. Japan*, **6**, 313.
46. CHAPMAN, D. and WHITTINGTON, S. G. (1964) *Trans. Faraday Soc.*, **60**, 1369.
47. TURNER, J. D. and LINGAFELTER, E. C. (1955) *Acta Cryst.*, **8**, 551.
48. SAKURAI, T. (1955) *J. Phys. Soc. Japan*, **10**, 1040.
49. VAND, V., LOMER, T. R. and LANG, A. R. (1949) *Acta Cryst.*, **2**, 214.
50. WARREN, B. E. (1933) *Phys. Rev.*, **44**, 969.
51. STEWART, G. W. and MORROW, R. (1927) *Phys. Rev.*, **30**, 232.
52. MORROW, R. (1928) *Phys. Rev.*, **31**, 10.
53. NORMAN, N. and MATHISEN, H. (1960) *The Structure of Linear Polymers*. U.S. Dept. of Commerce, Washington, PB.171181.
54. SEGERMAN, E. (personal communication).
55. BARTELL, L. S. and KOHL, D. A. (1963) *J. Chem. Phys.*, **39**, 3097.
56. TAUER, K. J. and LIPSCOMB, W. N. (1952) Acta Cryst., **5**, 606.
57. MALKIN, T. (1930) *J. Amer. Chem. Soc.*, **52**, 3739.
58. KOLB, D. G. and LUTTON, E. S. (1951) *J. Amer. Chem. Soc.*, **73**, 5593.
59. ABRAHAMSSON, S. and SELIN, K. (1963) *Acta Cryst.*, **16**, part 13, Suppl. A. 58, 5.40.
60. CARLISLE, C. H. and CROWFOOT, D. (1945) *Proc. Roy. Soc.*, **A184**, 64.
61. HOLTZBERG, F., POST, B. and FANKUCHEN, I. (1953) *Acta Cryst.*, **6**, 127.
62. JONES, R. E. and TEMPLETON, D. H. (1958) *Acta Cryst.*, **11**, 484.
63. BAUN, W. L. (1961) *J. Phys. Chem.*, **65**, 2122.
64. VON SYDOW, E. (1955) *Acta Chem. Scand.*, **9**, 1685.
65. STENHAGEN, E. and VON SYDOW, E. (1953) *Arkiv. Kemi*, **6**, 309.
66. VON SYDOW, E. (1956) *Acta Chem. Scand.*, **10**, 1.
67. LOMER, T. R. (1963) *Acta Cryst.*, **16**, 984.

68. ABRAHAMSSON, S. and FISCHMEISTER, I. (1959) *Arkiv. Kemi*, **14**, 57.
69. MULLER, A. and SHEARER, G. (1923) *J. Chem. Soc.*, **123**, 3156.
70. LUTTON, E. S. (1946) *Oil and Soap*, **23**, 265.
71. LUTTON, E. S. and KOLP, D. G. (1951) *J. Amer. Chem. Soc.*, **73**, 2733.
72. BENEDICT, J. H. and DAUBERT, B. F. (1949) *J. Amer. Chem. Soc.*, **71**, 4113.
73. CASPARI, W. A. (1928) *J. Chem. Soc.*, 3235.
74. TRILLAT, J. J. (1925) *Compt. rend.*, **180**, 1329.
75. CASPARI, W. A. (1929) *J. Chem. Soc.*, 2709.
76. MALKIN, T. (1931) *J. Chem. Soc.*, 2796.
77. SMITH, J. C. (1938) *Ann. Reports Prog. Chem. Soc.*, **35**, 257.
78. ALEBY, S. (1962) *Acta Cryst.*, **15**, 1248.
79. FRANCIS, F. and PIPER, S. H. (1939) *J. Amer. Chem. Soc.*, **61**, 577.
80. ALEBY, S. and VON SYDOW, E. (1960) *Acta Cryst.*, **13**, 487.
81. HEINTZ, W. (1849) *Jahresber.*, **2**, 342.
82. DUFFY, P. (1853) *J. Chem. Soc.*, **5**, 197.
83. BERTHELOT, M. (1853) *Liebig's Annalen der Chemie*, **88**, 304; (1854) **92**, 301.
84. GUTH, F. (1902) *Z. Biol.*, **44**, 78.
85. LAUTZ, H. (1913) *Z. phys. Chem.* (*Leipzig*), **84**, 611.
86. OTHMER, P. (1915). *Z. anorg. Chem.*, **91**, 237.
87. LOSKIT, K. (1928) *Z. phys. Chem.* (*Leipzig*), **134**, 135.
88. JOGTEKAR, R. B. and WATSON, H. E. (1930) *J. Indian Inst. Sci.*, **13A**, 119.
89. WEYGAND, C. and GRUNTZIG, W. (1932) *Z. anorg. Chem.*, **206**, 304.
90. CLARKSON, C. E. and MALKIN, T. (1934) *J. Chem. Soc.*, 666.
91. MALKIN, T. and SHURBAGY, M. R. E. (1936) *J. Chem. Soc.*, 1628.
92. BAILEY, A. E., JEFFERSON, M. E., KREEGER, F. B. and BAUER, S. T. (1945) *Oil and Soap*, **22**, 10.
93. FILER, L. J., SIDHU, S. S., DAUBERT, B. F. and LONGENECKER, J. E. (1946) *J. Amer. Chem. Soc.*, **68**, 167.
94. LUTTON, E. S. (1945) *J. Amer. Chem. Soc.*, **67**, 524.
95. LUTTON, E. S. (1950) *J. Amer. Oil Chemists' Soc.*, **27**, 276.
96. MALKIN, T. (1954) *Progress in Chemistry of Fats and Other Lipids*, Vol. 11. Pergamon Press, London.
97. RALSTON, A. W. (1948) *Fatty Acids and their Derivatives*, p. 545. Wiley, New York.
98. VAECK, S. V. (1948) *Mededel. vlaam. chem. Ver.*, **10**, 225.
99. CHAPMAN, D. (1962) *Chem. Rev.*, **62**, 433.
100. HOERR, C. W. (1960) *J. Amer. Oil Chemists' Soc.*, **37**, 539.
101. RAVICH, G., ZURIMOV, C., VOLOVA, V. and PETROV, V. (1946) *Acta Physicochim., U.R.S.S.*, **21**, 101.
102. CHAPMAN, D. (1955) *Nature*, **176**, 216.
103. CHAPMAN, D. (1957) *Spectrochim. Acta*, **11**, 609.
104. LUTTON, E. S. (1958) *J. Amer. Oil Chemists' Soc.*, **35**, 11.

105. CROWE, R. W. and SMYTHE, C. P. (1950) *J. Amer. Chem. Soc.*, **72**, 5281.
106. QUIMBY, O. T. (1950) *J. Amer. Chem. Soc.*, **72**, 5063.
107. TURNBULL, D. and CORMIA, R. L. (1961) *J. Chem. Phys.*, **34**, 820.
108. LARSSON, K. (1963) *Proc. Chem. Soc.*, **87**, March.
109. JENSEN, L. H. and MABIS, A. J. (1963) *Nature*, **197**, 681.
110. CHAPMAN, D. and HAYES, M. J. (1960) (unpublished work).
111. CARTER, M. G. R. and MALKIN, T. (1939) *J. Chem. Soc.*, 577.
112. CARTER, M. G. R. and MALKIN, T. (1939) *J. Chem. Soc.*, 1518.
113. MALKIN, T., SHURBAGY, M. R. E. and MEARA, M. L. (1939) *J. Chem. Soc.*, 1409.
114. MALKIN, T. and MEARA, M. L. (1939) *J. Chem. Soc.*, 103.
115. MALKIN, T. and MEARA, M. L. (1939) *J. Chem. Soc.*, 1141.
116. LUTTON, E. S., JACKSON, F. L. and QUIMBY, O. T. (1948) *J. Amer. Chem. Soc.*, **70**, 2441.
117. CHAPMAN, D. (1957) *J. Chem. Soc.*, 2715.
118. CROWE, R. W. and SMYTHE, C. P. (1951) *J. Amer. Chem. Soc.*, **73**, 2040.
119. CHAPMAN, D. (1958) *J. Chem. Soc.*, 3186.
120. JACKSON, F. L. and LUTTON, E. S. (1949) *J. Amer. Chem. Soc.*, **71**, 1976.
121. JACKSON, F. L. and LUTTON, E. S. (1950) *J. Amer. Chem. Soc.*, **72**, 4519.
122. JACKSON, F. L. and LUTTON, E. S. (1952) *J. Amer. Chem. Soc.*, **74**, 4827.
123. FEUGE, R. O., VICKNAIR, E. J. and LOVEGREN, N. V. (1952) *J. Amer. Oil Chemists' Soc.*, **29**, 11.
124. VICKNAIR, E. J., SINGLETON, W. S. and FEUGE, R. O. (1954) *J. Amer. Oil Chemists' Soc.*, **58**, 64.
125. FEUGE, R. O. and LOVEGREN, N. V. (1956) *J. Amer. Oil Chemists' Soc.*, **33**, 367.
126. JACKSON, F. L., WILLE, R. L. and LUTTON, E. S. (1951) *J. Amer. Oil Chemists' Soc.*, **73**, 4280.
127. CHEN, C. and DAUBERT, B. F. (1945) *J. Amer. Chem. Soc.*, **67**, 1256.
128. SIDHA, S. S. and DAUBERT, B. F. (1946) *J. Amer. Chem. Soc.*, **68**, 2603.
129. DAUBERT, B. F. and CLARKE, T. H. (1945) *Oil and Soap*, **22**, 113.
130. FILER, L. J., SIDHU, S. S., DAUBERT, B. F. and LONGENECKER, J. E. (1946) *J. Amer. Chem. Soc.*, **68**, 167.
131. MALKIN, T. and WILSON, B. R. (1949) *J. Chem. Soc.*, 369.
132. LANDEMANN, W., FEUGE, R. O. and LOVEGREN, N. V. (1960) *J. Amer. Oil Chemists' Soc.*, **37**, 638.
133. LAVERY, H. (1958) *J. Amer. Oil Chemists' Soc.*, **35**, 418.
134. BAUER, F. J., JACKSON, F. L., KOLP, D. G. and LUTTON, E. S. (1949) *J. Amer. Oil Chemists' Soc.*, **71**, 3363.
135. HOWE, R. J. and MALKIN, T. (1951) *J. Chem. Soc.*, 2663.

136. CHAPMAN, D. (1956) *J. Chem. Soc.*, 2522.
137. LARSSON, K. (private communication).
138. DAUBERT, B. F. and LUTTON, E. S. (1947) *J. Amer. Chem. Soc.*, **69**, 1449.
139. GROS, A. T. and FEUGE, R. O. (1957) *J. Amer. Oil Chemists' Soc.*, **2**, 239.
140. CARTER, M. G. R. and MALKIN, T. (1947) *J. Chem. Soc.*, 554.
141. CHAPMAN, D. (1958) *J. Chem. Soc.*, 4680.
142. FISCHER, E., BERGMANN, M. and BARWIND, H. (1920) *Ber.*, **53**, 1591.
143. REWADIKAR, R. S. and WATSON, H. E. (1930) *J. Indian Inst. Sci.*, **13A**, 128.
144. MALKIN, T. and SHARBAGY, M. R. E. (1936) *J. Chem. Soc.*, 1628.
145. LUTTON, E. S., JACKSON, F. L. and QUIMBY, O. T. (1948) *J. Amer. Chem. Soc.*, **70**, 2441.
146. CHAPMAN, D. (1956) *J. Chem. Soc.*, 55.
147. LUTTON, E. S. and JACKSON, F. L. (1948) *J. Amer. Chem. Soc.*, **70**, 2445.
148. ABRAHAMSSON, S., ALEBY, S., LARSSON, G., LARSSON, K., RYDERSTEDT-NUHRINGBAUER, I. and VON SYDOW, E. (1960) *Acta Cryst.*, **13**, 1044.
149. CHAPMAN, D., CROSSLEY, A. and DAVIES, A. C. (1957) *J. Chem. Soc.*, 1502.
150. BEAR, R. S., PALMER, K. J. and SCHMITT, F. O. (1941) *J. Cell Comp. Physiol.*, **17**, 355.
151. SCHMITT, F. O., BEAR, S. R. and PALMER, K. J. (1941) *J. Cell Comp. Physiol.*, **18**, 31.
152. EGERTON, M. J., GREGORY, G. I. and MALKIN, T. (1952) *J. Chem. Soc.*, 2272.
153. BAER, E. and KATES, M. (1951) *J. Amer. Chem. Soc.*, **72**, 942.
154. BEVAN, T. H., BROWN, D. A. and MALKIN, T. (1962) *J. Chem. Soc.*, 3495.
155. BEVAN, T. H. and MALKIN, T. (1951) *J. Chem. Soc.*, 2667.
156. FINEAN, J. B. (1953) *Biochim. Biophys. Acta* **10**, 371.
157. ELKES, J. and FINEAN, J. B. (1951) *Exp. Cell Res.*, **4**, 82.
158. FINEAN, J. B. (1959) *J. Biophys. Biochem. Cytology*, **62**, 123.
159. SEGERMAN, E. (1963) (private communication).
160. MCBAIN, J. W. and LEE, W. W. (1943) *Oil and Soap*. **20**, 17.
161. MCBAIN, J. W. (1950) *Colloid Science*. Heath & Co., Boston, D.C.
162. LUZZATI, V. and HUSSON, F. (1962) *J. Cell Biol.*, **12**, 207.
163. HUSSON, F. (1961) *Compt. rend.*, **252**, 945.
164. STOECKENIUS, W. (1962) *J. Cell Biol.*, **12**, 221.
165. HUSSON, F., MUSTACCHI, H. and LUZZATI, V. (1960) *Acta Cryst.*, **13**, 608.
166. SCHMITT, F. O. and BEAR, R. S. (1939) *Biol. Rev. Camb. Phil. Soc.*, **14**, 27.

167. SCHMITT, F. O., BEAR, R. S. and CLARK, G. L. (1935) *Radiology*, **25**, 131.
168. SCHMITT, F. O., BEAR, R. S. and PALMER, K. J. (1941) *J. Cell. Comp. Physiol.*, **18**, 31.
169. FINEAN, J. B. (1953) *Exp. Cell Res.*, **5**, 202.
170. FINEAN, J. B. (1954) *Exp. Cell Res.*, **6**, 283.
171. FERNÁNDEZ-MORÁN, H. (1959) *Rev. Mod. Phys.*, **31**, 319.
172. FERNÁNDEZ-MORÁN, H. (1950) *Exp. Cell Res.*, **1**, 309.
173. FERNÁNDEZ-MORÁN, H. and FINEAN, J. B. (1957) *J. Biophys. Biochem. Cytol.*, **3**, 725.
174. FINEAN, J. B. (1960) *J. Biophys. Biochem. Cytol.*, **8**, 31.
175. SCHMITT, F. O. (1959) *Rev. Mod. Phys.*, **31**, 455.
176a. FINEAN, J. B. (1958) *Exp. Cell Res.*, **5**, 18.
176b. FINEAN, J. B. and ROBERTSON, J. D. (1958) *Brit. Med. Bull.*, **14**, 267.
177. VANDENHEUVEL, F. A. (1963) *J. Amer. Oil Chemists' Soc.*, **40**, 455.

9. Future developments and other techniques

In the preceding chapter we have shown first the present state of development of the separation techniques for dealing with the complex mixtures in which they occur naturally. Then we have shown how spectroscopic and X-ray techniques enable both a more precise identification to be made in many cases and how they also provide structural information, e.g. about the way in which lipid molecules pack, the type of radicals which can occur.

There are many obvious gaps in our knowledge, even with the simple lipids, and particularly so with the important phospholipid molecules. Examples of this are the paucity of information available about their liquid–crystalline phase (a study of the effect of electric fields combined with X-ray data may be particularly important), the lack of single-crystal X-ray data on any phospholipid and even their poor characterization by infra-red spectroscopy, high-resolution n.m.r. spectroscopy or mass spectroscopy. In the future, as pure phospholipids are prepared and carefully checked by thin-layer chromatography, this situation will surely change.

When we come to the problem of the possible interactions between lipid and protein here we can see that infra-red spectroscopy and low-angle X-ray techniques may help to illuminate the situation. Other techniques such as surface studies, including the measurements of surface pressure, surface tension and surface potential, may also provide useful information [1–5]. A little of such work has been reported with pure phospholipids [6] and although such studies in the past were probably affected by impurities, this should not be the case in the future. The study of mixed films should also be useful and studies of cholesterol–phospholipid films are being carried on at present [7]. The importance of phospholipid micelles for the solubilization of cholesterol has been pointed out [8]. Calorimetry and thermal analysis may prove valuable.[1]

[1] These techniques are being applied to a study of pure phospholipids, in mixtures with cholesterol and also to natural membranes, e.g. myelin. Such studies may show why the phospholipids in biological tissues have a particular distribution of fatty acids associated with them.

Finally, the technique of electron microscopy, which we have mentioned briefly in the early chapters, may supplement the information obtained by the spectroscopic technique enabling us to visualize the complex patterns of the macromolecular organization which occur in the biological system. The modern electron microscope achieves resolution of the order of 5 to 10 Å with good preparative techniques. Artefacts abound in the preparation of the samples for study and false interpretations are easy to make [9, 10, 11] but important information is being rapidly revealed. The combination of X-ray and electron microscopy, particularly when the latter includes electron diffraction, is very powerful. Few such studies have been reported on the simple glycerides or phospholipids. The combination of the two techniques to studies of myelin sheath has been most valuable [12–14].

The combined electron microscope studies of Fernandez-Moran and the biochemical studies of Green and co-workers show the way in which information about the biological lipoproteins can be obtained. The work on mitochondria is particularly interesting [15–17]. An example of such studies are those made with negatively stained, water-soluble pure mitochondrial phospholipids. The lipid micelles used in this technique are embedded in thin films of buffered phosphotungstate. The buffered reagent tends to localize preferentially at the available aqueous interphase. An electron micrograph is shown in Fig. 118. Periodic dense lines 10–20 Å separated by light bands 25–30 Å having irregular spacing of 45–50 Å in the dried state and of 60–80 Å in partly hydrated specimens are interpreted primarily in terms of aqueous interphases at the hydrophilic and hydrophobic regions of adjacent lecithin bimolecular leaflets. This technique is said to be better than the techniques involved with standard osmium-picked and sectioned specimens. Serum lipoproteins have been studied and, after fixing, resolved in the microscope [18]. Electron microscopy has also been applied to the study of isolated mitochondria. This has shown a repeating structural unit of 80–100 Å in diameter, considered to be a basic component of the active mitochondrial membranes, which has been designated elementary particle (EP). The isolated particles contain all the major components of the respiratory chain and it is thought that they contain all the functional enzymic components of the electron transport chain. Green and co-workers [19–21] have, as a result of this work, been able to discuss the role of the lipid in the mitochondrial electron transfer process and oxidative phosphorylation. Studies have also been made with hydrated biological systems in such a way as to minimize desiccation, whilst the possibility of visualizing the organized water structures present in lipoprotein structures is also being explored.

Fernández-Morán has pointed to future developments in the study of biological systems using electron microscopy techniques at liquid helium temperatures [22]. Cooling to temperatures close to absolute zero is said not to appreciably impair critical life and this has been demonstrated with a variety of living organisms. Improved low-temperature preparation techniques of biological tissues have been developed, based on rapid freezing of fresh or glycerinated tissues with liquid helium at 2°K followed by freeze substitution and embedding in plastics at low temperatures under conditions which minimize ice crystal formation and extraction artefacts. Special low-temperature stages for examining specimens at liquid helium temperature have been constructed and a new type of miniaturized high-resolution electron microscope totally immersed in liquid helium is being developed. This will have superconducting lenses with ripple-free magnetic fields, operate in ultra-high vacuum and have optimum conditions for low voltage (1 to 10 kV) and high-voltage electron microscopy along with many other refinements which may make resolution approaching the theoretical limit (about 2 Å) attainable in direct examination of organic and biological structures.

The apparent similarity of the structural arrangements of the multilayered components in the myelin sheath, photoreceptors, chloroplasts and mitochondria makes clear the importance of further studies of lipids and particularly of lipid–protein interactions. An understanding of these interactions may enable the mechanism of membranes, the basis for photosynthesis, the structure of the brain and memory processes to be determined [23]. The causes of atherosclerosis and its ultimate control as well as technological advances in dealing with lipid molecules may also be rewards resulting from such studies.

REFERENCES

1. DANIELLI, J. F. and DAVSON, H. (1943) *Permeability of Natural Membranes*, p. 60. Cambridge University Press.
2. SCHULMAN, J. H. (1945) *Biochem. J.*, **39**, liv.
3. MATALON, R. and SCHULMAN, J. H. (1949) *Discuss. Faraday Soc.*, **6**, 27.
4. DOTY, P. and SCHULMAN, J. H. (1949) *Discuss. Faraday Soc.*, **6**, 21.
5. ELEY, D. D. and HEDGE, D. G. (1956) *Discuss. Faraday Soc.*, **13**, 221.
6. ANDERSON, P. J. and PETHICA, B. A. (1955) *Biochemical Problems of Lipids* (eds. G. Popjak and E. Le Breton). Proc. 2nd International Conf. Univ. Ghent, July, 1955.
7. STANDISH, H. H. and PETHICA, B. A. (private communication).
8. FLEISCHER, S. and BRIERLEY, G. (1961) *Biochem. Biophys. Res. Comm.*, **5**, 367.

9. DOURMASHKIN, R. R., DOUGHERTY, M. and HARRIS, R. J. C. (1962) *Nature,* **194**, 1116.
10. BANGHAM, A. D. and HORNE, R. W. (1962) *Nature,* **196**, 952.
11. GLAUERT, A. M., DINGLE, J. T. and LUCY, J. A. (1962) *Nature,* **196**, 953.
12. FERNÁNDEZ-MORÁN, H. and FINEAN, J. B. (1957) *J. Biophys. Biochem. Cytol.*, **3**, 725.
13. FINEAN, J. B. (1960) *J. Biophys. Biochem. Cytol.*, **8**, 13.
14. FINEAN, J. B. (1960) *J. Biophys. Biochem. Cytol.*, **8**, 31.
15. FERNÁNDEZ-MORÁN, H. (1959) *Rev. Med. Phys.*, **31**, 319.
16. FERNÁNDEZ-MORÁN, H. (1960) *Ann. N.Y. Acad. Soc.*, **85**, 689.
17. FERNÁNDEZ-MORÁN, H. (1962) *Ultrastructure and Metabolism of the Nervous System*, p. 235. Williams & Wilkins, Co., Baltimore.
18. HAYES, T. L. and HEWITT, J. E. (1957) *J. Appl. Phys.*, **11**, 425.
19. GREEN, D. E., FLEISCHER, S. and FERNÁNDEZ-MORÁN, H. (1963) *Science,* **140**, 381.
20. GREEN, D. E. and ODA, T. (1961) *J. Biochem. Japan*, **49**, 742.
21. GREEN, D. E. and FLEISCHER, S. (1963) *Biochim. Biophys. Acta*, **70**, 554.
22. FERNÁNDEZ-MORÁN, H. (1964) Royal Microscopical Society Bethesda, **83**, 183.
23. *Macromolecular Specificity and Biological Memory* (ed. F. O. Schmitt). M.I.T. 1962.

Index